GEOGRAPHY
FIELDWORK PROJECTS

JENNIFER FREW

Contents

SECTION 3 FIELDWORK PROJECTS 90

Your Fieldwork Project

Fieldwork is the discovery part of geography because it involves 'going out and finding out'. This is what geographers have done for centuries and it is the way in which our geographical knowledge of the world has been built up. Curiosity and a thirst for knowledge have made people go out and find out more about the world we live in. Think of the explorers of the past who discovered new sea routes, new lands and new mountains. Everybody, and that includes *you*, can make worthwhile discoveries while doing research for a geography project.

Through fieldwork people have found patterns in weather, farming, shopping, mountain chains and every other topic in geography; and fieldwork has provided the answers to why some of the patterns exist. Now you, too, have the opportunity to make your contribution to geography.

How this book can help you

This may be the first time you have done a fieldwork project, and the prospect can be quite daunting. If this applies to you then look first at Section 3. Each of the six topics covered there includes a Trial Run and a Short Project. If you work through one or two of these for practice you will soon see the various stages that work on your project will involve.

At the very beginning it is important to realise that every stage of your work must be organised so that your final report will be well structured and integrated from beginning to end.

Section 1: How this book can help you

Section 1 has been written to give guidance on how to achieve this through careful planning and organisation, and pages 8–9 explain **how to write your final report**.

Section 2 : Geographical Skills

The first part of Section 2 describes the **techniques** that you could use in the fieldwork (data-gathering) part of your project. The second part of Section 2 explains techniques for analysing data to help you towards drawing conclusions. Exactly which of the techniques you use will depend upon the aims of your project. Section 2 is like a 'pick and mix', but you must have a clear idea of what your final mixture will be in order to pick the most appropriate techniques.

Section 3: Fieldwork Projects

Section 3 is divided into chapters based upon topic areas. In addition to the Trial Run, each chapter contains a Short Project and an Investigation. An Extra Investigation for each topic is available on the Website accompanying this book (see below). **These are like recipes that tell you step-by-step how to complete a fieldwork project**. You may use them as they are or adapt them to your area and to what you find most interesting.

Appendix 1: Further Project Ideas

Appendix 1 is a list of other project ideas not covered in Section 3 that you might like to do for your fieldwork.

Appendix 2: Sources of Information

Appendix 2 suggests a variety of sources that you could use to find extra information for your project. The full list of information sources and contact details is supplied and updated on the accompanying Website (see below).

Glossary

There is a Glossary of geographical and fieldwork terms which you might find useful. Terms that are defined for you in the glossary are highlighted in ***blue like this*** when they appear in the book.

Website

There is a Website to accompany this book which provides Extra Investigations and a full list of Sources of Information to help you with your project. Please type in the following address: *www.geography-fieldwork.nelson.co.uk*

If your project forms part of an examination

If you are doing a project for an examination, such as for your GCSE Geography, it would be sensible to have a copy of the syllabus and find out exactly what you have to do to earn a high mark. The syllabus will suggest how long your final report should be by recommending how many words it should have. Maps, field sketches, photographs and diagrams will probably *not* be included in the length recommended by the examination board.

You will also be able to find out from the syllabus the way in which the project will be marked. A certain proportion of marks will be allocated to different aspects of the final report. For example:

- **Presentation:** How well you have presented the information in your own words and with illustrations.
- **Interpretation:** How you have analysed the results of your fieldwork.
- **Conclusions and evaluation:** What are the logical results when you draw the threads together? Do your conclusions answer your original aims and expectations? What weaknesses have you found in your techniques for data collection and data analysis? What improvements would you have made if you could have begun all over again?

Most exam boards provide sample projects with details of the way in which they have been marked. Similarly, in school there may be past projects that have been done in recent years. All of these can be very helpful but try not to imitate them. Nobody can do *your* fieldwork project as effectively as you can.

At any stage of your project you must not hesitate to ask your teacher for help and advice!

Coursework projects

You may be doing a coursework project that does not actually involve going out into the field to collect data. This book will be of great help to you in planning your project, carrying out your research and writing your final report. The skills you need to do this are the same skills as those needed for a project based on fieldwork. Obviously though you will not need to use the fieldwork skills explained in the first part of Section 2.

Before you begin your coursework project, look at the **Rivers Trial Run in Section 3 on page 126**. This is based entirely on secondary, or 'non-fieldwork', data and shows you what can be done. Appendix 2 will also be very useful because it suggests some of the very many sources from which you can obtain your data.

You can take your time more with your project than you can in an examination. This makes it a very good opportunity for you to show the examiners what you can do.

Step-by-step guide to doing your project

To complete a successful project you must work in an organised way and pay attention to detail. Famous geographers of the past who explored the world may appear to have worked on a grand scale, but their way of working was very like that of a student who is preparing a fieldwork report for an examination. Every successful explorer follows a step-by-step approach like this, and you must do the same.

1. Choose a topic area that interests you

The things we like best tend to be what we are good at, so choose a topic which you like. If you cannot decide, then glance through the Project Suggestions for each topic in Section 3 and Appendix 1 to help you to choose. Focus your mind on your chosen topic and find out as much as possible about it. Read chapters of books and articles in magazines, watch video films and television programmes, and explore CD-ROMs and the Internet. This sort of background work will help you to decide which aspects of your topic you want to concentrate your investigations on. Some people find it difficult to focus on aspects of the topic that are of manageable proportions for a fieldwork project. To help you there are examples in the Trial Runs at the start of each topic in Section 3.

A good way of helping yourself to do this is by asking a question about your topic to which there may be several possible answers. A question to which the answer is either a simple 'Yes' or 'No' will give little scope for a fieldwork investigation. Here are two of the sort to which there may be several answers:

(a) Why is there more traffic going into town than coming out first thing in the morning?

(b) How does the shape of a river's channel affect the speed of water flowing through it?

Both of these would be useful parts of an investigation. The title for (a) could be 'Patterns of Traffic Flow' and for (b) 'River Flow and River Channels'. However, the exact wording of the project title can be left until the end of your project just as long as you know exactly what it is you are investigating.

2. Choose a fieldwork area

Take care to find a fieldwork area which is safe to visit and which is the right size for you to investigate in sufficient detail in the time you have available. You should be able to complete your measurements and recordings within two or three days. Each chapter in Section 3 gives guidance to help you to find the right type and size of area for your topic.

3. Split your investigation into two or three sections

It is best to divide the research for your project into manageable sections. You should call these sections 'aims'. Each aim will focus on a different aspect of your investigation and help you with your enquiries.

Bear in mind that a successful project often results from looking at the inter-relationships between geographical features or comparing the features in your fieldwork area with examples in a book or article that you have read. ***Inter-relationships*** are connections between facts.

Aims may be worded as questions or as hypotheses. The main difference between the two is that a ***hypothesis*** is an idea that is worded as a statement. This can be tested to prove whether it is correct or not, whereas a question can be answered. Remember that a hypothesis always begins with the word 'That'. Here are two examples of hypotheses:

- That visitors to Country Parks come less frequently and stay for longer than visitors to parks in towns.
- That some types of industry continue to occupy old sites and premises.

Think carefully about how you should put your aims into words and, if in doubt, ask your teacher whether you should phrase them as questions or as hypotheses. All of your aims must be the one or the other: *not* a mixture of the two.

Aims written as questions or hypotheses are equally good, but you will have to go about your research in different ways depending on whether your aims are questions or hypotheses. Answering questions is a bit like being an explorer who is on a fact-finding mission to discover as much as possible about the area, whereas testing hypotheses is like being a detective who has a hunch about the crime which he is trying to solve and who is searching for clues to prove it.

Limiting yourself to two or three aims will enable you to investigate them thoroughly. For guidance, look at the wording of the aims in the Weather Trial Run in Section 3 on page 93 and also in the Leisure Trial Run on page 180.

Write your aims on pieces of card and carry them with you all the time.

4. Tackling your fieldwork

A map is the best starting point for this and it will save time if you study it before going out. A map on which you can write and record features in the field is called a **base-map**. It is important to choose the right scale to suit your purposes so look in Section 2 on page 11 for help. During your fieldwork your base-map will probably get wet and dirty but this does not matter because you will be able to make neat copies for your **final report**. Rough work may be needed as evidence so don't throw anything away.

Start by making a ***reconnaissance visit*** in your fieldwork area. This means making a quick visit before beginning properly. This will enable you to plan how to collect the information you need in as efficient a way as possible.

'Data' is a term used for information of all types: facts and numbers. Data collected in the field are termed 'primary data'.

Consider what information you really need to complete your aims, and when you are outside in the field collecting data adopt this rule: '**If in doubt, write it down**'. Never let your mind trick you into thinking that you will remember it; we have all heard people say 'But, I'm sure it *was* there'. You must be certain, so write your notes *in detail* as you collect your data during fieldwork.

All investigations will need the **basic fieldkit**, and each recipe in Section 3 includes suggestions of specialist equipment that you are likely to need.

Geography is probably only one of the subjects which you are taking, so your time in the field will be precious. Your data-gathering will probably present a time problem and you may decide to use a ***sampling technique***

Sampling is a recognised scientific method, but you must 'know what you are doing'. The sampling methods are described and their strong points explained in Section 2 on pages 15–18 of this book, so read them and, after your **reconnaissance visit**, consider carefully whether you need to use one, and, if so, which one would be the most reliable for you to follow. Your teacher will advise you, too.

Basic fieldkit

1. **Field notebook:** hard-backed notebook or clip-board with paper and a bulldog paper-clip. **Ballpoint pen** and **pencil** and spares and a **clear polythene bag** big enough to put these in and to write in if it rains. Include some **sheets of plain paper** for field sketches. Write your aims on the front page of your field notebook/clip-board and keep your **aims cards** in your pocket.
2. **Footwear** and **clothing** must be comfortable and suitable for the weather conditions and the sort of environment you will be working in.
3. A **base-map** of your fieldwork area. You may have to bring the map up to date in your field-work by adding new buildings and divisions of land, and by crossing out those which are no longer there. Maps of different scale are described on page 11 and each investigation in Section 3 recommends a scale of map.
4. **Timetable for public transport** you may use.
5. Money for public transport. Also the correct **coins** or a **phonecard** for use in a public tele-phone together with the **telephone number** you would ring if you needed help.
6. Your **camera** if you intend to use it.
7. A **compass**
8. A **whistle** and **torch** for use in emergency. If you are working in open countryside take high-energy food, such as chocolate, with you.

TWO RULES OF FIELDWORK:

1. If in doubt, write it down.
2. Don't throw any data away until you are absolutely sure that you have finished and handed in your project to be marked.

When investigating your aims, it is important to be as objective as possible. This means avoiding bias, such as interviewing only people who look helpful.

5. Doing additional research and collecting secondary data

Most projects benefit from extra data collected from books, pamphlets, newspapers, leaflets, etc. These are called **secondary sources** and information obtained from secondary sources is called ***secondary data***

There is an enormous amount of information available on almost every topic you could think of for a geography project, but you do need to know what is available and where to find it. Records kept in public libraries and other places enable you to compare the present with the past and to see trends and patterns over time.

Books and other published work are given in the Sources of Information pages in Appendix 2 and on the accompanying Website, together with an outline of the kinds of information they contain. These are followed by a list of addresses at which you could contact an Information Officer for help to obtain the most up-to-date information.

It can be difficult to know how much detail to include. A good general rule to follow is to use only the information that you can understand without too much difficulty. As a further precaution, ask yourself, 'Will this really help the reader to understand and enjoy my project more?'

CAUTION: Whilst secondary data are a very important source of evidence, it is important to use these data so that they form an essential part of your investigation. Take care not to copy chunks of data simply because you think it looks impressive.

The Country Code

The Country Code is a good guide to follow wherever you are.

- Guard against all risks of fire
- Fasten all gates
- Keep dogs under proper control
- Keep to the paths across farmland
- Avoid damaging fences, hedges and walls
- Leave no litter
- Safeguard water supplies
- Protect wildlife, wild plants and trees
- Go carefully on country roads
- Respect the life of the countryside

With secondary source material always make a note of the publication used: the title, author, publisher, date of publication and where you obtained it. Keep any letters which you receive; they are evidence of the work you have completed.

6. Analysing your data

When you have collected your primary and secondary data you will be in a position to **analyse** them. This means re-arranging them so that patterns and ***inter-relationships*** within them will appear. ***Data analysis*** allows you to make sense of your data, and to apply them to your original aims. So, before beginning this stage of your project, **read through your aims again**.

Ensure that you choose the techniques which will enable you to interpret your data and complete your aims. Trial Runs are included with the techniques in Section 2 and further suggestions are given in Section 3.

7. Drawing conclusions and evaluating your fieldwork

As you have explained how and why you have analysed your data, the logical outcome will have been reached. This is your **conclusion**. At the very end of your report, summarise your conclusions under the heading 'General Conclusion'.

Marks will probably be allocated for ***evaluation***. This means saying whether you feel that you have fully completed your aims, and if not, why not. You should describe any difficulties that you came across during your data collection both in the field and in secondary sources, and suggest ways in which you would have altered the fieldwork if you were to do it all again. Evaluations are included in Sections 2 and 3 of this book.

To summarise, **evaluation** means describing the degree to which you are satisfied with your work at every stage from:

the formulation of your aims

↓ *through*

gathering of data in the field and supporting them with reference to secondary sources

↓ *leading to*

analysis of your data in the light of the aims

↓ *to*

drawing conclusions and evaluating your work.

Using ICT in your project

Information and Communications Technology (ICT) can be a very useful way to improve your work. These are a few of the main ways you can use ICT to help you do your fieldwork project and produce your final report:

- Spreadsheets and other programs can quickly analyse your ***data*** and help you to produce various graphs, charts and tables.
- Using the Internet can help you obtain additional information to aid your research.
- Computers can process your fieldwork data in other ways, e.g. if you have a digital camera or want to scan photographs into your report.
- Wordprocessing your text will allow you to change your work without having to rewrite everything – and will also help you check your spelling.
- Producing your report on computer will improve the presentation of your work and allow you to make changes quite easily.

You will have the opportunity to use ICT whatever project you decide to do. **But remember**:

- Save and print your work as you go and always check the results carefully
- Check with your teacher that using ICT is the best way of doing what you want to do
- ICT is a tool to improve your work and save you time – you will **not** get extra marks for using ICT itself!

How to write your final report

Think how you can best arrange your information so that someone knowing nothing about your fieldwork area can understand completely what you have discovered and tested. It may help to prepare it as if you were going to write a book of your own. There will probably be a recommended length for your report. Check on this to make sure that you do not penalise yourself by writing much too much.

At every stage ask yourself 'Why am I writing this?' and 'How does it help someone reading it to understand more about my investigations in this area?' These questions will ensure that your final report is logical and well-organised.

It is useful to know that most people's handwriting measures about 150–200 words on an A4-sized sheet of paper.

Your final report must be worthy of the time and care which you have spent on planning and carrying out the whole of your fieldwork project. You will know better than anyone else just how long it has taken. Now it is worth spending time and care on your presentation even if it means re-arranging your material more than once.

It is a big help to number the pages and call all maps, diagrams, field sketches, photographs and other illustrations Figure 1, Figure 2 and so on, in order. Use pencil for numbering the first draft. The first impressions and the last impressions of a book are the ones that make the greatest impact on the reader. The same applies to your final report.

REMEMBER: Enthusiasm for your topic is very infectious. It will come across to your reader.

Begin by arranging your first draft in the order given below. Write your first draft in rough. Then leave it for a day or two so that you will return to it with a fresh eye and see immediately where you can improve it. When you re-read it, make notes in the margin about anything that you need to check up on by looking in a book or by asking your teacher.

1. **Title page.**
2. **Acknowledgements:** Thank anyone who has been particularly helpful to you, including your family and friends.
3. **Contents page:** Chapter headings.
4. **List of illustrations:** Maps, diagrams, field sketches, photographs, pictures numbered in order of sequence, as Figure 1, Figure 2, etc.
5. **Introduction:** This should explain the reasons why you liked your particular topic enough to choose it for your project. Keep your introduction to a maximum of two pages of writing: do not use up valuable project length in unnecessary detail here. A good way to help the reader to locate your area is by including maps: one of the region, one of the local area and one of the fieldwork area. Your fieldwork area could be outlined in a box. Imagine your area is an airport and as you fly towards it you are able to pick out more and more detail, so the scale of map becomes bigger.
6. **List of all aims.**
7. **Call each aim in turn a 'chapter'**, and write out your aim as the chapter's heading. In the written text of your chapter you must refer to your illustrations of all kinds so that the finished project will read as a well-integrated piece of work, along similar lines to an illustrated talk.

   In each chapter include the following:

   a Describe in detail when and how you carried out your **investigations in the field**, including what you did on your own and the part you played as one of a group if it was part of a class project. Describe, with examples as illustrations, the scale and types of maps you used, field sketches with notes which describe particular features, assessment schemes, measuring techniques and the equipment which you used, including your camera. Explain why you used particular methods of investigation and what you felt to be the good points or bad points of each.

   b Describe how, where and why you obtained the **secondary source material** which supports the evidence from your fieldwork.

   c Describe, with illustrations, the **techniques you have used to analyse your data.** Do your best to explain why you chose these particular techniques and what they told you about your original aim.

   d Write the **conclusions** you have reached.
8. **General conclusions:** Write a summary of the conclusions to each of your aims and assess the value of what you have achieved.
9. **Bibliography:** List in alphabetical order the author's name, the books you have used and any secondary sources such as newspaper records that you have used, e.g.

   Loynes, H. & Jennings, A., 'Does Worcester need an orbital road?', *Wideworld*, Vol. 6, No. 1, September 1994.

Your final report must be written in your best English. Use a dictionary to check your spellings and ask your teacher for help with grammar and punctuation. The use of good English is a real skill, and one that will enhance your final report.

Enjoy your project

All of this advice may sound very serious, but fieldwork is fascinating and fun. You will remember your geography project long after you have stopped thinking of all the lessons you spent in the classroom. You can be sure that, after your fieldwork, you will never look at the landscape in the same way again. The skills that you use in your project will stay with you for the rest of your life.

Good luck!

Introduction

This section of the book first tells you how to **collect** data in the field and then explains how to **analyse** your data. Remember that terms in ***blue italics like this*** are defined for you in the Glossary.

Techniques for collecting data

The first part of this section describes the techniques that you could use to collect ***data*** during your fieldwork. You need to consider exactly what data you must collect to fulfil the aims of your investigation. Next decide which of these fieldwork skills will enable you to collect your data as efficiently and accurately as possible. Do not hesitate to ask your teacher for advice if you are unsure.

The techniques have been divided into different types to help you pick out the ones that you feel will be most helpful to you, but remember that many of the techniques listed under each heading can be used or adapted for other types of investigation:

- Basic Techniques – general skills you are likely to need for any fieldwork project
- Surveying a Slope – skills for measuring slopes
- Measuring the Weather – skills for measuring all aspects of weather and climate
- Techniques for Rivers and Coasts – various skills for investigations of rivers and coasts
- Techniques for Towns and Traffic – various skills for investigations of towns and traffic.

Each Investigation in Section 3 lists techniques which have been introduced in Section 2 that will be useful in that Investigation.

Wherever possible, home-made equipment is recommended for your investigations. If you make your own equipment, remember to explain this in your final report. You may gain extra marks for the time and initiative taken!

Remember that data collected in the field like this through direct observation and measurement are termed 'primary data'.

Techniques for analysing data

The second part of this section describes the techniques that you could use to analyse the data you have collected. To help you pick out the ones you feel will be most helpful for your project, the techniques have been divided into two main types: those for analysing data in the form of maps and graphs and those for analysing data in the form of numbers. However, all these techniques aim to help you to use the data and draw conclusions in your final report. They explain ways to:

- illustrate your data – information displayed visually makes an impact on the reader
- interpret your data – patterns and inter-relationships, and their causes, are often more easily picked out from maps and diagrams.

You need to decide how best to illustrate and interpret the data in your final report. Look through the techniques in this section and ask yourself 'Could I use this for my data?'. Try the technique out in rough. Remember that you may have to cater for big numbers and small numbers on the same diagram, so practise getting the scale right. If the technique doesn't work, or the scale is wrong, try another technique.

Sometimes it is difficult to decide which technique is the best to use for the data you have collected. To help you practise, many of the techniques include a Trial Run. Working through the Trial Runs will help you to choose which technique is the most appropriate for your project.

It is wise to include more than one technique in your final report. You will realise, for instance, that bar charts and pie charts can be used to represent the same data, so use them both in your project but for different sets of data. You should also include in your final report maps and diagrams drawn both by hand and by computer. This will show that you have both skills.

Bear in mind that all maps, diagrams and pictures must give information to the reader.

Basic Techniques

Choosing the right scale of map

The Ordnance Survey maps of the Landranger Series (the maps with pink covers) are drawn to the scale of 1:50,000. This is a useful scale to look at first, but the OS map of scale 1:25,000 – the Outdoor Leisure or Explorer Series with yellow or orange covers respectively – are more detailed and show field boundaries which are very useful to find exactly where you are in the countryside. For built-up areas the 1:10,000 scale of map – the Landplan Series – shows buildings clearly. Larger-scale maps of the Superplan Series are expensive to buy but they show exceptional amounts of detail. Two of these are the 1:2500 and 1:1250 scales.

Figure 1 Extracts from OS maps of Petworth, Sussex, at 1:10,000 and 1:25,000 scales

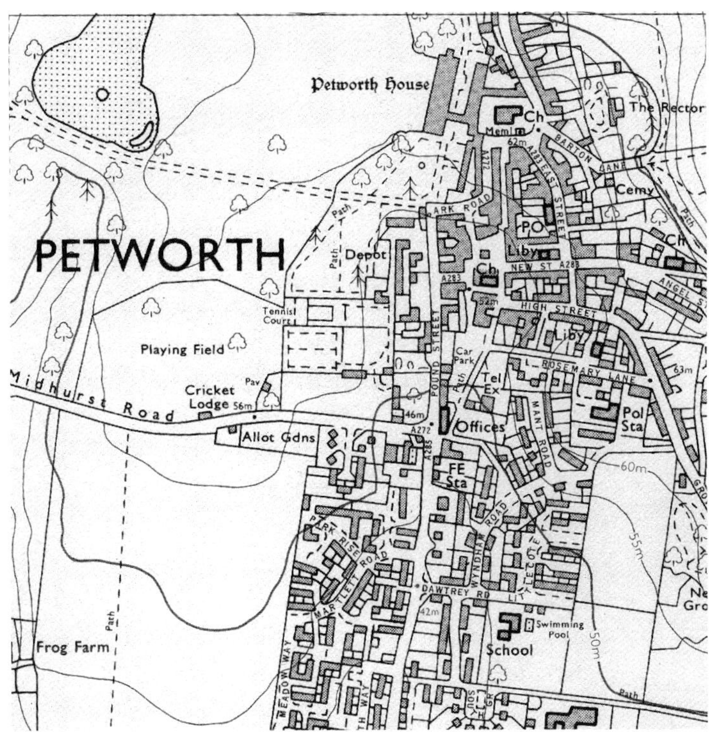

R.F. = 1:10,000

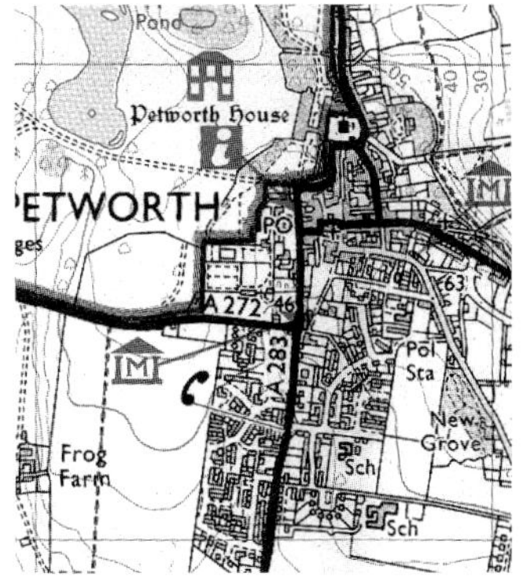

R.F. = 1:25,000

Field sketching

You may wonder how a field sketch could be better than a photograph, but field sketches have the following advantages:

- A field sketch can simplify what you see.
- When well labelled, a field sketch shows *your* interpretation of the landscape.
- Features of the landscape which you feel are important can be emphasised; others such as a bush in the foreground which gets in the way can be left out.
- No view is too wide to be sketched whereas a wide-angle camera lens may be needed for a photograph, and even then important features may be hard to recognise.

Field sketching is a real skill. If you are worried about your artistic ability a good way to get started is to practise sketching from slides shown onto a projector screen. It may help to imagine that you are looking at the landscape through a window with four or six panes of glass. Many people find a 'viewfinder' made to match the grid helpful. A viewfinder is easy to make. Draw a grid on your page and then make a viewfinder to match it, like the one in Figure 2. When sketching, place the main features in the appropriate panes.

Different areas within the viewfinder may be referred to as the background, middleground or foreground (1, 2 or 3), and the letters A, B and C may help further when writing notes about the features you are sketching. For example, a feature

Figure 2 How to make a viewfinder to help with field sketching.

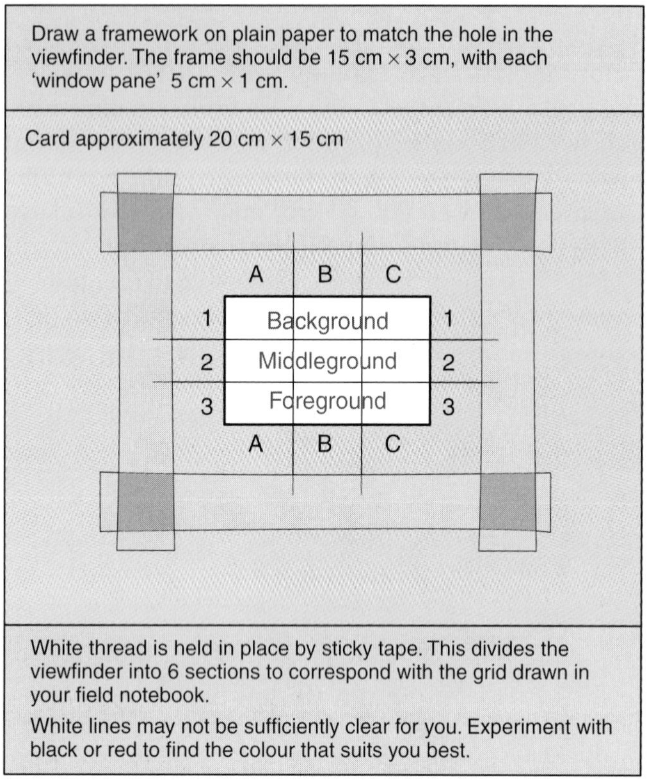

Draw a framework on plain paper to match the hole in the viewfinder. The frame should be 15 cm × 3 cm, with each 'window pane' 5 cm × 1 cm.

Card approximately 20 cm × 15 cm

	A	B	C	
1	Background			1
2	Middleground			2
3	Foreground			3
	A	B	C	

White thread is held in place by sticky tape. This divides the viewfinder into 6 sections to correspond with the grid drawn in your field notebook.

White lines may not be sufficiently clear for you. Experiment with black or red to find the colour that suits you best.

to the back of your view, and to the left, may be described as being in area 1A. For your sketch use a soft pencil and follow this order:

1. Draw the skyline.
2. Add important and obvious large features such as rivers, quarries and woodlands. For the horizontal distance hold your pencil at eye level and for the vertical distance hold it at arm's length. See Figures 3 and 4. You may estimate an angle as shown in Figure 5.
3. Next, add other features: railways, roads, canals, and then major buildings such as farms, factories and housing developments.
4. Shade your sketch by using lines to shade the slopes and other features. These lines are known as **hachures**.
5. As on a map, you need a scale and direction. A building or road will give an indication of the scale of your sketch. The number of storeys in a building can also be helpful.
6. Locate the direction of the left- and right-hand sides of your sketch. Add any notes in the margin and finally give your field sketch a title, such as 'Field sketch from the view of .... looking towards the .... (compass direction)'.

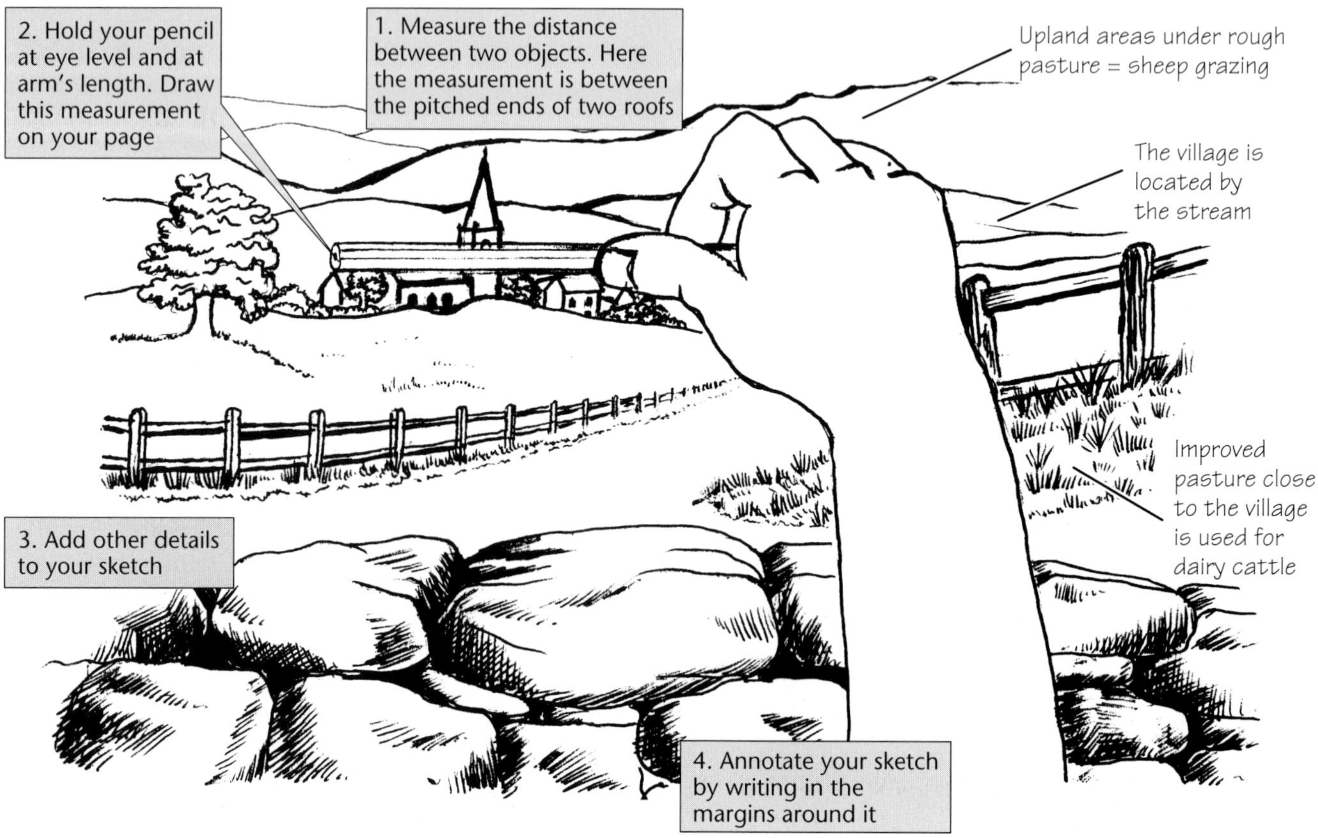
2. Hold your pencil at eye level and at arm's length. Draw this measurement on your page
1. Measure the distance between two objects. Here the measurement is between the pitched ends of two roofs
Upland areas under rough pasture = sheep grazing
The village is located by the stream
Improved pasture close to the village is used for dairy cattle
3. Add other details to your sketch
4. Annotate your sketch by writing in the margins around it

Figure 3 Finding the horizontal scale and annotating your field sketch.

Figure 4 Finding the vertical scale and annotating your field sketch.

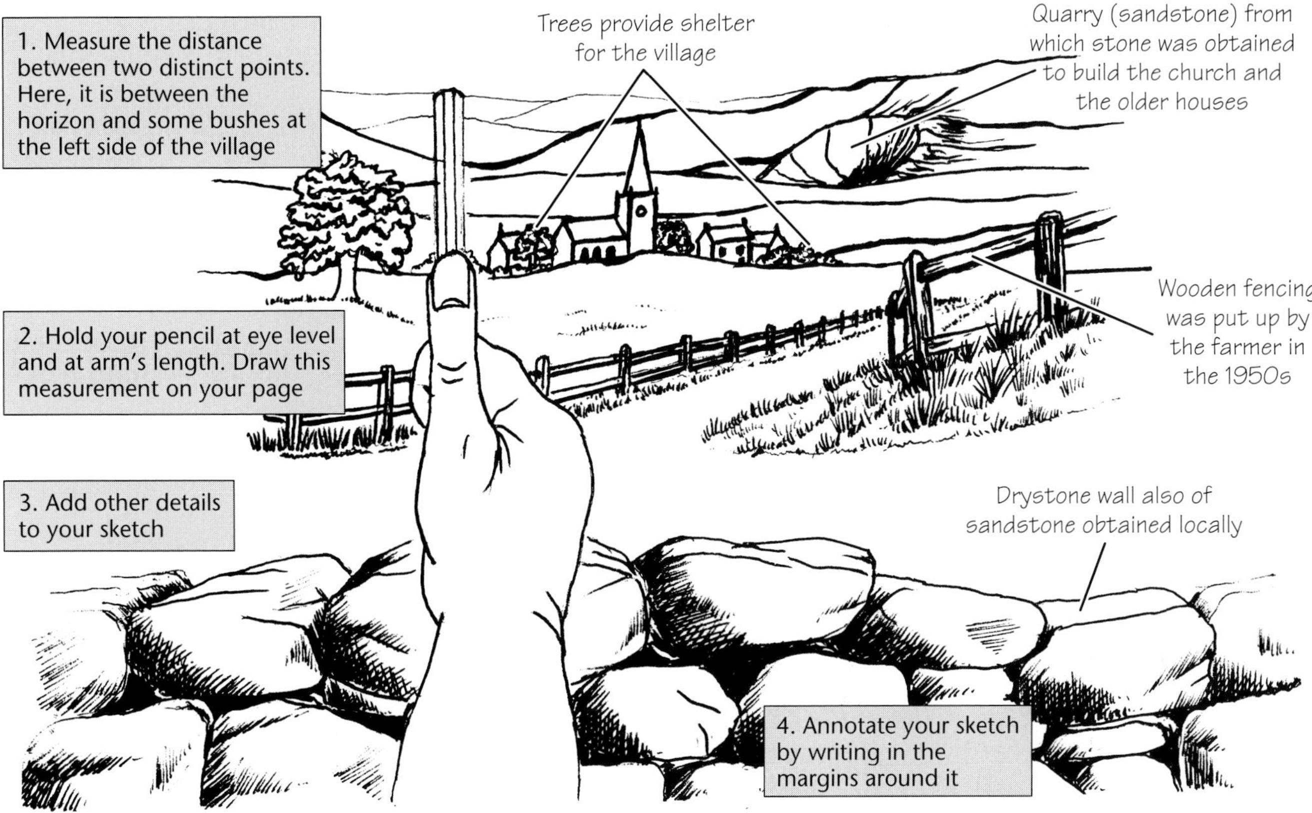

1. Measure the distance between two distinct points. Here, it is between the horizon and some bushes at the left side of the village
Trees provide shelter for the village
Quarry (sandstone) from which stone was obtained to build the church and the older houses

Wooden fencing was put up by the farmer in the 1950s
3. Add other details to your sketch
Drystone wall also of sandstone obtained locally

Figure 5 How to estimate an angle when field sketching.

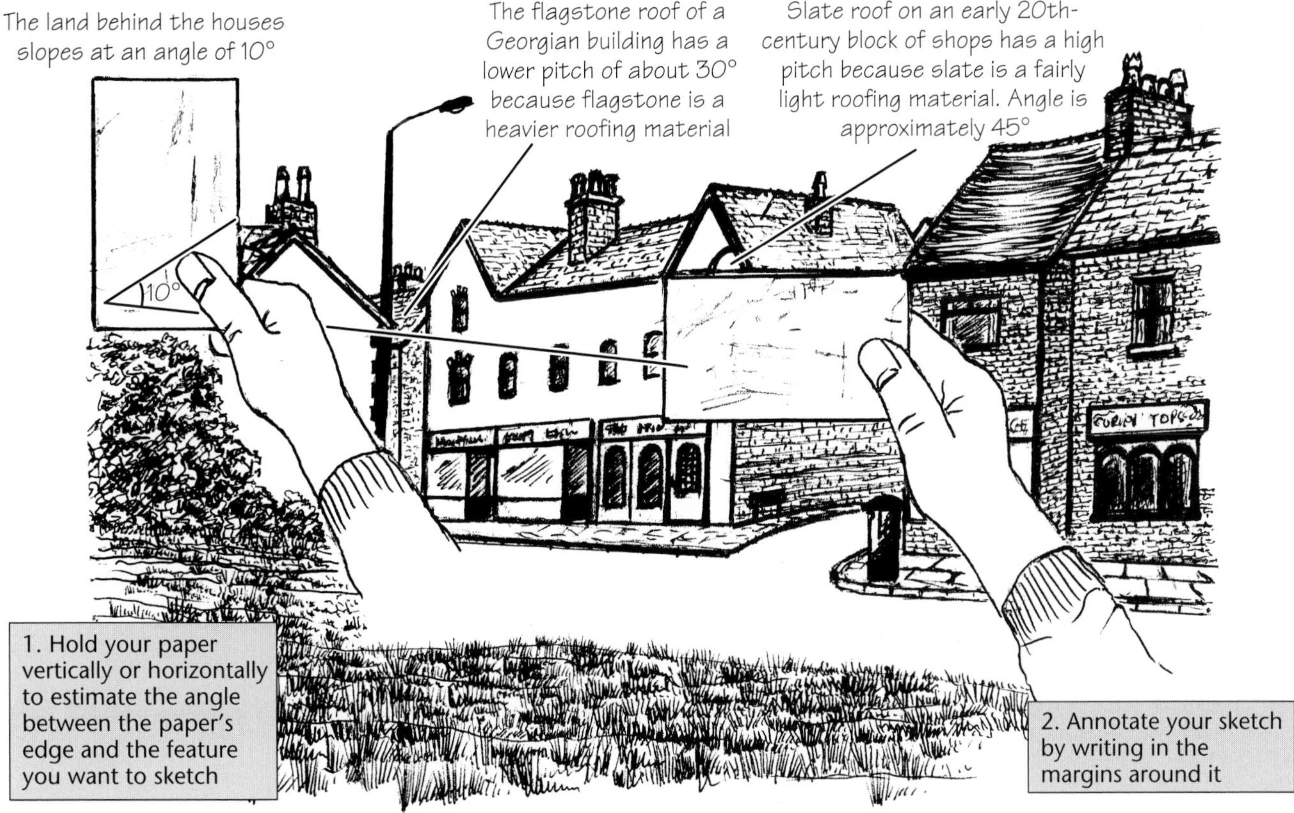

The land behind the houses slopes at an angle of 10°
The flagstone roof of a Georgian building has a lower pitch of about 30° because flagstone is a heavier roofing material
Slate roof on an early 20th-century block of shops has a high pitch because slate is a fairly light roofing material. Angle is approximately 45°
10°
1. Hold your paper vertically or horizontally to estimate the angle between the paper's edge and the feature you want to sketch
2. Annotate your sketch by writing in the margins around it

How to use a camera in your fieldwork

When you take a photograph, hold your camera so that the object you want to take **fills the viewfinder**. Make sure that your photograph contains an element of a scale such as people, a ruler or a pencil. Make a note in your field notebook of the photograph number. Refer to your Ordnance Survey map and record with a grid reference the point at which you took the photograph, and the compass direction in which the camera was pointing.

How to lay a line of transect

A ***transect*** is simply a line or a route along which you make observations and/or take measurements during your fieldwork. Lines of transect help you to be organised and ***objective*** in data-gathering. There are two kinds of transect:

1. A small-scale transect is likely to be literally a line that you have placed on the ground such as a washing-line (most are 10 m long) or a 30 m tape measure. Place your line of transect carefully to allow yourself to measure or observe the features which are important to your aim.
2. A large-scale transect is a line which you have drawn on your base-map. This is a useful method to follow when you cannot survey the whole area. There is an example on the map in the Rivers Trial Run in Section 3, page 127. Another example would be if your aim were to discover the distinctive features of different zones in a town: you could draw on the map lines of transect radiating outwards from the town centre, and work along each. This type of transect is a ***sampling technique***.

You can see that the placing of a line of transect needs some thought, and this is just one reason why a preliminary reconnaissance visit is important before beginning your data collection. When you have decided on a line of transect, explain the reasons why you chose this particular one. It may help you when you write the ***evaluation*** of your work.

Pacing out distance

Find the length of your average stride to the nearest quarter of a metre by taking average, even strides. Stop on the ball of your 'back' foot with your 'front' foot flat on the ground. A friend can measure with a metre rule or tape measure from the toes of your 'back' foot to the toes of your 'front' foot. Count the number of strides needed to cover 50 m and/or 100 m and write this down in your field notebook.

Using quadrats for surveying

A **quadrat** is a square frame which can easily be made by joining together four lengths of timber reinforced at the corners. To estimate accurately and quickly the amount of the square that is covered by grass or other plants, or sand, pebbles or litter, the square can be threaded from side to side with sturdy string to make 100 smaller squares. This automatically indicates percentages.

Make a quadrat with sides 50 cm in length (250 cm^2 or one-quarter of a square metre) or 1 m in length (1 m^2).

The quadrat should be tossed behind you instead of placing it with care, so that it will cover material picked out at random. However, you must be sensible with this and take care not to cause any damage to anybody or anything (see Figure 7).

Figure 6 Laying a line of transect

Figure 7 Using a quadrat to carry out a survey of vegetation

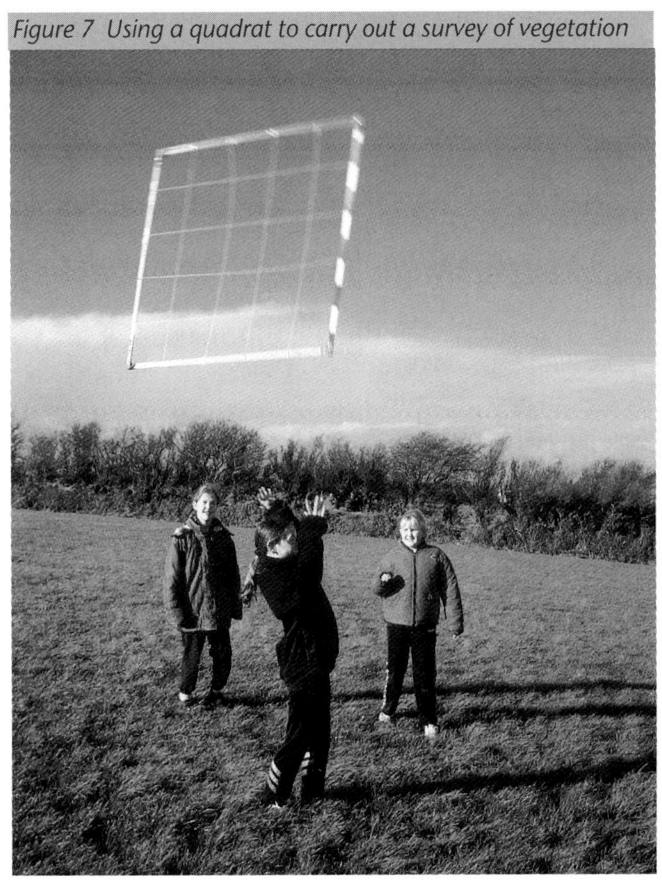

Classifying information

A class is any set of objects or people that have some feature or quality in common with one another. That feature or quality distinguishes the set from others.

Classifying is a skill and it can be important at the planning stage of your investigation, and later in your ***data analysis***. At the planning stage of your investigation it is very important to decide which data you will collect within certain categories or classes. These can be subdivided. It is important to be sensible about the amount of detail you want to give. Look at the example in Figure 8.

You will see straight away that the classes are not 'watertight'. The important thing is to be able to justify your subdivisions. For example, would you place apples into the 'tree crop' class or the 'fruit crop' class? Your reasons should be given in your **final report**.

It may help you to make up your own classification by looking at official ones such as the ten classes in the MAFF's *Land Classification* or those of the Geographical Association in *Land Use UK*.

Sampling

What is it? How to choose the most appropriate method

If you were to record every single thing you wanted to investigate in your fieldwork area you would have recorded what is known as the ***total population*** Usually, this is impossible in the time you have available, but your records must reflect the total picture as closely as possible. All sampling methods tell you the points at which to collect your data.

Figure 8 Classification of types of farming.

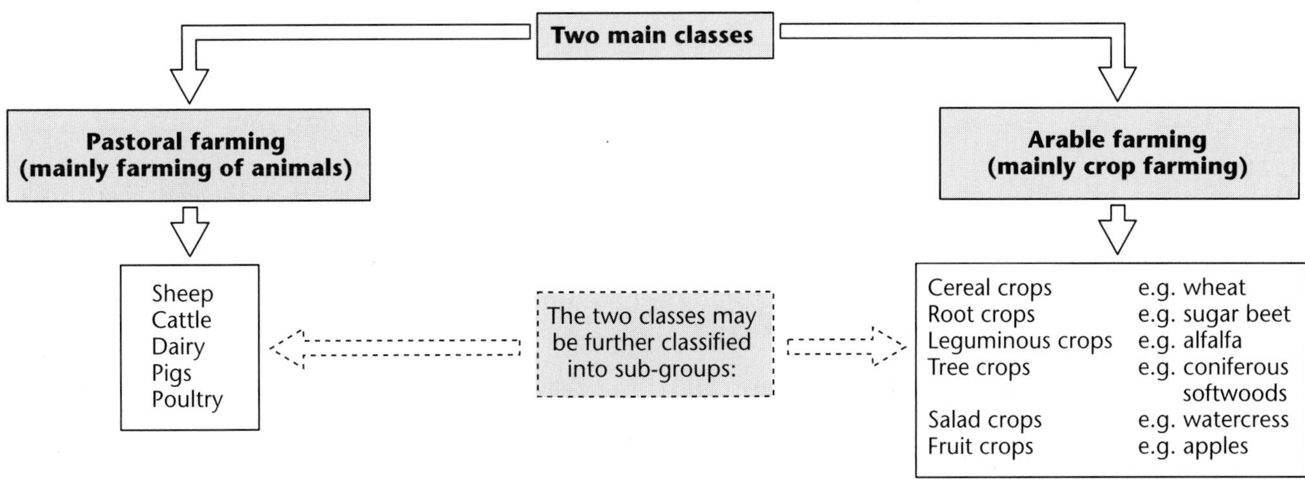

Choosing the best method of sampling

It is important to choose the method of sampling that is best for your particular investigation. To help you, the three main methods are described below. Each method is illustrated by a map based on an investigation to discover whether farm land use varies with height. Land use on both sides of the transect will be recorded at each of the sample points marked by a cross.

Each part of Figure 9 has been drawn to scale so try measuring the distance between the sample points and check on the way in which they were chosen.

Make a note of what you think is good and bad about each of the different methods. Next, consider which would best suit *your* investigation. During your ***reconnaissance visit*** you may decide to try out more than one sampling method. If so, describe this in your **final report**: it is an important part of your project. Before beginning your fieldwork decide carefully which method will be the best for *your* investigation.

Systematic sampling or regular sampling (Figure 9a) means carrying out investigations at regular intervals. Examples are:

- measuring the depth of a stream every 10 cm across your base-line (*more detail is given on page 53*)
- interviewing every 10th person who passes a particular place on the pavement (*see page 22*).

Random sampling (Figure 9a) means that the intervals at which you carry out investigations will be completely at random, based on numbers to guide you. A simple way of achieving this is to use numbers on counters such as dice or numbered corks or ping-pong balls. Keep these hidden from view inside a box or bag. Shake it, then pick out one or more of the counters. Use the number as the interval between the first and second investigations. Repeat the procedure to find the distance between the second and third investigations, and so on.

Figure 9a Points for investigation chosen by using the method of systematic sampling.

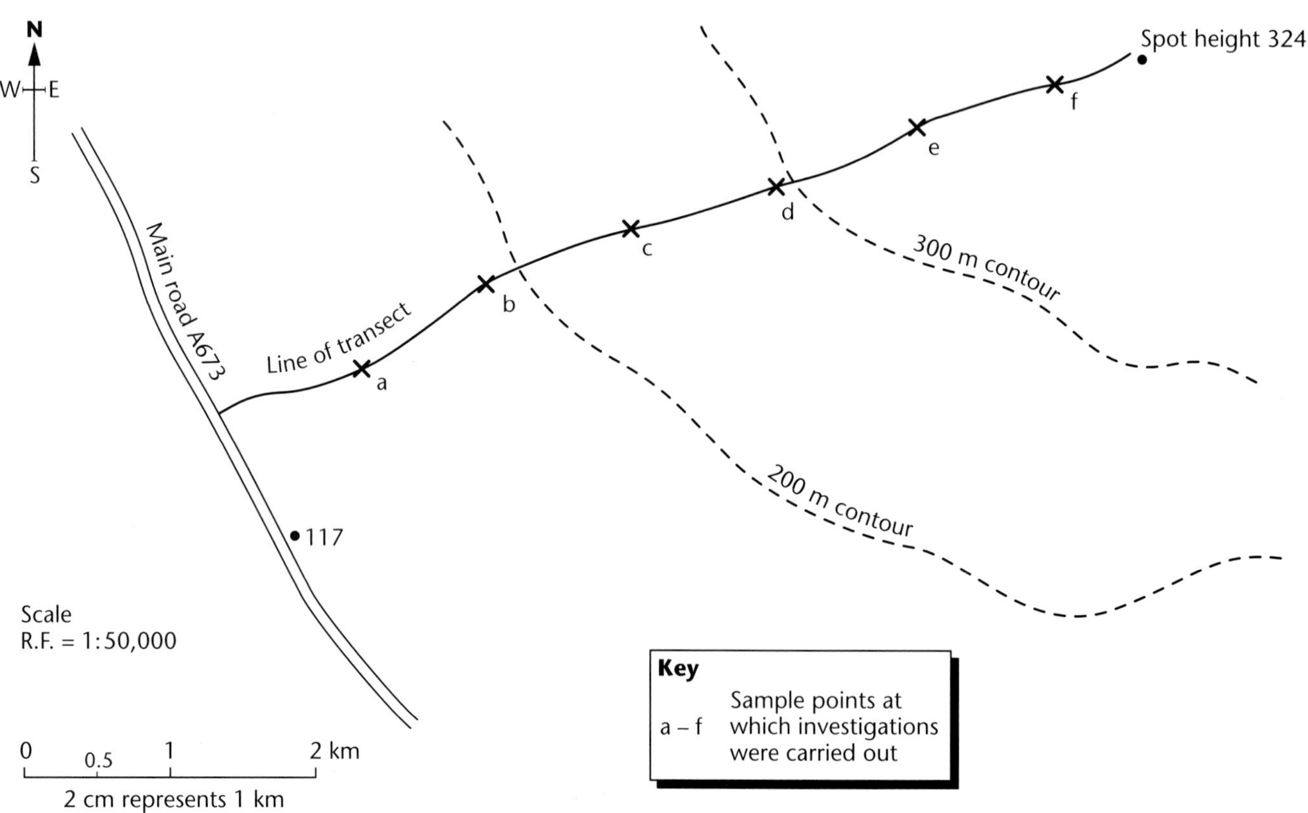

Figure 9b Points for investigation chosen by using the method of random sampling with numbered counters.

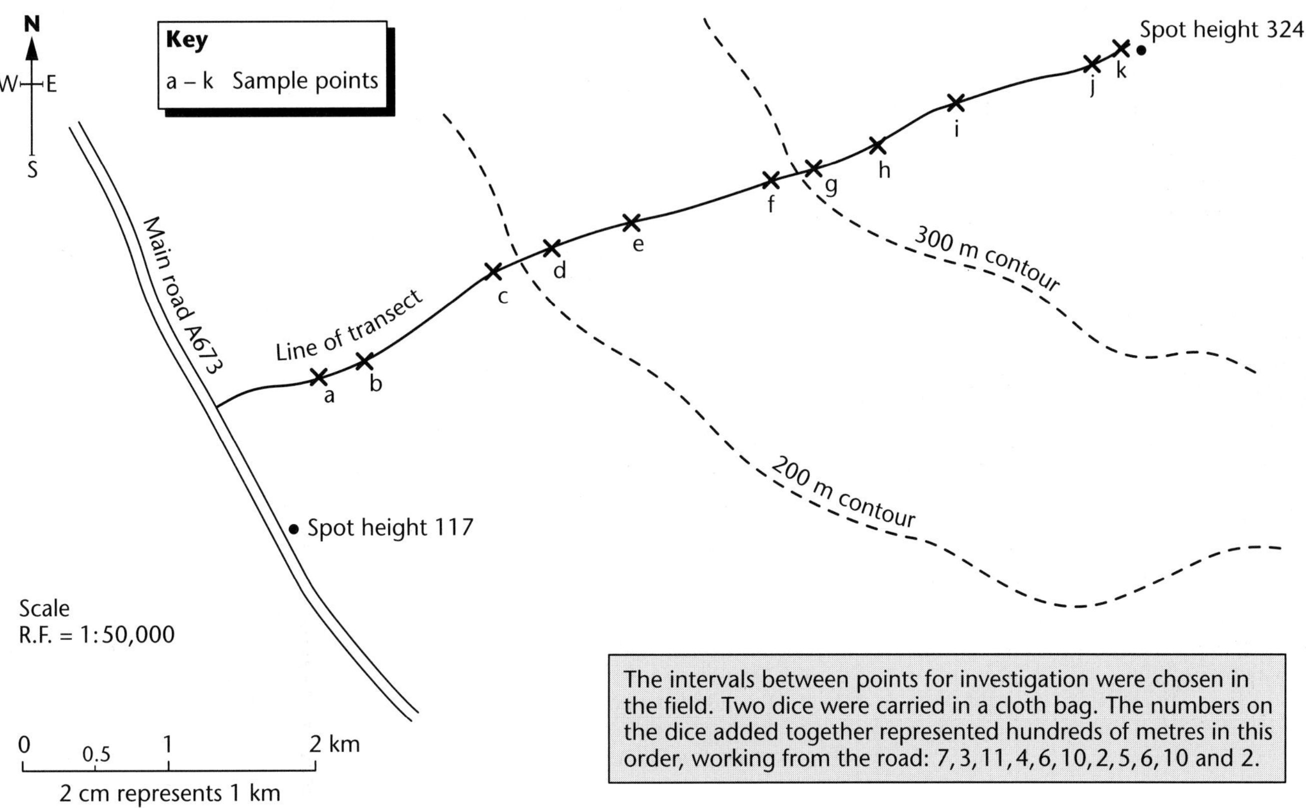

Figure 9c Points for investigation chosen by using the table of random numbers on page 18.

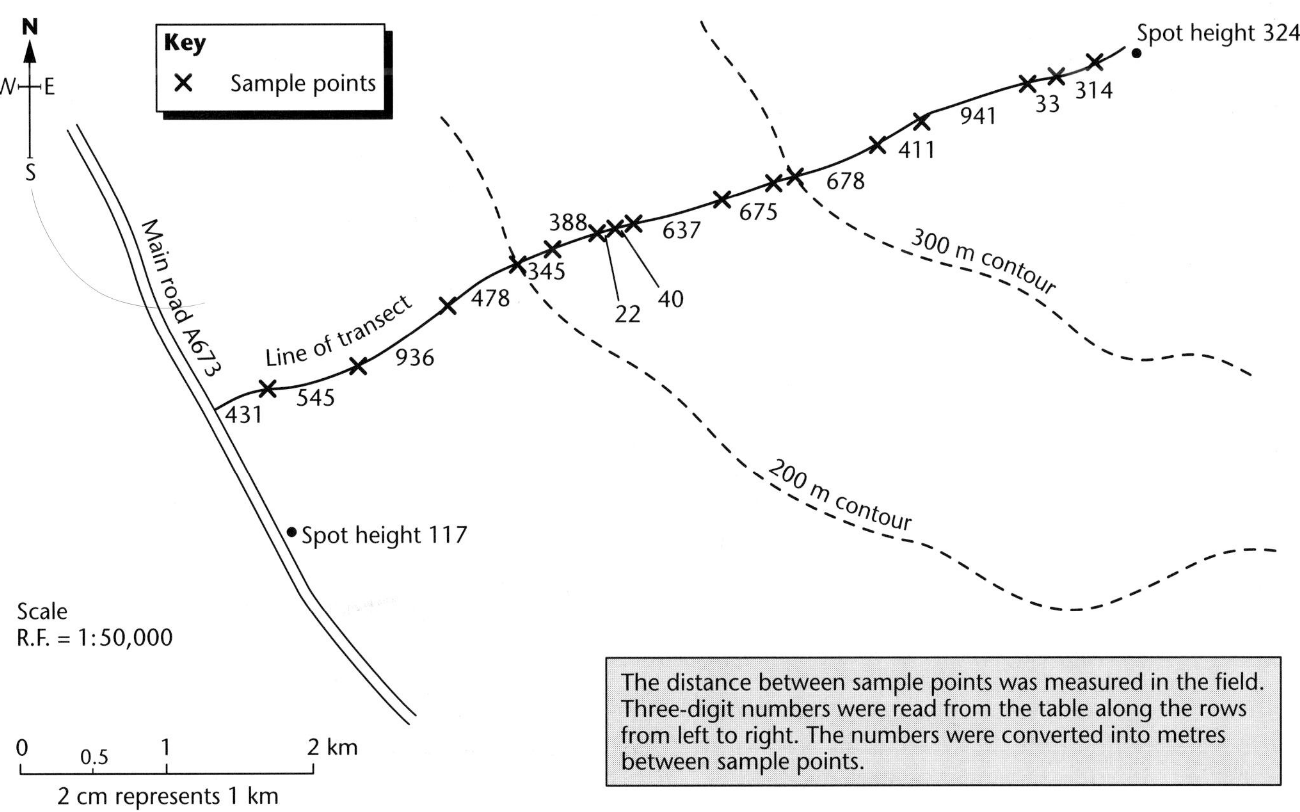

Figure 9d Stratified sample sites. The number of points for investigation corresponds to the percentage of the transect that lies at different heights.

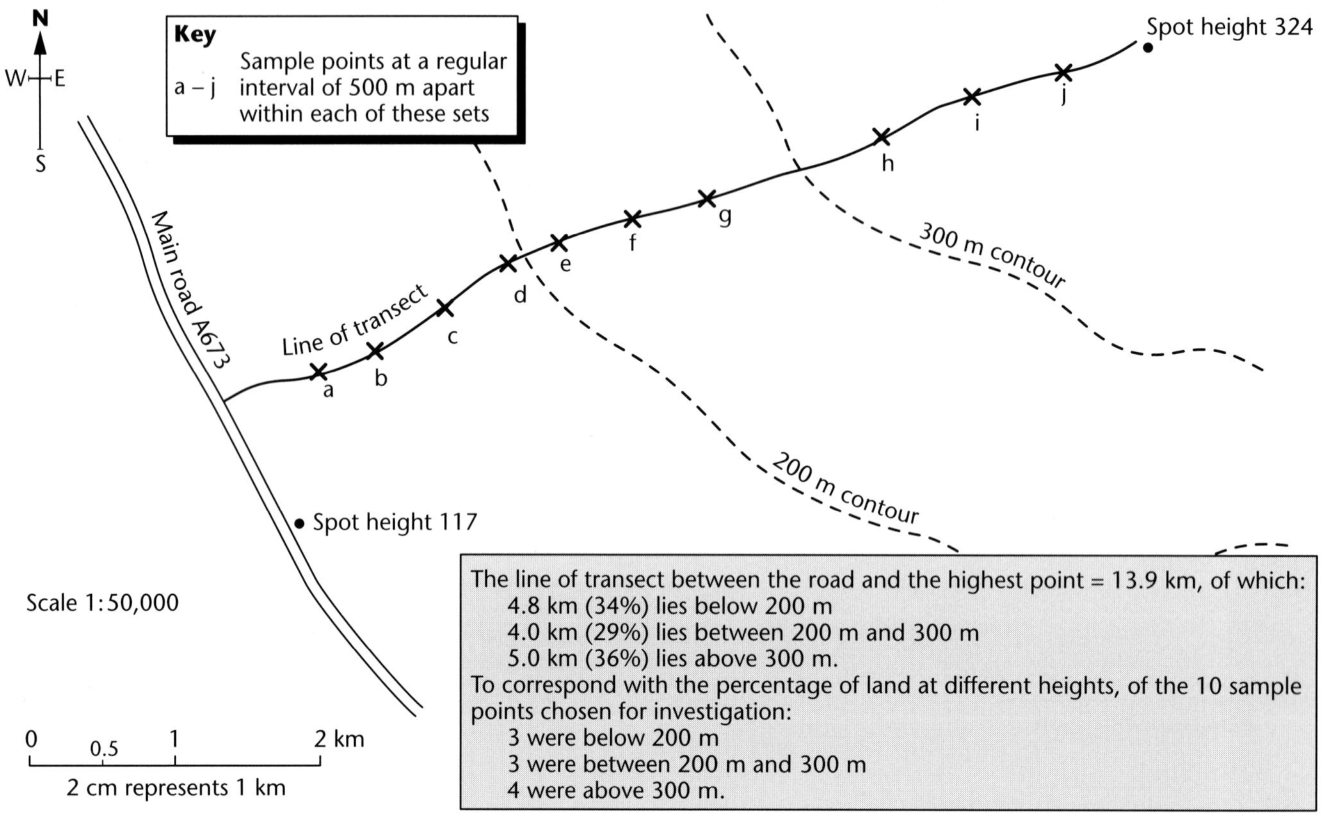

Random number tables may be generated by a computer. You must decide whether to use numbers as single digits or as pairs or in threes. Decide whereabouts on the page of numbers to begin and be consistent in the direction in which you read them: across from left to right, line by line, or from the bottom to the top, column by column.

	ROWS									
COLUMNS (as in a building)	43	15	45	93	64	78	34	53	88	02
	20	40	63	76	65	67	34	11	94	10
	33	19	00	14	19	28	40	51	92	69
	12	85	65	30	00	97	56	30	15	48

Use single digits such as 4, 3, 1 and 5 across from left to right, or combinations such as 12, 33, 20 and 43 up the left-hand column. The combination used in Figure 9c is three digits.

Stratified sampling (Figure 9d) ensures that you have a 'balanced' sample. If, for example, you know that 90% of the buildings in a town are dwellings and the remaining 10% are services of various types, your results would best reflect the total population if you were to carry out 90% of your investigations on dwellings and 10% on 'other' buildings.

Most market research companies use stratified samples. They often call it 'quota sampling'.

Letter-writing to request information or permission to visit

You may need to ask for information or for permission to visit a fieldwork area. If approached courteously most people are very helpful, particularly when you explain that you are doing a geography project. Give your name and that of your school or college. Begin by making a short, polite telephone call. Ask for the name of the person to whom you should write, and send your letter promptly. If you need a written reply enclose an A4-sized stamped envelope addressed to yourself.

Examples of letters that you could use are given below.

To request information:

Your address

Date

Name and address of the person to whom you are writing

Dear Sir/Madam (*use the name of the person if you know it*)

As explained in our telephone conversation*, I am doing a project in geography at (*name of school*). I should be very grateful if you could supply me with information on the following between the dates .... to ....

Examples: the number of visitors
the weather
river discharge and water purity

This will be a great help to my project.

I enclose a stamped addressed envelope and look forward to receiving your reply at your earliest convenience.

I hope that my request will not cause you too much trouble.

Yours sincerely

(*your signature*)

To request permission to visit:

Your address

Date

Name and address of the person to whom you are writing

Dear Sir/Madam (*use the name of the person if you know it*)

As explained in our telephone conversation*, I am doing a project in geography at (*name of school*). I should be very grateful if you would allow me permission to visit (*name – if it is part of a rural area it would be helpful to give Grid References*) on (*Mon*)day, the *date* between *time* and *time* to enable me to collect data. I shall make sure that I cause no damage during my visit, and hope not to cause any inconvenience.

I enclose a stamped addressed envelope and look forward to receiving your written permission at your earliest convenience/look forward to calling for your written permission as we arranged by telephone (*whichever applies*).

Thank you for your help.

Yours sincerely

(*your signature*)

*NB Leave this out if you cannot get through on the telephone.

When you have received the information or have visited the location be sure to write a letter of thanks. It always pleases people to know that they have helped, so tell them how you will use their information.

Be prepared to wait for quite a long time before receiving a reply so allow for this possibility as you plan your investigation. A polite telephone call can speed things along!

Questionnaires and interviews

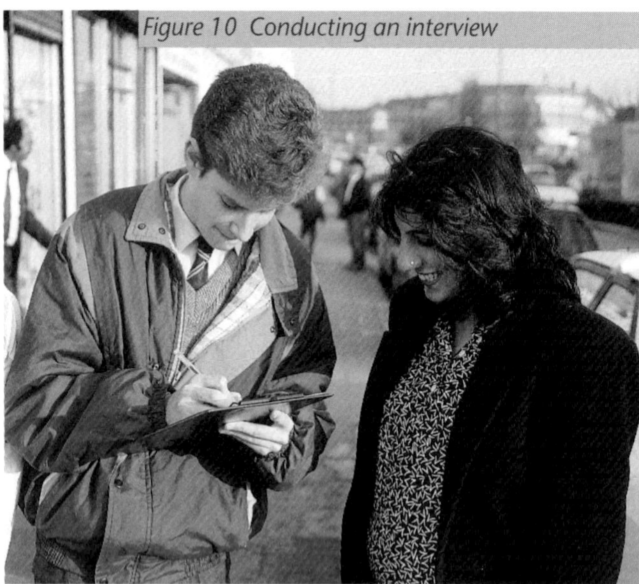

Figure 10 Conducting an interview

You interview people to obtain information that is not available anywhere else. When you do so you impose upon people's goodwill and time, so design your questionnaire carefully. You may find the following checklist helpful.

1. What information do I want to discover, and how will this help my investigation? (Information can be facts or opinions/values.)
2. Which questions will produce the information I need?
3. How can I word the questions to obtain a direct answer?
4. How will I be able to analyse the answers when I have completed the interviews?
5. How long will the interview take? Keep it as short as possible, and never longer than 10 questions.

It is a good idea to discuss the design of your questionnaire with friends, and then to try it out on your family. Getting the precise information that you need is more difficult than some people think!

The easiest type of questions for everybody – interviewer, interviewee and data-analyst – is the type which is answered by a straight 'Yes' or 'No'. Examples are:

Question: Do you regularly buy the local newspaper?
Answer: Yes/No.
Question: Do you have a dog?
Answer: Yes/No.

There is nothing geographical about these questions in themselves, but think what they may lead to. Answers to the local newspaper question could help to delimit the boundary of a town's ***catchment area/market area/ sphere of influence***. People who have dogs may take them for walks in the local public park, a Country Park or a National Park, so they provide evidence to show the use made of the facilities and times at which they are used.

Other **easy-to-use** and **easy-to-analyse questions** are those where a tick is placed in a box. Here is an example:

Do you live
- within 1 km of the town centre? ☐
- between 1 and 4 km from the town centre? ☐
- 5 or more km from the town centre? ☐

Opinions can be phrased so that they can be translated into number values such as: 1 = good; 2 = moderate; 3 = poor. For example, the opinion of the range of leisure facilities in a public park produced the following response:

	1st interviewee	2nd interviewee
Benches	2	2
Flower beds	3	2
Facilities for children aged under 5 years	2	1

Leave two or three lines at the end of each sheet of questions for any comments which a helpful person might wish to give you. These can often be very useful when you ***interpret*** your data, but be careful to point out that the sample size of 'freely given' comments may not be the same as that for the interviews.

›etting out your questionnaire

'eople are reassured by an official-looking interview ˌheet, headed by the name of the school, and a brief explanation of the purpose of the interview. Make sure that people know that it is anonymous. Remember to thank the person whom you have interviewed. An example of a questionnaire is given in Figure 11.

Figure 11 Example of a questionnaire.

SCHOOL NAME

PUPILS from this school are conducting a survey of the shopping and professional services in this area. It would help our study if you would please answer the following questions. The results will be anonymous.

Location of survey: ______________________ Time of survey: ______________________

1. What is the name of the town or village where you live? ______________________

2. How far is your home from (*name of town in which you are working*)? ______________________

3. How have you travelled here today, e.g. by bus? ______________________

4. Have you come here for any particular reason, e.g. Christmas shopping, to visit friends?

   ____

5. How often do you come here for the following services:

	How often do you come? e.g. weekly, monthly, yearly
(a) Specialised shop which sells expensive goods	
(b) To buy butter or margarine	
(c) Shoe shop	
(d) Post Office to buy stamps	
(e) Doctor (General Practitioner)	
(f) Solicitor	
(g) Christmas shopping	
(h) Do you ever buy a local newspaper containing news of this town?	

Extra comments if offered: ______________________

____

____

Thank you very much for your help.

Where to interview?

The **place** of the interview is important. A wide street or pathway where people are not in a great hurry or crowded together is an ideal place. Stand back from the main stream of people passing, and take care for your own safety.

Whom to interview?

Unless it is a very quiet time of day, it is unlikely that you will be able to interview everybody in your fieldwork area. If you cannot do this then use a sampling method as explained in detail on pages 15–18. Choose the one which suits your investigation best, and write down the reasons why you chose it. Here is a summary of the three methods:

Systematic sampling. Select your interviewees at a regular interval such as every 3rd, 5th or 10th person crossing an imaginary line of your choice. This 'line' could be where a cliff path leads onto a beach.

Random sampling. The interval between people to be interviewed will be chosen by the random numbers you select: either numbered counters or those in a table of random numbers as on page 18.

Stratified sampling. Commercial market research firms often call this 'quota sampling'. You would expect many more young people to go to a pop concert than to a concert of chamber music. You would, therefore, interview a proportionate number of younger and older people at both concerts.

Conducting the interview

A pleasant smile can work wonders! Approach people courteously, and show them your interview sheets. It is a good idea to have with you a letter of authority or other form of identity from school. Let the person you are interviewing see what you are filling in on the sheet. People are often interested to know how their information will help you, so be prepared to tell them.

In spite of keeping strictly to your unbiased/objective approach by using a sampling technique, it is inconsiderate to ask people who are obviously in a great hurry, are carrying many bulky bags and parcels or are accompanied by young children. Ask the next person if you receive a refusal. Just select the next person along. Make a note of this in your field notebook and then explain it in the ***evaluation*** part of your final report.

Always remember to thank the person for his/her help and time.

Using the Internet to conduct research

The Internet can be an excellent source of information to help you with the research for your project. The Internet is a worldwide network of computers that links together individual people, groups, schools, companies and organisations from all around the world. It is similar to an enormous library – only it is electronic and it comes to your computer!

These are the main ways you can use the Internet for your fieldwork project and final report:

You can obtain up-to-date information and the latest facts and figures from a particular source, e.g. from libraries, museums, tourist information centres, companies, government departments, local councils, pressure groups and many others.

You can search for websites that contain secondary data and background information that might be relevant to your project. This can be downloaded and saved on your computer or on disc.

You can send messages and 'talk' to people via e-mail, asking for ideas or extra information and statistics or even diagrams and pictures. You can even compare your fieldwork with a similar project in another school somewhere else in the world!

Be careful. The Internet can be very time-consuming and expensive. It is tempting to keep browsing and not always stick to the point of your research. Just like using a library you should know exactly what you are looking for before you start.

How do you search for material?

There are two main ways to search for information on the Internet, depending on whether you know the actual website you want or if you are just trying to find out more on a topic.

1. If you know exactly which organisation you want to contact you can type in their website address (URL or Universal Resource Location) if you know it. This is the fastest way of obtaining information. Your teacher probably has a list of the main ones you are likely to need. These may be stored on your school network (intranet) or you can look at the Website for this book which

has hotlinks to many useful contact websites (go to: *www.geography-fieldwork.nelson.co.uk*). It is a good idea to record all the useful websites you visit to save time looking for them again in future. Write these down in your notes or 'bookmark' them on your computer (if you have your own one).

2 If you don't know the website address for an organisation, or if you want to do a more general search on a topic, you will need to use the 'search' facility to look for information on the Internet. In simple terms this acts like an index in a book. You need to type in the name of the organisation you want, or a key word or phrase from your topic, e.g. 'National Parks', and the search 'engine' will find a list of relevant (and not so relevant!) web sites for you to visit. You then need to decide which ones seem the most likely to be useful and go to them only. This can be very time-consuming. You can help by being as precise as possible with your search, e.g. type in 'Exmoor National Park' if that is what you want.

Remember:

- *Don't overload your report with too much detail.* The Internet will have a massive amount of material and you will need to choose carefully only the most important and up-to-date information for your project. Always check the date of the information on the website!
- Don't include any information or words and ideas in your final report that *you do not understand* yourself.
- Not all the information will be useful or relevant to your research so *just ignore it.* Ask your teacher for advice if you are unsure what will be useful to you and what you should ignore.
- *Don't just copy the information you collect.* You still have to decide what to do with it – just like when you find a page in a book.

Surveying a Slope

Lay a line of ***transect*** along the ground across the steepest angle of the slope. For this, use something like a washing-line secured with a tent peg at each end. This will keep you on the right track. There are several different ways of measuring slope, three of which are described below. Choose the one that you feel to be best for *your* investigation and, in your **final report**, explain why you chose it.

Hints on explaining why you chose this method:

Gradient or angle?

Distance between readings?

Number of people needed?

Types of equipment available?

Or was it just simple to do?

You will need the following equipment:

- 1 spirit level
- 1 sighting instrument called a 'level'. An alidade or Abney Level is often used, but a piece of timber with a non-transparent ballpoint pen tube attached will give accurate readings
- 1 tripod or other apparatus on which to rest your sighting instrument
- 2 ranging rods painted red and white alternately at fixed intervals such as 25 cm
- 1 tape measure

1. Levelling

Levelling is the traditional method of slope surveying. The advantage of levelling is that **it gives you a gradient immediately**.

Figure 12 shows you how to carry out levelling on an imaginary pebble beach. The slope is measured as the difference in height between two points. The points are identified on ranging rods by sighting through the level. The person holding the ranging rod marks the point with his or her thumb.

First, set your level in place and make sure with the spirit level that it is horizontal. Now place the ranging rods at changes in slope to enable you to measure the height on the foresight rod and the height on the backsight rod. Measure the distance between the two ranging rods (d1, d2, etc. in Figure 12). Record these three measurements on the Levelling Recording Sheet (Figure 13).

Always subtract the height recorded by the foresight from that recorded by the backsight. If the backsight reading is the smaller one, the difference is a minus quantity and this indicates that the land is sloping down:

$h_1 - h_2$	=	difference in height between A and B
$h_3 - h_4 (h_3 - 0)$	=	difference in height between B and crest
$h_5 - h_4 (h_5 - 0)$	=	difference in height between crest and C

Levelling immediately gives you a gradient and not an angle.

Figure 12 Levelling on a pebble beach using a level, tripod, ranging rods and tape measure.

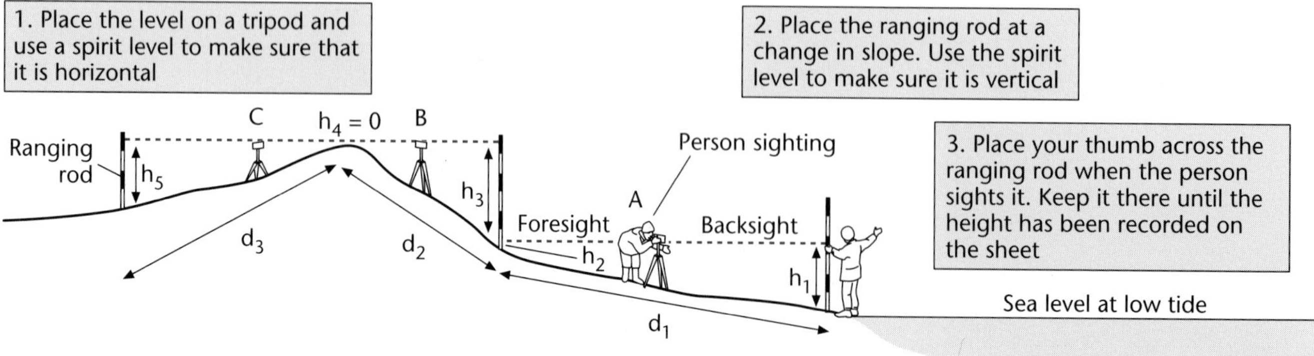

As slope measuring is a team effort it is vital that every member of the team does his/her particular part of the work with the utmost accuracy. If not, the results of the whole team's work will be inaccurate.

Figure 13 Recording sheet to use when levelling.

Levelling recording sheet (for method using level, tripod ranging rods and tape measure)								
Level location	Backsight height (m)	Foresight height (m)	Difference (m)	Height above sea level (m)	Distance between ranging rods (m)	Gradient	% slope	Comments
A	h_1 1.8	h_2 0.4	+ 1.4	1.4	d_1 14.0	1 in 10	10%	Ridged slope
B	h_3 2.7	h_4 0	+ 2.7	4.1	d_2 7.3	1 in 27	37%	Assorted pebbles, seaweed + driftwood
C	h_4 0	h_5 −1.6	− 1.6	2.5	d_3 8.2	1 in 5	20%	Big flat pebbles

2. Pantometer method

Figure 14 shows you how to survey a slope using the pantometer method. 'Step' your way with the pantometer downhill or uphill along your line of transect, and enter your recordings on a sheet similar to that shown in Figure 15.

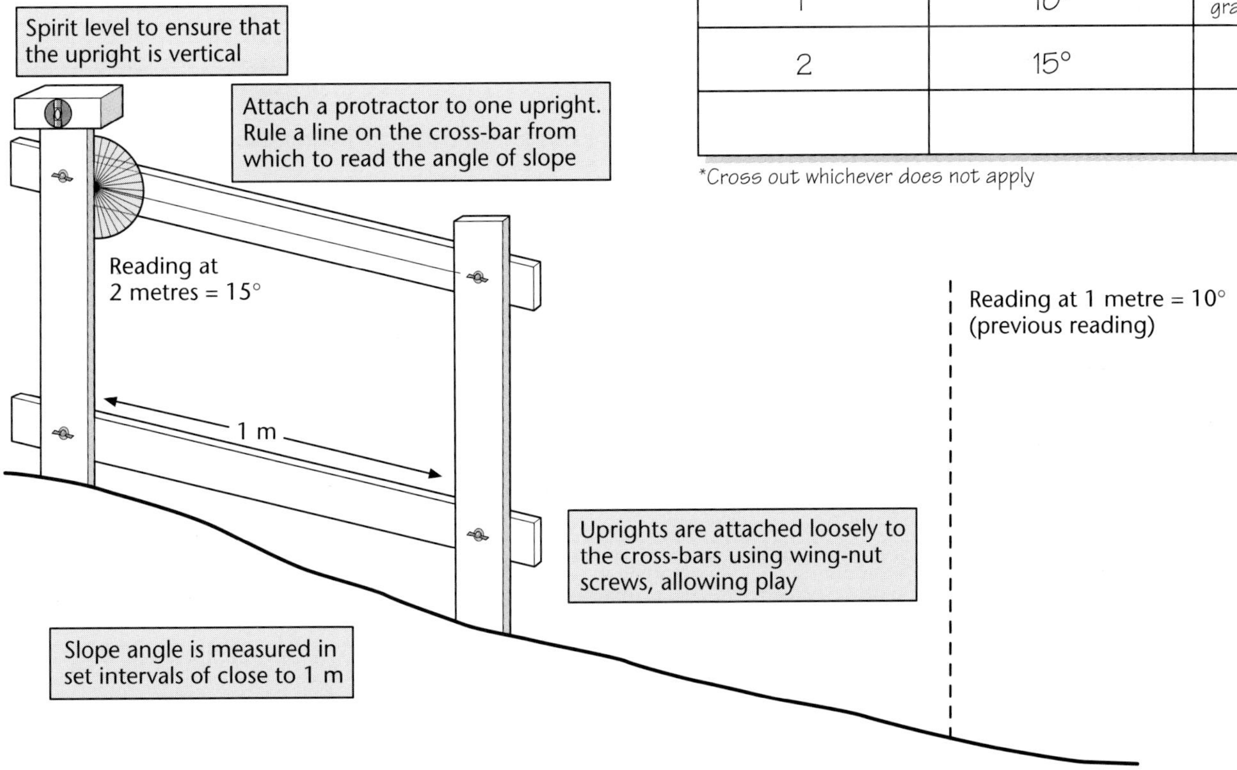

'Pantometer' comes from the Greek words for 'slope' and 'measure'.

Figure 15 Recording sheet for pantometer readings.

Pantometer slope recording sheet		
Metres upslope/downslope*	Angle in degrees from the horizontal	Comments
1	10°	Grassy grazing land
2	15°	

*Cross out whichever does not apply

Figure 14 Using a pantometer to measure the angle of slope.

Spirit level to ensure that the upright is vertical
Attach a protractor to one upright. Rule a line on the cross-bar from which to read the angle of slope
Reading at 2 metres = 15°
1 m
Reading at 1 metre = 10° (previous reading)
Uprights are attached loosely to the cross-bars using wing-nut screws, allowing play
Slope angle is measured in set intervals of close to 1 m

3. Clinometer method

Figure 16 How to make a clinometer.

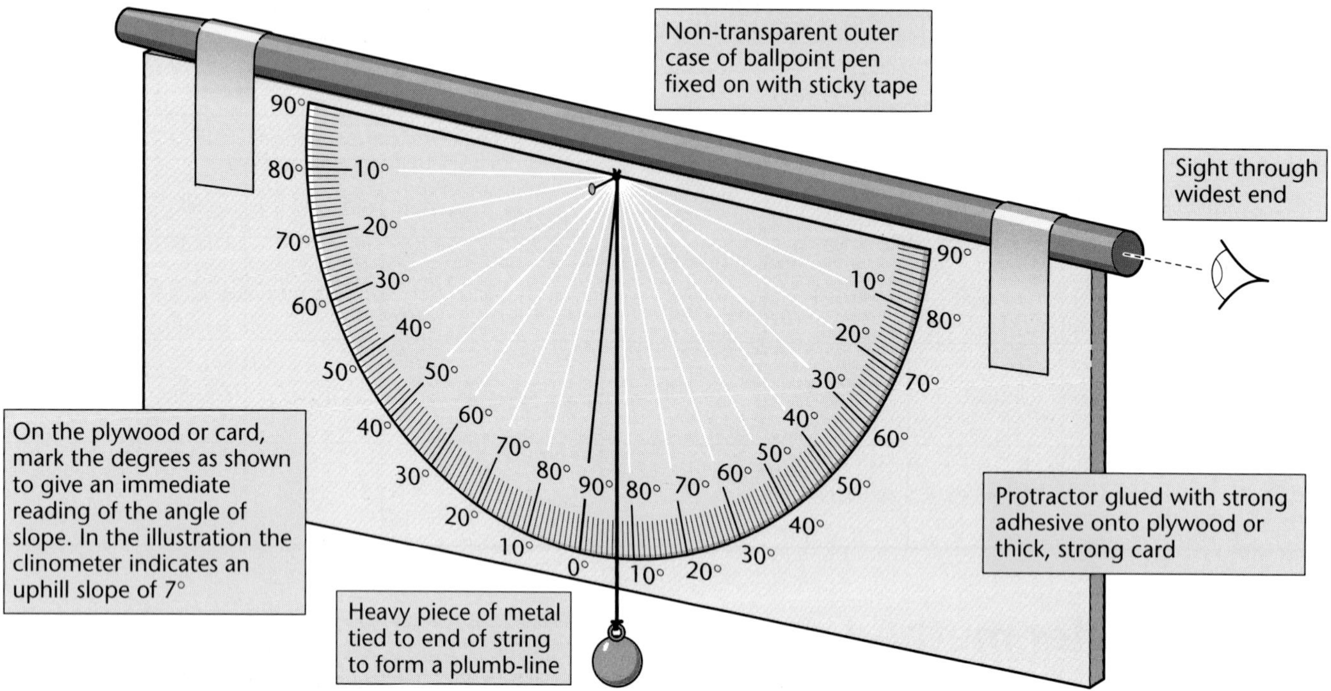
Non-transparent outer case of ballpoint pen fixed on with sticky tape
Sight through widest end
On the plywood or card, mark the degrees as shown to give an immediate reading of the angle of slope. In the illustration the clinometer indicates an uphill slope of 7°
Heavy piece of metal tied to end of string to form a plumb-line
Protractor glued with strong adhesive onto plywood or thick, strong card

The method for surveying a slope with a clinometer is shown in Figure 17. Call the person using the clinometer 'the sighter'. Measure the height of your eye from the ground. Mark the sighter's eye-height on an upright pole such as a broom handle, and call this a 'ranging rod'. Measure your distance from the ranging rod and record it (see Figure 18).

Figure 18 Clinometer slope recording sheet.

Clinometer slope recording sheet			
Location	Distance between sighter and ranging rod	Angle in degrees from the horizontal	Comments
A			
B			
C			

Figure 17 Measuring the angle of slope with a clinometer, ranging rod and tape measure.

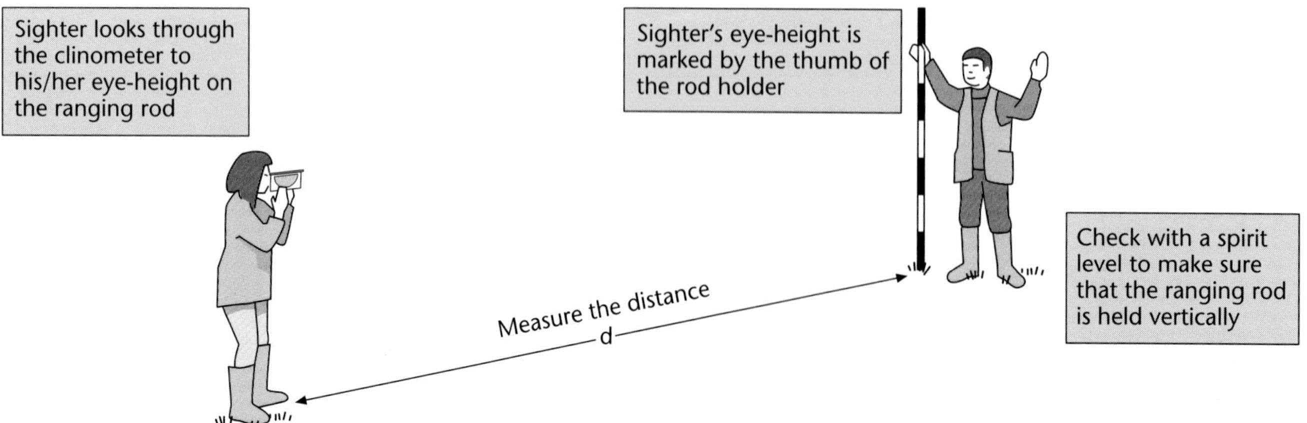
Sighter looks through the clinometer to his/her eye-height on the ranging rod
Sighter's eye-height is marked by the thumb of the rod holder
Measure the distance
d
Check with a spirit level to make sure that the ranging rod is held vertically

Converting the distance between positions on the slope into horizontal lengths

For complete accuracy, the distance between sighting positions should be horizontal, but the difference between the length of sloping ground and the horizontal length is usually very small. On a slope of 20% (1 in 5), or an angle of 10°, the difference for a descent of 1 m is only 10 cm (see Figure 19).

Whichever method you use to survey the slope, the recorder will be able to draw the profile as the work progresses. On the graph paper use 1 mm to represent 10 cm for both the horizontal and vertical measurements. It may be necessary to exaggerate the vertical scale but this can be done at home.

The other two methods use easy-to-make equipment.

Figure 19 Scale diagram to show the difference in length between sloping ground and the horizontal.

Scale 1 cm represents 1 m

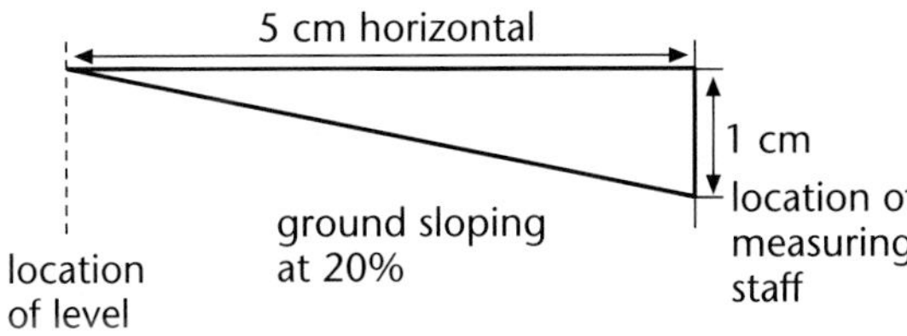

The horizontal line measures 5 cm which represents 5 m.
The sloping line measures 5.1 cm which represents 5 m and 10 cm.
The slope as a gradient is 1 in 5 or 20% and as an angle, the slope is 10°

Converting an angle of slope into a gradient

1. First calculate the tangent of the angle. The tangent is the horizontal distance divided by the vertical rise in slope:

   The tangent of x:

   $$\tan x = \frac{o}{a} = \frac{1}{4} = 0.25$$

2. Next divide 1 by the tangent:

   $$\frac{1}{\tan x} = \frac{1}{0.25} = 4$$

3. The gradient is expressed as being

   $$1 \text{ in } \frac{1}{\tan x} = 1 \text{ in } 4$$

Gradients may be expressed as percentages
1 in 10 = 10%

Measuring the Weather

You must keep careful records of the aspects of weather which you investigate. Make a table by adapting the very detailed version shown in Figure 20. Call this your 'weather log'. **Practise using the equipment you need before beginning your project.**

Figure 20 Detailed weather recording sheet for your weather log. Adapt this so that you can include the weather elements that are important for your project. Any extra details can be put in the 'Remarks' column.

Date	Cloud cover in oktas	Cloud type*	Temperature (remember to reset the thermometer when you are recording)			Relative humidity			Precipitation (empty gauges after recording)	Visibility distance and light intensity	Wind		Pressure (mb)	Remarks
			°C Max	°C Min	°C Mean	Dry bulb °C	Wet bulb °C	%			Mean direction	Mean speed		
am														*e.g. thunder, lightning smoke, haze, gusts, wind chill*
pm														
am														
pm														

* Use the abbreviations for cloud types given with Figure 22.

Atmospheric pressure

Figure 21 A barometer

The weight of the air in the atmosphere presses down on the earth and exerts a force called 'pressure'. Cool air is denser or 'heavier' than warm air, and when it sinks and presses on the ground it causes high pressure.

The instrument which measures pressure is a barometer, and the unit of measurement is the millibar (mb). There are mercury barometers, but at home you may well have an aneroid barometer. 'Aneroid' means 'without fluid'.

Altimeters in aeroplanes are aneroid barometers calibrated to indicate height rather than atmospheric pressure.

The pressure is the same indoors as it is outside, and, as barometers can become corroded, it is best to keep yours indoors. The readings will be more reliable if you keep it out of sunlight and away from draughts.

Clouds

Clouds are made up of water droplets or ice crystals, so they help to indicate the moisture content and temperature of the air. Different types of cloud have their base at particular heights. When people sometimes remark that 'the sky is high' they really mean that the cloud base is high and it is unlikely to rain.

Water vapour is an invisible gas.

The World Meteorological Organisation has produced an *International Cloud Atlas* which illustrates every possible type of cloud. Eight major types are shown in Figure 22.

Carry around with you a picture of cloud types to help you to identify the ones you see in the sky.

Figure 22 Major cloud types and the conditions they bring. Clouds are classified by their shape and the height of their base.

International abbreviations for clouds					
Cirrus	Ci	Altostratus	As	Nimbostratus	Ns
Cirrostratus	Cs	Fairweather cumulus	Cu	Stratus	St
Altocumulus	Ac	Cumulonimbus	Cb		

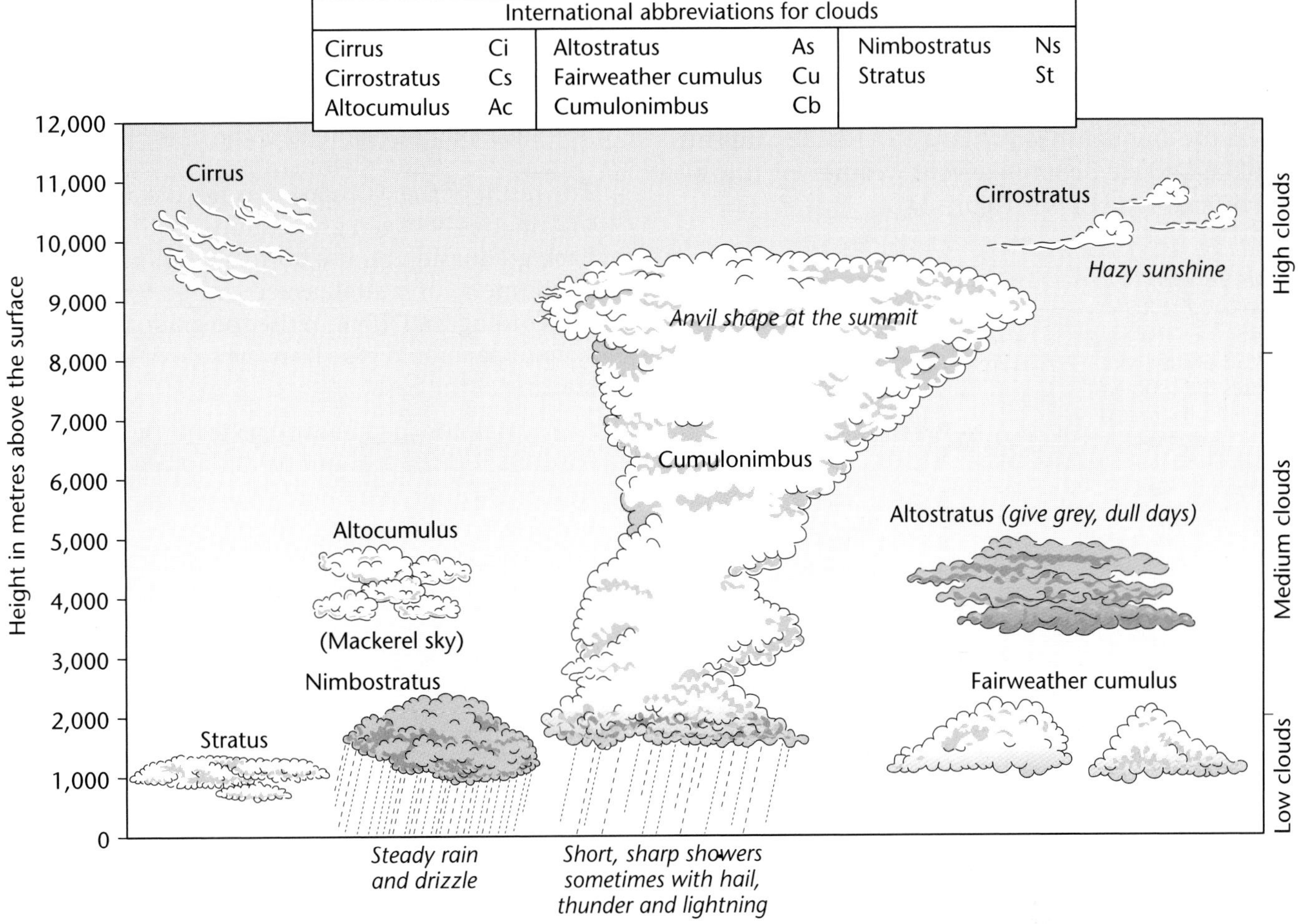

TRIAL RUN 1

Different types and amounts of clouds often follow one another in sequence and recording the sequence and amount of cloud cover will enable you to forecast the weather over the next few days.

Here are some clues which clouds give as a help towards forecasting:

- **Cirrus clouds** after a spell of settled weather are the first indicators that the warm front in a depression is soon likely to pass over at ground level.
- **Stratus clouds** make the sky darker and there is the likelihood of drizzle and rain later.
- **Cumulonimbus clouds** often bring thunder, lightning and hail because there is great turbulence within the cloud. These clouds form at the cold front of a depression, and cold sector air will soon follow at ground level.
- Small fluffy cumulus clouds, like those in a child's drawing, are called **fairweather cumulus**, and often tell us that a depression has passed across. We are now in cold, polar air with high pressure, blue sky and sunshine.

Keep your own record in the form of a list with these headings:

Date	Time of day	Type of cloud	My forecast for tomorrow

Make your own forecast for the following day. At the end of the day look at a weather map in a newspaper to find out what the Meteorological Office forecast was for the day. Award yourself marks for the accuracy of your observations and forecast: 'very good', 'good' or 'not bad'.

The amount of sky that is covered by cloud is measured in eighths. The Greek word '**okta**' is used to describe the amount of cloud cover. Make a **cloud cover recorder** using a cardboard tube 4 or 5 cm in diameter and 20 cm long (see Figure 23). Hold the tube vertically, look through it with one eye and assess the amount of sky that is covered. Record this in oktas and later complete your weather log using the official symbol (see Figure 24).

Figure 23 How to make a cloud cover recorder.

Figure 24 Symbols to indicate the amount of cloud cover.

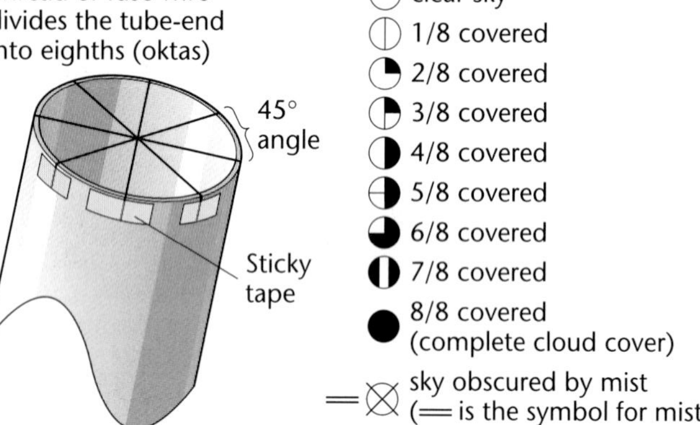

Precipitation

Precipitation is any liquid or solid that condenses from water vapour, so rain, drizzle, snow, hail and sleet are all forms of precipitation. Precipitation is always measured in liquid form, using a rain gauge. The amount is expressed in millimetres or centimetres.

Snow melts to approximately 1/10th of its depth, but try experimenting with ice cubes and frost from the freezer in your kitchen.

People on expeditions to cold areas weigh the snow. Why do you think they do this? Why not try weighing some snow yourself?

A **rain gauge** is easily made. The most important feature is to have a funnel to catch the rain so that it will not splash back upwards and out of the container. Here are two good ways of making a rain gauge:

1. Take a clear cylindrical glass bottle – round with straight sides – and a plastic funnel bought from a hardware or do-it-yourself shop (see Figure 25).

   To ***calibrate*** (create the measuring scale on) the bottle, first measure the diameter of the base of the bottle and the top of the funnel and then do this calculation:

$$\frac{\text{the square of the diameter of the top of the funnel}}{\text{the square of the diameter of the base of the bottle}}$$

   The result of the calculation is the distance in millimetres between graduations on the bottle. Each graduation on the bottle will then represent a millimetre of rainfall as recognised by the Meteorological Office. Write the graduation on a strip of paper and glue it to the side of the bottle, starting at the base.

2. Use a straight-sided, clear plastic bottle with a flat base. Cut off the top and turn it upside down to fit into the base. No calculation is needed here because the base and the funnel have the same area. The graduation will be in millimetres, so mark these on a strip of paper and glue it to the side of the bottle, starting at the base.

Figure 25 How to make a rain gauge from a cylindrical bottle and a plastic funnel.

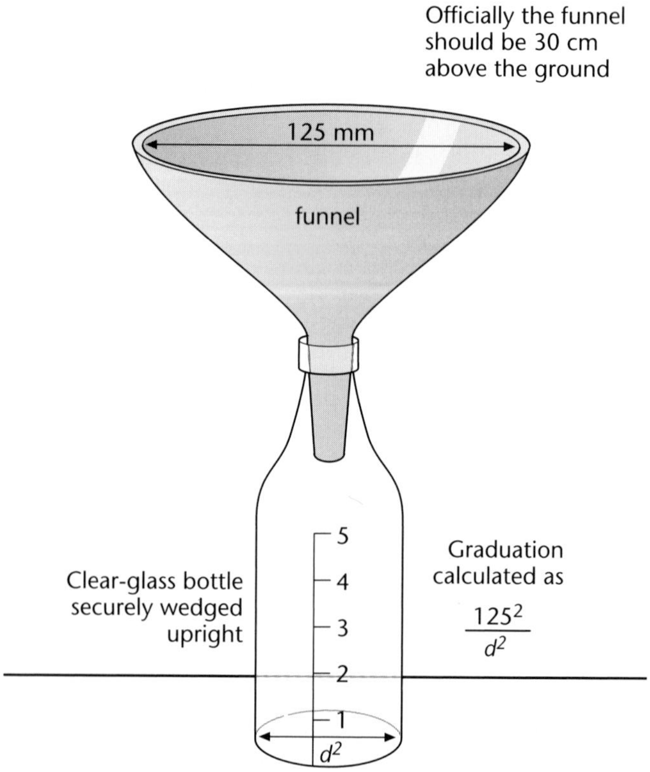

Officially the funnel should be 30 cm above the ground

125 mm

funnel

Clear-glass bottle securely wedged upright

Graduation calculated as $\frac{125^2}{d^2}$

5 4 3 2 1

d^2

Rain does not always fall down vertically. It is often driven by the wind at an angle. This is the sort of rain that does the most damage to buildings, and it is measured with a **driving rain gauge**. Try making one as shown in Figure 26.

Figure 26 How to make a driving rain gauge from a plastic bottle.

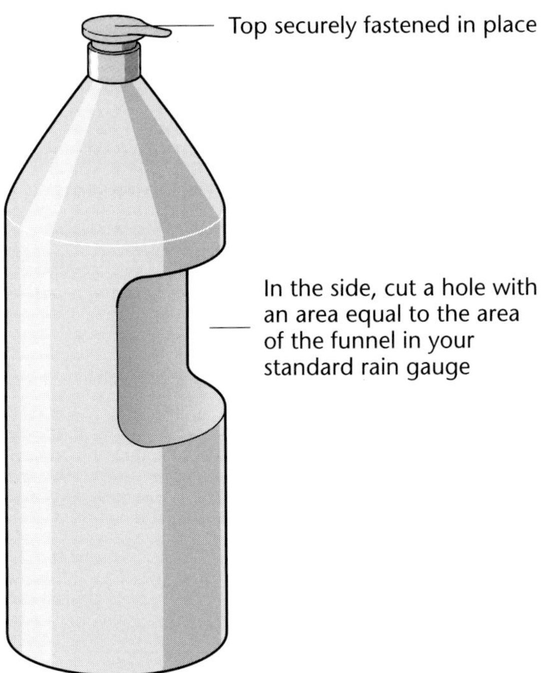
Top securely fastened in place
In the side, cut a hole with an area equal to the area of the funnel in your standard rain gauge

Figure 27 Homemade portable thermometer screen

Two or more driving rain gauges may be placed to catch the rain driven from different directions. Make sure that you have different columns clearly labelled on your weather log: one for the standard rain gauge, and one for each of the driving rain gauges. A rain gauge should be firmly fixed so that it remains upright, ideally with the funnel 30 cm above the ground.

If your thermometer has a metal indicator which shows either the maximum or minimum temperature, remember to reset the instrument immediately after you have written the measurements in your weather log.

The Stevenson Screen is named after its inventor who was a lighthouse engineer and the father of the author, Robert Louis Stevenson.

Temperature

Officially, atmospheric temperature is recorded by a thermometer placed inside a Stevenson Screen. This is a box on legs 1.2 m above the ground. It is painted white to reflect the sun, has a double roof and slats in the sides to allow the air to circulate gently around the instruments inside. You may have seen one at school or elsewhere. However, you can make a simple thermometer screen at home. Use two lengths of down-piping of different diameter. Paint these white and place one inside the other. Place the thermometer inside the small cylinder so that air circulates freely around it. This type is often used on geographical expeditions because it is light in weight and can be easily carried.

Before buying thermometers consider exactly what information you want for the aims of your project. Special thermometers are needed for special measurements.

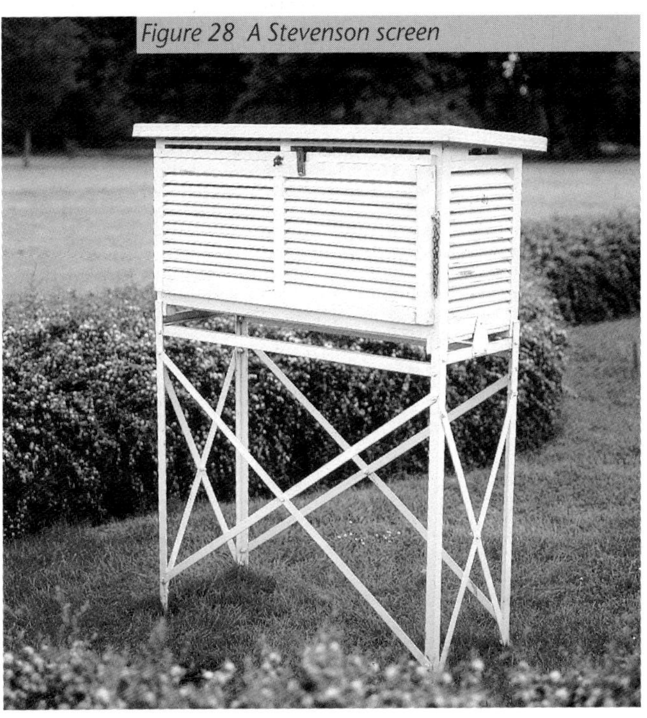
Figure 28 A Stevenson screen

Different designs of thermometer are appropriate for particular purposes. You may have used thermistors and thermocouples in science lessons and will know their uses. Geographers usually use thermometers which are in the form of glass tubes containing mercury or alcohol and graduated accordingly.

Some types of thermometer and their main uses

A **standard household thermometer** simply shows the temperature of the air and is sensitive enough to be read within 15 minutes of being put in position.

A **maximum and minimum thermometer** or **Six's thermometer** (see Figure 29) is usually read once within each 24-hour period. This is the thermometer that is most frequently used by farmers, gardeners and groundsmen. They know which temperatures are most critical for their different plants and animals.

Readings are taken at the base of each metal indicator and, after recording, each is pulled back by a magnet to rest on the mercury.

Maximum and minimum thermometers are usually placed in a thermometer screen. Carefully sited in a thermometer screen, readings from a maximum and minimum thermometer could provide an 'outside control' set of measurements, for comparison with those of thermometers kept in other places.

A **standard minimum thermometer** works on a principle similar to that of the maximum and minimum thermometer. A standard minimum thermometer can also be used to discover the temperature of surfaces such as tarmacadam, brick, glass, copper and aluminium. **Frost forms on different surfaces at different temperatures**, and this is important for investigations of local climate and microclimate. The Meteorological Office or your local weather station will tell you exactly where to place them for measuring different surfaces. If you have difficulty in obtaining a standard minimum thermometer you can improvise by using the minimum arm of a maximum and minimum thermometer.

Figure 29 A maximum and minimum thermometer (or Six's thermometer).

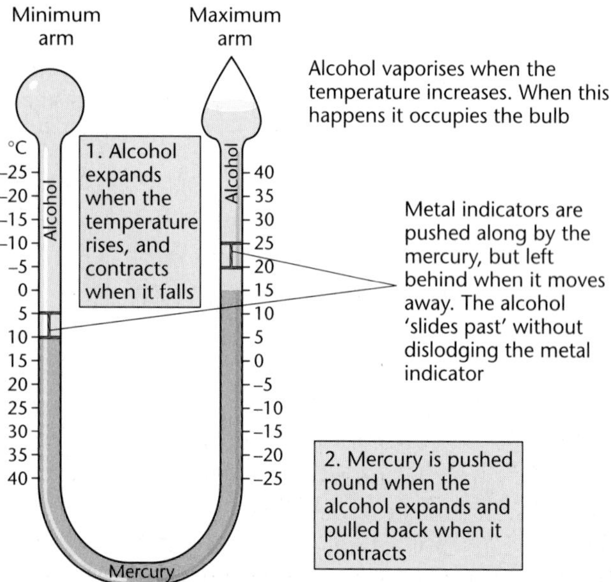

TRIAL RUN 2

Look at the diagram of a maximum and minimum thermometer in Figure 29.

1 Look carefully at the diagram and then, as if you were the manufacturer, write for the customer: (a) an explanation of how the thermometer works and (b) instructions on how to use the thermometer. You may combine the two.

2 Practise taking daily temperature readings, making sure that you keep a record of them. If you have more than one thermometer, keep one outside, without the protection of a thermometer screen.

TRIAL RUN 3

1 Suggest people whose jobs are likely to involve the use of the different thermometers.

2 Which type of thermometer would you recommend using for each of the temperatures listed below?

Here are some temperatures that are needed for practical purposes:

- grass minimum temperature
- concrete minimum temperature
- copper minimum temperature
- river water temperature
- tarmacadam maximum and minimum temperatures
- sea surface temperature
- glass minimum temperature
- maximum temperature of air at 1.2 m above ground level
- minimum temperature of air at 1.2 m above ground level

A **soil thermometer** is encased in a metal cover which enables it to be hammered into the ground. Soil thermometers may be bought at a garden centre.

Thermometers for use in streams need protection similar to that of a soil thermometer.

Work out carefully the best places in which to site your thermometers according to the aim of your investigation. Official meteorologists read them twice a day, at 0900 hours GMT and at 2100 hours GMT. **Remember to reset thermometers which have metal indicators immediately after you have recorded the temperature.**

Relative humidity

Relative humidity relates the amount of moisture in the atmosphere to the temperature. If the air is saturated then the relative humidity (RH) is 100%. Relative humidity is measured by using a **wet and dry bulb thermometer**, sometimes known as a **hygrometer**. You can easily make one of these as shown in Figure 30.

Figure 30 How to make a wet and dry bulb thermometer unit to measure the relative humidity.

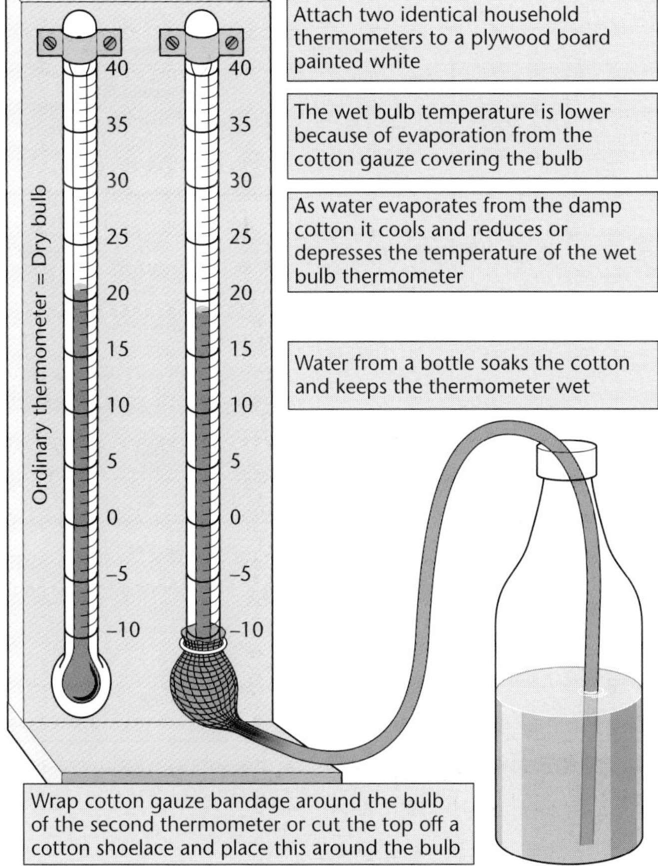

Figure 31 Relative humidity table for use with a wet and dry bulb thermometer (a hygrometer).

Dry bulb °C	Depression of wet bulb									
	1	2	3	4	5	6	7	8	9	10
40	93	87	82	76	71	66	61	56	52	47
35	93	87	81	75	69	64	58	53	49	44
30	92	86	79	73	67	61	55	50	44	39
25	92	84	77	70	63	57	50	44	38	
20	91	83	74	66	59	51	44	37		
15	90	80	71	61	52	44	35			
10	88	76	65	54	44	34				
8	87	75	63	51	40					
6	86	73	60	47	35					
4	85	70	56	42						
2	84	68	52	37						
0	82	65	48							
–2	80	61	42							

Cotton gauze wrapped around the bulb of the second thermometer keeps it wet. As water evaporates from the damp cotton it cools and reduces or 'depresses' the temperature of the wet bulb thermometer.

The relative humidity is calculated by the difference between the wet bulb temperature and the dry bulb temperature using either a table as in Figure 31 or a slide rule. If the readings on both thermometers are the same, then the air is saturated. If there is a small difference between the readings, the humidity is high. If there is a large difference between the readings, the humidity is low. When using the table, find the dry bulb temperature down the left-hand side. Trace this across to the difference from the wet bulb reading, which is given along the top of the table, and read off the relative humidity.

Simpler, but less fun to use, is a **dial humidity gauge**. This uses either paper or human hair which stretches when moist and shrinks when dry.

The importance of relative humidity is that it is the measurement of the amount of water vapour actually in the air, compared with the amount of water vapour that the air *could* hold. It is very important in forecasting. Clouds exist only where RH is 100% so by estimating the height of cloud base as described on pages 28–29 you can tell whereabouts the atmosphere is saturated. The RH is important for its connection with drying clothes outside, drying pavements and puddles, condensation on windows, within hothouses and when air conditioning is in operation. Ask people how they feel in different conditions of relative humidity. People often complain during hot 'sticky' summer weather, and air-conditioned shops find that their sales go up!

Wind

Wind speed

The **Beaufort scale** is a very effective reference chart for assessing wind speed (see Figure 32).

Instruments designed to measure wind speed are called **anemometers** and **ventimeters**. They tend to be expensive but you may have one in school. The most usual type of anemometer has metal cups which are rotated by the wind. This movement is transmitted electrically to a meter which shows the speed of the wind. Another type uses hot wire, and others, using mica turbine blades, are so sensitive that they can even measure convection currents above a radiator.

Officially, wind speed should be measured at 10 m above the ground or water surface, and if you use a hand-held instrument it should be held at arm's length to minimise turbulence caused by your body.

A simple version of an anemometer can be made by using a free-swinging pendulum as in Figure 33. Hold the anemometer parallel to the direction of the wind and ask a friend to read it for you.

You can ***calibrate*** the height of the swing indicator by using a fan or a hair-dryer or, on a calm day and on a quiet road, by holding it out of the window of a car moving at a known speed. It is best to calibrate your own as all will vary slightly. You should find your calibration similar to that given below.

Guidelines for a swinging-pendulum anemometer:

Angle from the horizontal	80°	60°	40°	20°
Wind speed in km/h	13	24	34	52
Wind speed in m/s	0.36	6.66	9.44	14.44
Beaufort force	0	4	5	7
Description	calm	moderate breeze	fresh breeze	near gale

Figure 32 The Beaufort scale of wind speed.

Beaufort force	Wind speed (m/s)	Official wind speed symbol on weather map	Description	How to recognise wind speed	Comfort to people walking
0	0 – 0.5		Calm	Smoke rises vertically	No noticeable wind
1	0.5 – 1.5	1 half feather	Light air movement	Smoke drifts, leaves move	
2	1.5 – 3.5	1 full feather	Light breeze	Flags flutter, small branches move	Wind felt on face
3	3.5 – 5.5	1 full feather	Gentle breeze	Flags extended	Clothing flaps
4	5.5 – 8.0		Moderate breeze	Wind sock lifted half-way up	Hair blown about
5	8.0 – 10.5	2 full feathers	Fresh breeze	Crests (white horses at sea)	
6	10.5 – 13.5	3 full feathers	Strong breeze	Wind whistles, big branches sway	You have to lean against the wind when walking
7	13.5 – 17.0		Near gale	Wind sock extended, whole trees sway	Umbrellas blow inside out, difficult to walk steadily
8	17.0 – 20.0	1 flag	Gale	High waves at sea	Difficult to balance in gusts
9	20.0 – 25.0	1 flag and 1 full feather	Strong gale	Tiles are blown from roof tops	People are blown over
10	More than 25		Storm	Trees uprooted	

Admiral Beaufort devised this scale for measuring winds at sea in 1805. His scale was given symbols and adapted for use on land. We still use it today.

Figure 33 How to make a swinging-pendulum anemometer.

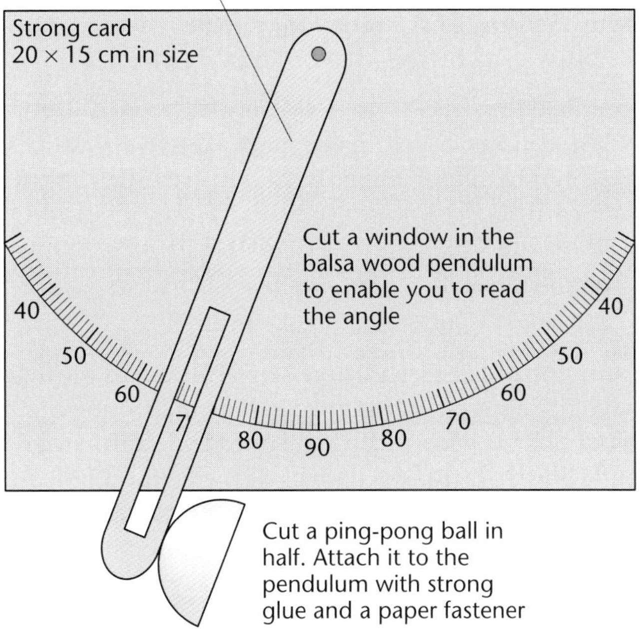
Strip of balsa wood 2 cm wide attached by a strong paper fastener. It must swing freely
Use a protractor to draw the angles on the card
Strong card 20 × 15 cm in size
Cut a window in the balsa wood pendulum to enable you to read the angle
40
50
60
70
80
90
80
70
60
50
40
Cut a ping-pong ball in half. Attach it to the pendulum with strong glue and a paper fastener

If you make a **wind sock**, as described below, this can help to estimate wind speed. If the sock is extended straight out, it means that the wind speed will be about 30 knots (56 km/h); if the sock is limp the conditions are calm, and halfway up indicates a wind of about 15 knots (27 km/h).

Ventimeters are used by sailing boat enthusiasts and these can be bought relatively cheaply from a chandler (sailing shop). Ventimeters depend upon the pressure of wind blowing into a hole in the side of a cylinder, which causes a disc to rise up a graduated tube.

Within the general wind speed there may be short-term but sudden changes in wind strength known as **gusts** and **lulls**. These may be related to **eddying** and other forms of **turbulence**.

Dry leaves or bubbles from a child's bubble-blowing kit are excellent ways of seeing the occurrence of a gust and its direction, and a child's windmill will pick out variations in the speed of very gentle winds.

High-sided lorries on roads in exposed areas can be affected by turbulence and this can be hazardous.

When measuring the speed of the wind, decide upon a sensible length of time for your observation. Experiment before you begin your investigation in earnest.

Wind direction

Don't forget: take care to remember that wind direction is recorded as the point of the compass from which the wind is blowing.

The time-honoured methods of observing wind direction are to turn your face to the wind, or to suck your finger, hold it up and it will dry first on the side from which the wind is blowing. You need to orientate yourself first, and know the points of the compass, too. There may be a **weather vane** on a nearby church or other building and this will save you a lot of trouble, but you may like to use a **wind sock** as airfields do.

Wind socks are easily made, and can help to give the speed of the wind as well as its direction. Cut a square metre of light but sturdy material into a wide funnel shape, from 90 cm at one end to 30 cm at the other. Sew it together and, using curtain rings, attach the widest end to a piece of heavy wire or a metal coathanger formed into a circle. Attach the sock to a broomhandle, or ideally to a sturdy pole 10 m in height. Cut out a plywood circle and mark it with the 16 points of the compass, then slide this over the pole to enable you to read the direction. Take care to align the north correctly.

Figure 34 A wind sock

Wind chill

Wind has the effect of lowering body temperature by blowing heat away from the surface and by evaporating perspiration. The chilling effect generally increases as the wind speed increases, until a speed of 65 km/h (18 m/s) is reached. There is little additional chilling effect at wind speeds greater than 65 km/h.

Tables of wind chill have been produced but the results are not exact. The relative humidity of the air, and local conditions such as sunshine and shade, complicate the issue. The wind chill effect on people varies according to the individual's size and the clothing worn.

The American forces have an interesting but gruesome rule of thumb for survival in cold and windy conditions. They call it '30–30–30'. It means that at a temperature of –30°F with a wind speed of 30 mph, human flesh will freeze solid in 30 seconds! This calls for split-second decision-making!

If you have measured both the wind speed and temperature at sites on open ground exposed to the wind, use Figure 35 as a guide to calculating the wind chill factor. Remember that, although fairly accurate, it is only an estimate. Describe its use for the purpose of placing park benches for people to take advantage of winter sunshine, or where to plant a belt of quick-growing conifers to provide shelter in a new garden.

Figure 35 Wind chill factor table.

Wind speed	Air temperature in °C (dry bulb thermometer reading)				
0 calm	15	10	4	0	–1
8 km/h 2 m/s Beaufort force 2 Light breeze	14	9	3	–1	–3
16 km/h 4 m/s Beaufort force 3 Gentle breeze	9	4	–2	–6	–9
24 km/h 7 m/s Beaufort force 4 Moderate breeze	6	2	–5	–10	–13
32 km/h 9 m/s Beaufort force 5 Fresh breeze	3	0	–8	–13	–15

Visibility and light intensity

Visibility is partly related to the relative humidity of the air. Smoke, other solid particles and other types of pollution can affect visibility too.

Here are some of the terms for different degrees of visibility used by the Meteorological Office:

airfield fog (thick) = visibility less than 200 m
motorists' fog = visibility 200–1000 m
poor visibility = visibility 1–4 km
moderate visibility = visibility 4–10 km
good visibility = visibility 10–30 km
excellent visibility = over 30 km

Estimating visibility is more straightforward during daylight. From an Ordnance Survey map, choose a set of objects such as church spires and multi-storey buildings at various distances. If the farthest object can be seen faintly, the visibility is probably just over that distance whilst, if it is clear and all colour and detail stand out, the visibility may be unlimited. A map such as that shown in Figure 36 is known as a visibility map. Visibility can be altered temporarily by showers, or by low cloud in hilly areas.

Figure 36 How to draw a visibility map by tracing it on an Ordnance Survey map.

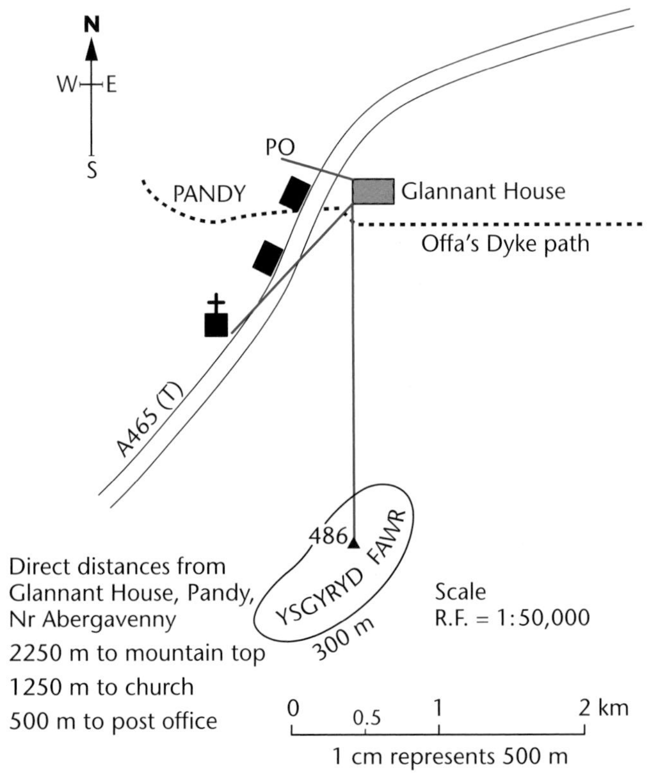

Light intensity is related to visibility conditions. The intensity of the light can be measured with a luxmeter (*lux* is the Latin word for 'light'). These are very expensive, so you could use a photographic exposure/light meter and convert the readings into Lux:

Photographic exposure meter reading	Lux
10	4.8
9	4.3
8	3.8
7	3.3
6	2.8
5	2.3
4	1.8
3	1.3
2	0.8
1	0.3

Air pollution

What is air pollution?

We are all familiar with technical terms such as 'acid rain' and 'ground-level ozone'. Probably you already also know all about photochemical smog. Air quality is continuously monitored and nowadays it is sometimes included in the weather forecast.

Air pollution may be defined as the accumulation of any substance in the atmosphere, in a greater than natural quantity. The main pollutants of the air are:

- oxides of nitrogen (NO_X)
- oxides of sulphur (SO_X)
- hydrocarbons (HC), i.e. combinations of hydrogen and carbon
- carbon monoxide (CO)
- particulates, which are particles in the air, either solid or liquid.

You will already know that each of these is classed as a primary pollutant, and some of them may combine during the calm and sunny conditions of anticyclones in summer to form photochemical smog which contains ground-level ozone (O_3).

Photochemical smog and ground-level ozone are secondary pollutants.

All of these pollutants, both primary and secondary, are monitored by the Government and by local authorities, and their results are available to the public. These official results could form useful evidence to support the discoveries you make during your fieldwork investigations. You can obtain them by writing to the Environmental Health Department of your local authority or the Government's monitoring station at Abingdon. The address is given on the Website.

Official monitoring agencies use sophisticated electronic equipment. This is designed to pick out and measure the quantity of individual pollutants such as carbon monoxide or sulphur dioxide in the air. Your school may have some of this equipment, too. However, as geographers, we tend to be more concerned about the effects of ***pollution*** upon buildings, plants and animals than about any one individual pollutant. When we have recorded the effects of pollution we can then work backwards to discover the possible causes. So that you can do this it is important to know what the pollutants are and how they got there in the first place.

Acid rain

Acid rain is one of the most destructive forms of pollution. It attacks limestone and marble, cement and sandstone, metal bridges and girders. It affects crop growth and forests and can damage life in rivers and lakes.

The term 'acid rain' was first used in 1872 by the British chemist, Robert Angus Smith, in the publication which he called *Acid Rain: The Beginnings of a Chemical Climatology*. He described ***precipitation*** which had been polluted by acids such as sulphuric acid and nitric acid. So acid rain has been around for a long time, and there were a lot more smoky chimneys from factories and homes in the 19th century than there are today.

How acidic is acid rain?

Normal precipitation – rain, hail, sleet and snow – is slightly acidic, with a pH of 5.6. Precipitation is classed as acid rain when the **pH is below 5.0.**

What causes acid rain?

Precipitation becomes acid rain when it **combines** with one or more of several chemical compounds. These include oxides of nitrogen, known collectively as NO_X, which mainly come from the exhausts of motor vehicles, as does **carbon monoxide**. Obviously these are given off at street level, which means that the greatest damage occurs on busy roads and in big towns. Buildings in towns often have a 'splash zone' of damage at this level.

Most (60%) **sulphur dioxide**, SO_2, begins as gases from electric power stations which use coal or gas. The gases rise up into the clouds where they combine with water vapour and oxygen to form sulphuric acid. This can be blown by the wind for hundreds of kilometres. Some people in Germany and the countries of Scandinavia blame 'British' sulphur dioxide for damaging their forests and crops.

The term 'Waldsterben', meaning 'forest death', is sometimes used for forests which have been very badly affected.

Nitrogen-based artificial fertilisers contribute to the amount of NO_2 in the air. Here is a surprising fact: 10% of the artificial fertilisers used in the USA are applied to golf courses. Can you guess what the percentage used in this way could be in your area?

Steel corrodes between two and four times more quickly in industrial towns than it does in the countryside.

Figure 37 Damage to a building caused by acid rain

Particulates in the air

Solid and liquid particles are mainly composed of hydrocarbons, soot and smoke being the main types. The major sources are again fossil-fuel-burning electric power stations, motor vehicles and factories, but fine ***particles*** of soil and other dust of silt-size and clay-size can be blown about in dry, windy weather. They range in size from particles of soot and smoke to minute particles which are so tiny that they cannot be seen even with a powerful microscope. The finest particles are often termed 'aerosols'. They are like the fine spray from an aerosol canister in our homes. The particles can accumulate on the surfaces of buildings where acids may attack them and salts grow into crystals. They also accumulate on plant leaves and reduce the plant's ability to make food by photosynthesis. A final problem is the way in which they reduce visibility.

You will have noticed that the Victorians often used tiles and glazed bricks, such as the shiny red Accrington bricks from Lancashire, in their buildings. These were an early anti-pollution measure, because fewer particulates stick to shiny surfaces.

Photochemical smog and ground-level ozone

Photochemical smog is the brownish haze which forms over large towns during the calm, sunny warm weather of ***anticyclones*** in summer. Ground-level ozone (O_3) is present in photochemical smog.

In the calm, warm air the following reaction takes place:

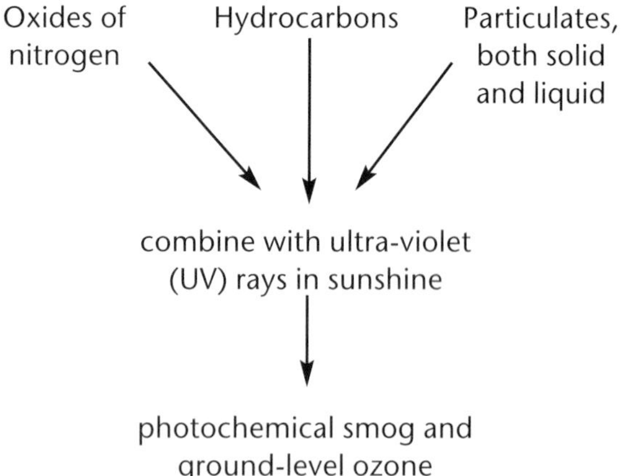

Ozone is a poisonous gas to human beings. Plants are very sensitive to it. In fact it is now considered to be more damaging to forests than even acid rain. To the south of Los Angeles, farmers can no longer grow citrus fruit trees. Ozone blemishes the skins of the fruit so badly that they cannot be sold.

Ozone causes rubber to crack and damages car tyres. It also speeds up the disintegration of plastics.

The ozone level is highest in towns, and varies during the day. The level is usually highest between midday and sunset, when the temperature begins to fall.

The French were the first to use giant fans to clear fog and smog from airport runways. They were introduced in the 1970s.

How to investigate air pollution

Unless your school has sophisticated electronic monitoring instruments, it is difficult to isolate the type of pollutant. However, when you have investigated the **effects of pollution** you may be able to discover what the major pollutants are likely to be from the records kept by the Environmental Health Department of your local authority or by the Government's monitoring station at Abingdon.

Some of the pollutants can remain in the air for a very long time and the wind can carry them far away from the source, so it is impossible to track down the exact source of the pollution with any certainty.

The important things to investigate in your fieldwork area are:

(a) How severe is the air pollution?

(b) What effects has it had on building materials?

How to estimate the severity of the air pollution

Your collecting jars and sticky tiles will have to be left in place for about a week. They must be put into safe places where they could not cause a problem or danger to people or animals. A ***reconnaissance visit*** will help you to find suitable sites. You may need to ask for permission to leave your equipment in place.

Lichens as indicators of air pollution

Examine the bark of trees, and stone walls and rocks, to discover whether lichens are growing there. Identify the species by comparing them with the pictures and descriptions in Figure 38. Record the species and the level of air pollution, if any (Figure 39).

Equipment for each of your investigation sites:

- Plastic containers about the size of a jam jar for collecting samples of rainwater. Put a label, preferably a waterproof one, onto each.
- Ceramic tiles covered with sticky plastic, for discovering the amount of solid particles (particulates) in the air. Put a label on each.
- White paper tissues for wiping surfaces to collect solid particles. Use a separate polythene bag for each one used.
- **Lichen chart** for identifying the level of air pollution (see Figure 38).

CAUTION: Never work in lonely places, and never work alone. Three people together should be the minimum for safety's sake. The third can go for help if needed.

Fieldwork area

You may find it helpful to look at pages 150–156 in the Transport section.

If air pollution is a major part of your project, it would be interesting to investigate sites along a ***transect*** through a town, ideally parallel to the direction of the main winds to see whether they affect the level of pollution, or begin in one town centre and go through to the centre of the next town. A transect of about 10 km may well reveal interesting patterns in the pollution levels, particularly if your town has manufacturing industry and/or streets congested with motor traffic.

Fieldwork method

1. Different types of lichen form reliable indicators of the level of air pollution. Lichens grow directly (without roots) on tree trunks and branches, on paving stones and on bare ground. They are composed of green algae and colourless fungi which behave as one organism: the algae provide food, whilst the fungi give moisture and protection from the sun. You will recognise this as an example of **symbiosis**.

   Lichens grow very slowly. When the pollution level is high, they can become dormant for several years and then begin to grow again as the pollution level falls. However, the **types** of lichen

Figure 38 Lichen types

Lichen desert High-level pollution	No lichens at all. The only growth on the trees is bright green and slimy-looking. This is the alga *Pleurococcus*	*Pleurococcus*
Crusty lichens Moderate-level pollution	*Lecanora* grows on trees. It is non-slimy, whitish-grey-green in colour and looks like crazy paving *Xanthoria* grows on stone as orange-coloured scaly patches	*Lecanora* *Xanthoria*
Leafy lichens Low level pollution	*Parmelia* and other leafy lichens grow on trees and walls. They are pale-green in colour, and grow in flat rosettes up to 15 cm across. They have a cabbage like appearance, with fan shaped lobes	*Parmelia*
Shrubby lichens No pollution	Many types of lichen flourish here. Two of these which indicate pure air are: *Evernia* *Evernia* has flattened branches which fork several times The upper surface is greyish-green and wrinkled. The lower surface is white *Usnea* *Usnea* has many stems from which a tangle of hair-like threads grow. It is commonly called 'Old mans beard' and can reach 15 cm in length	*Evernia* *Usnea*

Figure 39 Recording sheet for lichens.

Investigation site: ______________________ Date: ______________

Grid reference: ______________________

On rocks and stone walls	Pollution level	On tree barks	Pollution level
______________	____	______________	____
______________	____	______________	____
______________	____	______________	____
______________	____	______________	____
______________	____	______________	____

in an area are more important than the size of individual ones, so at each of your sites begin by looking for *Evernia* or *Usnea* and if you cannot find them come down to the next level, which is indicated by the presence of *Parmelia*. Record your results at each site on a copy of the recording sheet.

2. Put in place your collecting jars and sticky tiles. Record the site of each by its Grid Reference and write a description of the site: is it sited close to a wall, and if so, which compass direction does it face? How is the land surrounding the site used: garden, farmland, building site, built-up residential? How far is it from a road?

Leave the jars and sticky tiles for up to a week, if possible. Record the dates on which you left them and for how many days. When you collect them make sure that they are carefully labelled and close the water jars securely. Put the sticky tiles into a clean polythene bag trying not to dislodge any of the particles as you transport them. Notice the way that confectioners pack fragile cream cakes and try a similar method for your tiles.

3. At each investigation site, particularly if it is a dry day, find a surface that is horizontal or almost horizontal. Wipe it with a new tissue, as if you were dusting at home, to collect solid particles. Put each into a separate polythene bag and label it carefully.

Investigating your samples at home or at school

1. Test the acidity of each sample of water, using small-range pH papers, Universal Indicator fluid or an acidity probe. You may also choose to test each to discover some of the chemicals that are affecting the rainwater. Use a test kit of the kind sold at garden centres. (See 'How to assess water quality', pages 47–52).
2. Pass each water sample through a filter paper shaped into an up-turned cone. Leave each filter paper to dry out and then examine the solid particles on it. Estimate the proportion of the filter paper that is covered by particles. The use of a microscope will show you the shapes of the particles. (See Rivers Investigation, page 138-9, for particle shapes).
3. Estimate the proportion of each tile that is covered with solid particles, and, again, use a microscope to see the shapes of the particles.
4. Compare the colour of the dustings on the tissues from your investigation sites. To make your description more objective, try making a scale of darkness, giving each shade a value-number, and then compare your samples with it. In your **final report**, explain how and why you did this.

Drawing conclusions

In drawing your conclusions, it may be helpful if you mount all of your samples side by side on A1-sized white paper. Put your lichen discoveries along the top. A display of this kind will help you to pick out the similarities and contrasts between your different investigation sites. Describe these and suggest as many reasons as you can why they exist.

Interesting extra ideas

1. Compare your results with weather records for the month leading up to your fieldwork investigations. Obtain the records from your local Weather Station or from the Meteorological Station (see Appendix 2).
2. Obtain the results of continuous monitoring of the atmosphere from the Environmental Health Department of your local authority or from the Government's centre at Abingdon (see Appendix 2). If possible, find out what the 'official' site was like. Remember that local conditions affect the weather and result in what is known as the ***local climate*** (see the Weather Investigation). Explain this in your **final report**, and include the ways in which you consider the climate to have been affected by the local conditions as part of your evaluation.
3. Conduct traffic surveys (see pages 57–59 of Section 2) and relate your results to the number of vehicles passing at different times of day and on different days of the week. Can you pick out any ***inter-relationship*** between the two sets of results?

Investigating buildings for the effects of air pollution

This investigation would make a good link between Geography, Science and Technology.

As you already know from Geography, Science and Technology, different materials react to particular types of air pollution. This means that a whole project could be based on the investigation of building materials and air pollution. Alternatively, the damage done by pollution to buildings is important evidence and should be included in many other projects.

An investigation into the effects of air pollution damage upon buildings can reveal two important kinds of evidence:

1. The type of material and the way in which it has been damaged give important clues to the type of air pollution. Choose buildings composed mainly of the material of two or more from the following list:

limestone	sandstone	glazed brick
chalk	unglazed brick	tiles
marble	cement/concrete	granite

2. The **rate** or **speed** of damage by air pollution can be assessed by examining the damage on two buildings, ideally of the same material, of

different ages. Dated stones and town plans can give you the date when a building was constructed; and there are hints on how to estimate the age of buildings in 'How to investigate town development through time' on pages 59–63.

St Paul's Cathedral in London is built from Portland limestone. Investigations on St Paul's Cathedral, using very sophisticated equipment, show that the average rate of lowering of the surface is, at present, 0.062 mm per year.

Your fieldwork will be more accurate and done more quickly if you practise techniques in your reconnaissance visit.

There are two obvious but important things to know **before beginning**:

1. You must be able to recognise different building materials and to know which minerals they are composed of. Find out the chemical compounds which make up the minerals. Use a book on rocks to find out what different rocks look like. Coloured photographs on card can be bought at gift shops, or make your own. These can be useful to take along during your investigation. Call it your 'Rock Identification Chart'. In your **final report** describe how and why you made it.

   Note that bricks, cement, mortar and other artificial materials have been made to imitate rocks.

Rocks, minerals and chemicals are like, 'The House that Jack Built'! Rocks are made up of minerals; minerals are made up of chemical compounds.

2. The following is a brief summary of the ways in which different types of pollution affect building materials.

   Acid rain greatly increases the rate of **solution**, which is a form of **chemical weathering**. Minerals that are affected are:

   - **Calcite**, which is found in limestones, chalk, marble, concrete, cement and mortar. Calcite is calcium carbonate ($CaCO_3$). This dissolves in rainwater and is washed away.
   - **Feldspars** in granite may be changed into clay minerals which form a fine white powder. The powder may be washed away or, if dry, blown away.

   Crystal growth within the pore spaces of rocks, also know as 'dry deposition', can cause the rock surface to split, loosen and flake away. Sulphuric acid pollution combines with calcium in materials containing calcite, causing the growth of calcium sulphate crystals. As these crystals grow they prise up the surface layers. In limestones the surface lifted in this way may dissolve in acidic rainwater, but the surface of sandstones becomes fragile and can be flaked off by your fingernail. In sandstones the quartz grains are often held together by a cement made of calcite. The same effect can occur at the seaside. Crystals of salt, which is sodium chloride ($NaCl$), grow quickly because the air and rainwater contain large amounts of salt – but would you class this as pollution? Give your reasons as part of the **evaluation** of your work.

Figure 39 Crystal growth breaking up stone

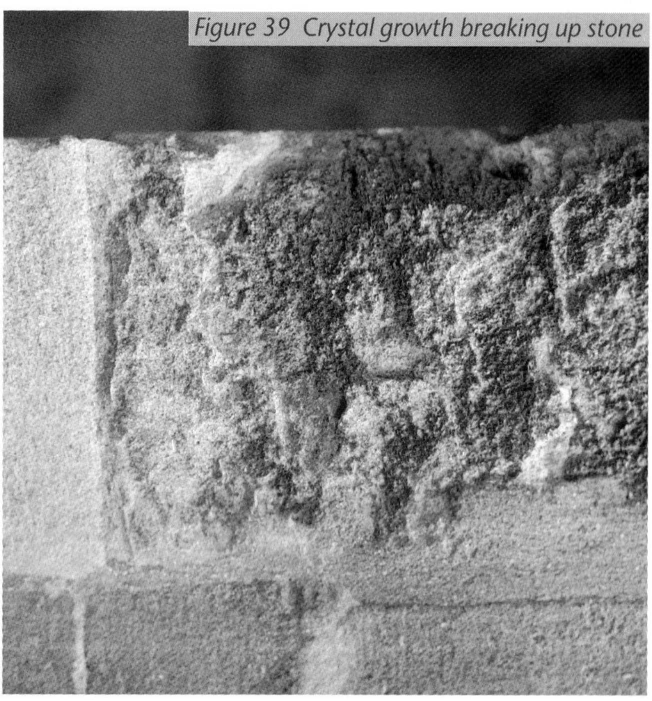

In frosty weather, exposed bridges such as the Humber Bridge and the Severn Road Bridge are treated with a mixture of urea and sand. This is to prevent damage caused by crystal growth following salting. Such bridges are extremely expensive to repair if they are damaged.

Fieldwork area

The number of buildings you investigate will depend on whether or not this is to be a major part of your project. About five buildings can be investigated in an hour if you are well practised and have done a good ***reconnaissance visit***

You may choose buildings along a transect as suggested on pages 14–16. Try to choose the same angle of surface on each – vertical or horizontal –

and try to make sure that the surface is facing in the same direction so that the comparisons you make between your results will be more reliable.

If you have time, and if access is possible to the **windward** and **leeward** sides of the same building, you may find interesting contrasts. Similarly, compare the **splash zone** of a building, which is immediately beside the pavement on a busy street, with the wall higher up. The extra damage caused by vehicle splashes in wet weather can be astonishing.

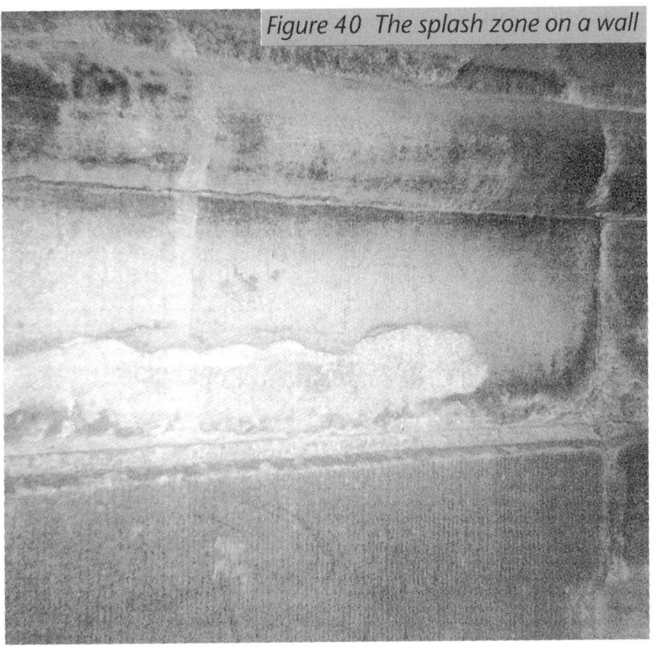
Figure 40 The splash zone on a wall

Some buildings have inscriptions carved into the rocks. The date when the inscription was made is usually given, and so is an important clue to the rate of weathering. Compare inscriptions on surfaces exposed to the wind and the rain with those on the sheltered leeward side. Is one easier to read than the other, or not?

CAUTION: A memorial garden or graveyard may seem a good fieldwork area for this project because such places usually contain a variety of types of stone, and each contains the date when it was put up. Memorials mean a great deal to families connected with them **so take care not to appear disrespectful: do nothing to cause damage**. It would be sensible to obtain permission to carry out your investigation there before beginning, so find out who is in charge. Carry with you your letter of written permission or a letter of authority from your school. **Most important of all is your own safety. Never work on your own in such places. There should be at least three of you – one to go for help if needed. Make sure that you are there only in broad daylight.**

Do a **reconnaissance visit** to find buildings which you could investigate. You may need to obtain permission, and it would be polite to explain to the person in charge of the building what you intend to do and why. Discover the **materials** of which the building is constructed, and, if you are investigating the rate of damage by pollution, find out the **date** when it was constructed.

Practise looking for signs of damage from air pollution. A surface affected by acid rain attack or salt crystal growth/dry deposition becomes flaky, pitted or grooved, and when you run the palm of your hand over the surface it will feel rough. Look at the equipment listed below. Suggestions are given to help you to estimate the degree of roughness and surface pitting. Try them out and adapt them or invent your own methods: initiative always earns extra marks.

Equipment that you will need:

- Pieces of **sandpaper** of different coarseness to enable you to compare the feel of different surfaces. Take these with you when you do your fieldwork.
- **White cartridge paper** cut into squares 10 cm × 10 cm in size, and thick wax crayons for surface rubbings of stones. Hold the paper onto the surface and rub it with a crayon, as if you were doing a brass rubbing.
- An **Ordnance Survey map** or **compass** to find the direction in which a building faces.
- A **profile former** and **ruler** marked to measure the depth of pitting of the surface. These are easily made as shown in Figure 41.

CAUTION: When carrying the profile former always wrap it in foam rubber and place it in a hard tube, such as a piece of down-pipe 5 cm in diameter.

Fieldwork method

1. Record the **name of the building**, the **material** and the **type of surface**: wall, windowsill, doorstep, pillar or inscription. In which **direction** does the surface face? Record the date of construction, if you are assessing the rate of pollution damage.

Figure 41 Profile former and ruler to use when measuring the depth of damage caused by pollution.

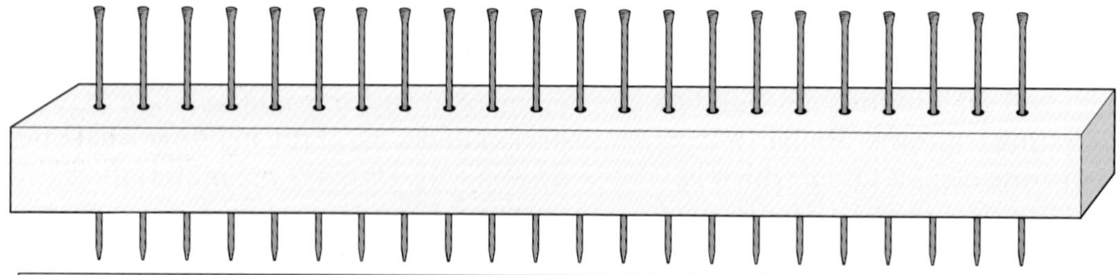

Use a piece of hardwood 30 cm long by 1.25 cm wide and 1.15 cm deep.
Drill a series of holes, with the centres of the holes at intervals of 1 cm.
The nails used are panel pins 4 cm long. These will need to move freely within the drilled holes but not so freely that they will fall out.
To obtain the perfect size of each hole, cut off the head of a normal panel pin and use it in an electric drill to create the holes.

Cover a ruler with graph paper on which you have drawn horizontal lines 1 mm apart. Cover this with sticky plastic.

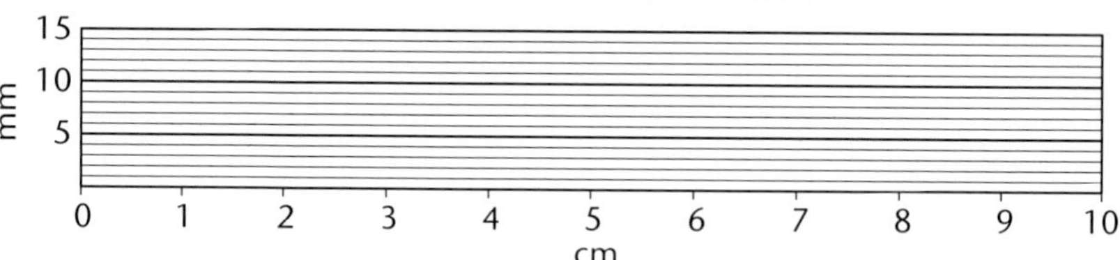

2. Begin your investigation of the degree of surface pitting by discovering whether or not the surface of the material was smooth when first built. Some stones such as granite can be polished to have a glass-like finish, whereas sandstones, concrete and the surfaces of most bricks are less smooth.

   Devise a **scale of values** to indicate the severity of weathering such as:

   1 = minimal (hardly weathered at all)
   2 = moderate
   3 = severe

   The practice in your **reconnaissance visit** will have trained you to recognise these.

At each site, begin by running the palm of your hand over the surface. Describe the feeling of roughness in your **field notebook**. Does it feel smooth, or like fine sandpaper or coarse sandpaper? Compare the feel with your samples of different sandpapers.

Your profile former will reproduce the surface exactly. First make sure that all the heads of the panel pins are level and in a line parallel to the timber. Hold the profile former at the ends and press it firmly with the sharp ends of the pins against the surface to be measured. The panel pins will move within the profile former to reproduce the precise shape of the surface. Next, measure with your ruler the length that the individual pins have moved. The deepest pits or grooves are the most important. **Record your results in your field notebook.**

Analysing your results to draw conclusions

Your 'stone rubbings' and 'profiles' from the profile former are important visual evidence in your results.

1. **Relating pollution damage to building materials.** Arrange your results so that the materials you have investigated are in an order from the most damaged to the least damaged. Write a short paragraph to describe each material and the degree of damage. Draw graphs and bar charts to make your results more clearly understood.

   Are you able to suggest which is the more important type of damage: acid rain or crystal growth? This may be difficult to do, and your reasons are as important as your evidence. Do certain materials seem to be more susceptible to one type of damage than to the other?
2. **Assessing the rate of pollution damage.** On buildings of the same material but of different ages, suggest the rate of weathering damage.
3. **Compare the severity of damage at the splash zone with that at a higher level.** Similarly do different sides of a building show different degrees of damage? You may be able to show different degrees of damage at buildings along your ***transect***. Reproduce the profiles you took with the profile former during your investigations. You may have to go back to check on these, and, if so, say so in your **final report**.

Interesting extras to investigate

1. Discover ways in which building materials may be preserved and protected. There are many stone-preserving companies, and you could write to one in your local area and ask for information. Suggestions on how to write a letter are given on pages 18–20.
2. From the records kept by the Environmental Health Department of your local authority or the Government's laboratory at Abingdon (see Appendix 2), discover how the level of air pollution in your area has varied over the years.

What is being done to reduce air pollution?

This would make an interesting and worthwhile coursework project or a section in your fieldwork project. Make sure that you support what you write by reference to records of air quality monitoring in your fieldwork area. The Environmental Health Department of the local authority will have records, as does the Government's laboratory at Abingdon (see Appendix 2). Records through time should reveal the results of the various measures taken. It would be interesting to compare records for the 1950s or even earlier and the end of the 20th century.

Here are some suggestions:

- Look at the roof of a large Victorian building. Estimate the width of the chimney stacks or count the number of chimney pots. It is worth remembering that 'acid rain' is a term coined well over a century ago. Find out about **The Clean Air Act of 1956** in Britain and other, later, similar acts.
- Motor car exhausts are capable of giving off carbon monoxide, hydrocarbons and oxides of nitrogen. From Science you will know about the two types of catalytic converter designed to be fitted to car exhausts:
  - (a) The oxidation catalyst system alters the air:fuel ratio and converts carbon monoxide into carbon dioxide, and hydrocarbons into water.
  - (b) The three-way catalyst system has the added advantage of reducing the emission of oxides of nitrogen, but this type of catalytic converter cannot be fitted to all cars.

Figure 42 is the printout of the results of a test carried out on the exhaust emissions of a motor car. These tests are compulsory on cars of three years of age and older. They are often referred to as 'MOT Tests'. Discover why and when they were introduced.

Figure 42 The results of a test for exhaust emissions carried out at a vehicle testing centre authorised by the DETR (Department of the Environment, Transport and the Regions). These tests are usually referred to as 'MOT Tests'.

Crypton Gas Analysis

Catalyst (closed loop) MOT Gas Test Results

					Diagnosis	**Limits** Min	Max
Engine oil temperature		=	85	°C	OK	80	–
Fast Idle Test					FAIL		
Engine speed		=	2860	rpm	PASS	2750	3150
CO level	at 2860 rpm	=	0.52	%	FAIL	–	0.30
HC level	at 2860 rpm	=	138	ppm	PASS	–	200
Lambda	at 2860 rpm	=	1.02		PASS	0.95	1.09
Second Fast Idle Test					FAIL		
Engine speed		=	2872	rpm	PASS	2750	3150
CO level	at 2872 rpm	=	0.31	%	FAIL	–	0.30
HC level	at 2872 rpm	=	135	ppm	PASS	–	200
Lambda	at 2872 rpm	=	1.01		PASS	0.95	1.09
Natural Idle Test					PASS		
Engine speed		=	877	rpm	PASS	800	1000
CO level	at 877 rpm	=	0.17	%	PASS	–	0.50
Overall result exhaust emissions test					FAIL		

Since 1990, all cars manufactured in the United Kingdom have been fitted with catalytic converters and made to run on unleaded petrol. However, they are only some of the 200 million motor vehicles in the world, which, every year, cover 300 thousand million kilometres.

- Investigate alternatives to, or ways of limiting the use of, motor vehicles. For example, tramways and other light rail transit systems in big cities; rail transport instead of road transport containers; and the piggy-back system of rail transport for cars on long journeys. In the mid-1990s in the UK the volume of goods transported by lorry was 15 times greater than that transported by rail.

  Look at ways of reducing the numbers of cars in big cities, such as the Certificate of Entitlement Scheme which operates effectively in Singapore. In Lagos, particular number plates are not allowed on certain days of the week.

- Find out more about the use of **flue gas scrubbers/flue gas desulphurisation (FGD)** in power stations and factories to reduce the quantities of sulphur dioxide and **nitric** oxide that are given off. Find out more about the effects of very tall chimneys at power stations and factories. Find out about the international Thirty Percent Club which was set up in 1984.

If you find out the cost of setting up some or all of these measures, you could write a ***cost–benefit analysis*** as part of your project. For example, the cost of FGD (flue gas desulphurisation) costs more than £200 million per power station, but the benefit is that 90% of the sulphur dioxide can be removed from the gases given off.

Techniques for Rivers and Coasts

How to assess water quality

People often talk about '***pollution***', and when they refer to 'pure water' they usually mean water that is fit to drink. What exactly are 'pure water' and 'polluted water'?

Technically speaking, 'pure water' is distilled water. It tastes 'flat' and is not usually used for drinking. Pollution is anything that prevents the water from being used for a particular purpose: old bicycle wheels, tin cans and other rubbish in rivers create an eyesore and prevent the rivers from being used for leisure. Water that is saline (salty) can be used for irrigating crops but not for drinking water for humans and preferably not for animals either.

How does water become polluted?

Most pollution is completely unintentional, and we all play a role in the problem.

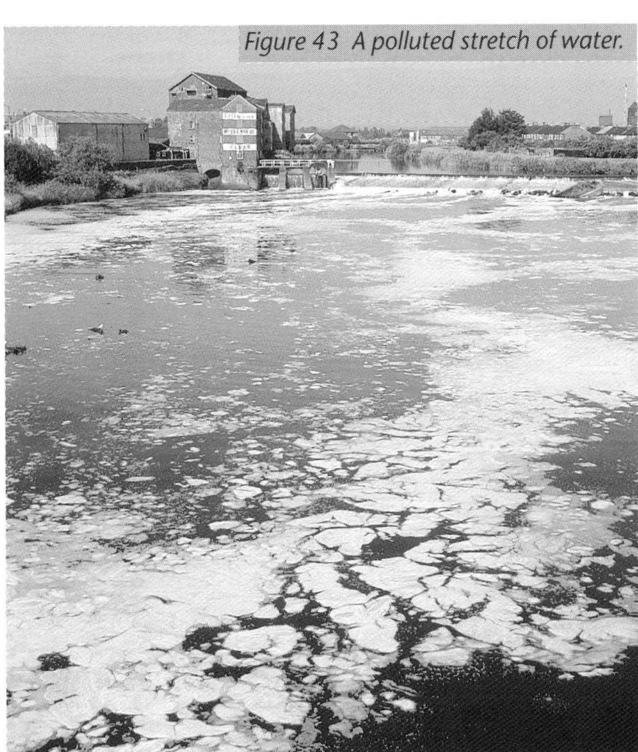

Figure 43 A polluted stretch of water.

- Farms – Over the last fifty years **fertilisers** such as NPK, **herbicides** to kill weeds, and **pesticides** to kill insects and other animal pests have been developed. A 'down' side to these fertilisers is that nitrates and phosphates can reach rivers and lakes where they enrich the water and encourage the growth of algae and other simple plants. These take over and use most of the oxygen in the water with the result that other forms of plant and animal life die. Herbicides and pesticides are designed to kill, and if they are found in rivers and lakes they damage the plants and animals in the water. Slurry from intensive animal farms is another source of enrichment used by simple plants.
- Towns – **Sewage treatment plants** were developed in Victorian times. Whilst the treatment plants have been enlarged and up-graded it has become difficult for them to service towns completely nowadays: there are more bathrooms now than ever before, and we all use a lot of detergents and other household products which contain phosphates. So towns can enrich water and lead to the profusion of algae in the same way that farms do. **Traffic** in towns produces leakages of oil and other hydrocarbons. **Refuse collections** from homes and offices are put into landfill sites or incinerated. Unwanted substances can find their way into water via the hydrological cycle.

> 1 litre of petrol can cover a water surface of 1 hectare.

- Industry – Water is used (a) in **industrial processes** and (b) for **cooling machinery**. Heavy metals such as copper, mercury and lead may find their way into river water and make it toxic. The release of cooling water can raise the temperature by as much as 8 °C below a power station or factory; when this occurs it is described as '**thermal pollution**'.

How to investigate the quality of water

Do as much as you can during fieldwork, and bring back samples of water to complete your investigations in school or at home. Your results can be compared with those of the Environment Agency, the Environmental Health Department of your local authority or a water company. Label each sample clearly as soon as you collect it (use waterproof labels).

Observations can be helped if you take along a clear bottle of 'pure' water. Distilled water can be bought from motor accessory shops. Alternatively, take along a bottle of mineral water, but make sure that it is in a clear – not tinted – container. Use your 'pure' water as a control for your assessments.

Your investigations may be extended to include depth, following the method in the Extra Investigation on Rivers on the Website.

Adapt the table in Figure 44 for recording your results.

Pollution affects rivers and lakes by altering

- the types of plants and animals that live in the water and the proportions of different types
- the oxygen content of the water
- the acidity of the water
- the temperature
- the transparency of the water, which can be termed the 'turbidity' of the water
- the water's chemical content

As you read through the different ways of investigating water quality you will soon see that there is some overlap between the different properties of water.

Plants and animals that live in the water

Each species, particularly animal species, has a narrow range of environmental conditions that suit it best, so an investigation of the species can tell you a lot about the condition of the water. Most of your other investigations will simply confirm the picture of what the life – or the lack of it – in the water has already shown. Those other investigations are, nevertheless, very valuable evidence.

Animals are the more useful indicators of water quality, but it is interesting and useful to investigate the plants present at your fieldwork site. With both plants and animals, the frequency of occurrence of one species is less important than the **variety of species present**.

In fast-flowing water, plants are cushion-shaped (mainly mosses) or have strong and flexible stems, such as the water crowfoot, which is a type of buttercup. Floating plants such as pondweed may be found in gently flowing rivers.

Algae flourish in waters enriched by nutrients. Two types are easily recognised: **blanketweed** forms thick mats with tangled bright green filaments often several metres along. **Algal blooms** are masses of microscopic algae living on the surface. They often appear to be bluish-green in colour. Thermal pollution increases their rate of growth. Algae grow at the expense of animals and other types of plant. They may use up a lot of the dissolved oxygen and reduce the speed of flow of the river. This prevents the river from re-oxygenating itself efficiently. They also reduce the sunlight below them, preventing plants from photosynthesising.

Figure 44 Water quality recording sheet.

Name of investigation site:__________________ Date:__________

Grid reference of investigation site: (*can be completed later*)__________ Weather conditions:__________

Before beginning write a short description of the site:__________________

Depth	**Water life** Record the species present and estimate the proportions of each as a fraction or a percentage of the whole of the animal or plant life		**Oxygen content** How much of the water is smooth/glass-like; or frothy or bubbly turbulent; or white water turbulent?	**Acidity**	**Temperature**	**Transparency**	**Chemical test results**	**Others**
	Animals	**Plants**						
			Record the result if an electronic meter is used					

Figure 45a Moss next to a waterfall

Figure 45b Duckweed

Figure 45c Water crowfoot

Figure 45d Algae

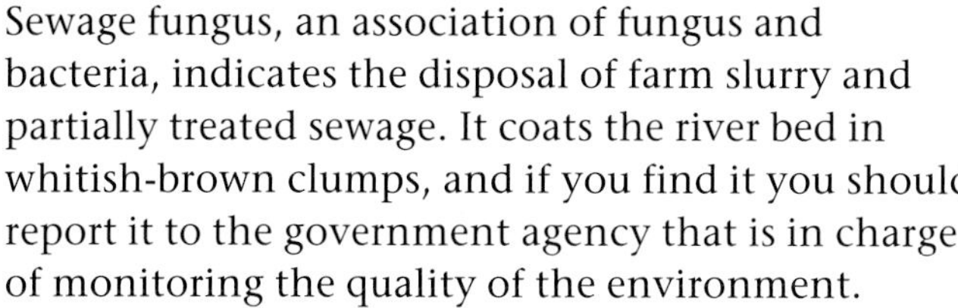
Sewage fungus, an association of fungus and bacteria, indicates the disposal of farm slurry and partially treated sewage. It coats the river bed in whitish-brown clumps, and if you find it you should report it to the government agency that is in charge of monitoring the quality of the environment.

CAUTION: Fish are very sensitive to vibrations so move as carefully as you can.

Fish and riverbed creatures

If there are **salmon** in the water it is of a very high quality, whereas the **roach** is tolerant of water of a much lower quality. Even in canals of relatively low-quality water, roach are found, but their growth has usually been stunted and they are seldom bigger than 15 cm in length.

Creatures that live on the bed of the river or pond are reliable indicators of water quality. Many live

Figure 46 Chart of animals useful for indicating water quality. Tick the boxes as you find the animal species. Note that not all types may be present.

High-quality water —— Increase in tolerance to pollution ——→ Lower-quality water

Date	Location of investigation site	Stonefly nymph (2 tails)	Mayfly nymph (3 tails)	Caddisfly larva	Freshwater shrimp	Water boatman	Water beetle	Snail or limpet	Leech	Water slater	Tubifex worm

under or on the downstream side of rocks and pebbles. They cling to the surface either with suckers or hooked claws to avoid being swept away by the current, and are well-camouflaged because they are a good source of food for fish. Insects such as the stonefly take a year or more to grow as nymphs in water before they hatch. In warm summer weather they may be seen as winged flies hovering above the water having hatched from the nymph chrysalis. Use the chart in Figure 46 to help you to identify the animal life on the bed of your river, pond or lake.

Oxygen dissolved in water

Water normally contains dissolved oxygen to a quantity of ten parts of oxygen per million parts of water, i.e. 10 ppm. A lack of oxygen can be fatal to many forms of aquatic life. Shallow rivers with turbulent flow (when the water looks bubbly) oxygenate themselves rapidly. The type of fish in the water is a useful indication of the oxygen content.

People fishing sometimes build little temporary weirs from stones to entice fish into the richly oxygenated water immediately beyond them.

Water dissolves oxygen where it comes into contact with the air, so turbulent, bubbly flow constantly oxygenates the water. Another source of oxygen for animals that live in the water is that given off by plants in the water during photosynthesis.

In places where vast quantities of bacteria and algae live, as when water is enriched with nitrates and phosphates, the dissolved oxygen content becomes largely used up. This creates what is known as the Biochemical Oxygen Demand (BOD). You will find out more about this in a science textbook. Fish cannot live in water with a BOD of more than 5 ppm. Dissolved Oxygen (DO) can be measured with an electronic meter, but you can discover a lot by looking at and recording the plants and animals in the water.

The types of fish in rivers, lakes and ponds are useful indicators of the following aspects of water quality:

oxygen supply	dissolved substances
temperature	transparency/turbidity of the water

The secretary of an angling club in your fieldwork area will be able to tell you where different types of fish occur. Write a letter explaining why you would like to have this information (see page 18).

Average BOD values:

Clean rivers	1–5 ppm (parts per million)
Treated sewage	10–20 ppm
Crude sewage	200–300 ppm
Farmyard runoff	1500–2000 ppm

Take care to remember that this is the oxygen **demand**, *not* the oxygen content.

Salmon, trout and dace are active fish, particularly at a temperature of around 8 °C. They need a good supply of oxygen and this is found in fast-flowing, turbulent rivers. **Chub**, found in England, also need large quantities of oxygen, whereas the pike is a less active fish and is found in slower-flowing, deeper water. The roach is also content with a low oxygen content.

Acidity

Most fresh water in Britain is slightly acidic, with a pH of less than 7. The acidity mainly reflects the geology and soils of the catchment area. Look at maps of the 'solid geology' and 'drift geology'.

Test the acidity by using small-range pH papers or universal indicator fluid or an electronic acidity probe. If you find a sudden change in the pH level of the water, detective work will eventually find the reason why. Related to acidity is the hardness of water. This comes from rocks within the catchment area which contain calcium and magnesium carbonate. Crustaceans and molluscs tend to be more plentiful in hard water because they need calcium carbonate for their shells. Whilst hard water is less acidic and suits crustaceans and molluscs, few vertebrate animals can live in acidic water. The peaty water of moorland streams supports only a small variety of plants and animals.

Temperature

The dispersal of warm water from a power station or factory can raise the temperature of river water by as much as 8 °C and the water may remain warmer than normal for several kilometres downstream.

A difference of only a few degrees Celsius can result in completely different forms of life in water. Salmon and trout die if the water moves outside the range of 5–20 °C.

Two effects of an increase in the temperature of the water are:

- less oxygen is carried and active animals soon disappear
- the life-cycle of insects is disrupted.

The river needs to be monitored over several months before these effects are discovered, but the government's monitoring agency will be able to supply you with details (see Appendix 2).

You can measure the temperature of the river with a thermometer (see page 33) upstream and downstream of a factory, or above and below the point where a tributary joins your river.

Water transparency/turbidity

If the water is 'cloudy' or opaque, less sunlight reaches the river bed and this reduces the number and types of green plants that can grow there. In turn, this affects the animals which feed on the plants, and the effect is passed through the food chain.

Pondweeds which grow in still water and algae in rivers can reduce the sunlight reaching the bottom, as can the overhanging branches of trees. A large load of clay and silt-sized ***particles*** has the same effect.

Figure 47 Turbidity measuring disc.

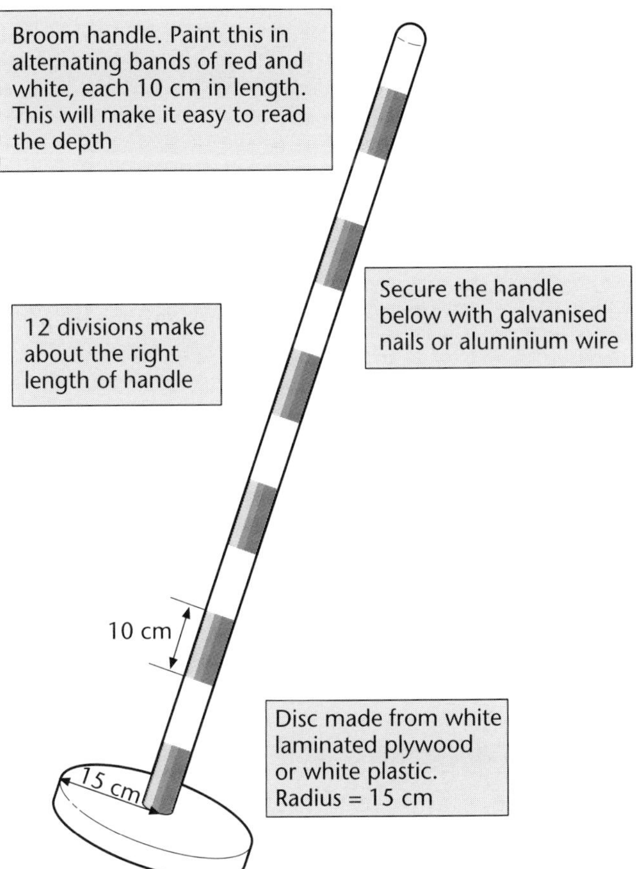
Broom handle. Paint this in alternating bands of red and white, each 10 cm in length. This will make it easy to read the depth
Secure the handle below with galvanised nails or aluminium wire
12 divisions make about the right length of handle
10 cm
15 cm
Disc made from white laminated plywood or white plastic. Radius = 15 cm

Collect a sample of water in a clear glass watertight container. If you are investigating a river or lake with a lot of vegetation or murky-looking water, use a turbidity measuring disc. You can easily make one by attaching a circle of white, laminated plastic to a broom handle, graduated in intervals of 10 cm (Figure 47). Dip this into the water and measure the depth at which the disc becomes less clear. Eventually it may no longer be visible. The level of transparency can change after heavy rainfall, so it would be interesting to take measurements in different weather conditions, and to relate the two.

The water's chemical content

Test kits can be bought cheaply from garden centres. Some are produced for measuring water in ornamental ponds, but even those for testing soil can be used for water in rivers and lakes, because they are designed to test the water in the soil. Collect a sample of water and test it for the presence of nitrates, phosphates and calcium.

A river's total solution load can be measured by using a conductivity meter. This measures the electrical conductivity. The greater the conductivity, the greater is the concentration of dissolved metals.

Investigations back at school or at home

Complete any of the tests that you were unable to do during your fieldwork. In addition:

1. Pass each of your samples through a filter paper made into the shape of a cone. Use a microscope to examine the fine particles that were making the water less clear/more turbid. Compare the quantities you find in your samples collected from different sites. (See page 41 in Air Pollution for more detail on particles.)
2. Put a small quantity of each sample onto an agar plate and label each one clearly. Make two controls for comparison: put 'pure' water onto one plate and put water treated with calcium hypochlorite onto another plate. Cover each plate and leave them. A few days later the samples will show signs of the activity of micro-organisms in the water. You may need help from a teacher with both the preparation of the sample plates and the interpretation of the results. Don't be too surprised if you find that your pure water contains more creatures than you expected!

Comparing your results with those of an official monitoring agency

The government's monitoring service, such as the Environment Agency in England and Wales, has continuous gauging stations on many rivers. These results are available to the public. Two extra sets of records may also be available:

1. The consented values are those agreed between the government's agency and the people who use the rivers to dispose of waste and/or water. For example, farmers have to dilute effluent to a consented level and industrialists have to reduce effluent to a non-toxic level.
2. The River Quality Objective follows European Union guidelines.

Ask for the results from a monitoring station in an area similar to the area in which you are carrying out your fieldwork: a river of the same ***stream order*** would add further weight to your comparisons between the official tests and the results of your investigations.

Look for the address and telephone number in the local telephone directory or contact one of the sources given in Appendix 2 or on the Website.

Looking for more relationships

Compare your results of water quality with the results of investigations of any or all of the following:

- the speed of flow of the river
- the discharge of the river
- the river's load
- local weather conditions at your investigation sites
- the use made of the river today and in the past.

The Meteorological Office will supply you with details of the weather in the month before your fieldwork.

It can be interesting to discover more about the way your river has been used. You could find out more from the Local History section of your Public Library or from the archives of your local newspaper.

The Watch Trust for environmental education as part of the Wildlife Trusts Partnership (RSNC) organises a riverwatch project and will supply equipment for water testing.

Measuring the speed of flow of a river

Along straight stretches of its course a river flows fastest in the middle of its channel. Where it meanders, it flows fastest on the outer side of the bend but at a distance from the bank. The average flow takes place at 4/10ths of the depth as measured

Fieldwork equipment

- **EITHER**

  Floats and stopwatch or digital counter such as a wristwatch

  Oranges make excellent accurate floats for measuring the speed of flow of the surface. In shallow streams the peel of a quartered orange, dog biscuits or courgettes serve the same purpose. None of these will pollute the stream, but it is best to take all of your measurements with the same type of float. To be as accurate as possible, take the measurements at least three times at each point and then work out the average of these. Work out beforehand the number of floats you are likely to need. It may be helpful to put a dab of paint of a particular colour on the floats to indicate the place at which you put them in the water. Red could be used for the float closest to the left bank and green for that in the middle, and so on.

  OR
- **A flowmeter with a digital counter**

  This will give you an instant reading probably in metres per second. Adjust the height of the vane to enable you to take measurements at 0.4 of the depth (see Figure 48). It would be interesting to compare this with the speed of flow at the surface.
- **A length of cord, such as a washing-line**, to span the river and act as a base-line along which to take measurements. When using floats it is helpful to have a second cord across the river at your chosen distance downstream.
- **A tape measure** is useful for measuring the distance downstream over which you intend to use floats to time the speed.
- **A metre rule** to measure the depth and/or the intervals between measuring points. Take a spare one with you.

upwards from the bed (see Figure 48). This is the point where the friction with the channel and the atmosphere is least.

Figure 48 Speed of flow of rivers.

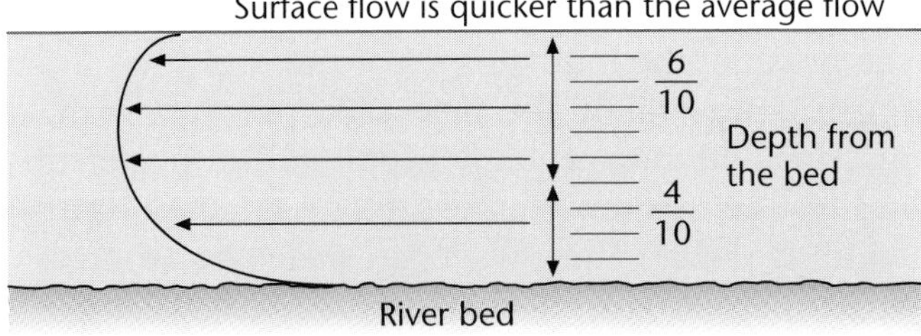

Method using floats and a stopwatch or digital counter

1. Use one cord to span the river at right-angles to the direction of flow. Secure it on both banks with a tent peg or tie it around a tree root. The person(s) placing the floats in the water will stand at this line.
2. Measure or pace out your chosen distance of 10 or 20 m downstream and put the second cord in place there. The person timing the floats and then catching them will stand here and call to the person recording when a float arrives at the line.
3. Choose intervals across the river at which floats will be placed in the water. The distance between them will depend on the width of the river and the amount of detail you wish to investigate. The intervals will form a ***sample*** and this is explained in more detail on pages 15–18. Here are some suggestions:
   - Divide the width of the river into four and measure the speed at the left-bank side, in midstream and at the right-bank side.
   - Choose a regular interval such as 1 m, 50 cm or 10 cm. This is a **systematic sample**.
   - Take a **random sample** using numbered counters or a table of random numbers.

Figure 49 Measuring rate of flow of a stream

4. Your floats should be placed in the water at the same time for each set of measurements. Ideally this would involve the same number of people as there are floats. This may not be possible. When you put the floats into the water alert the 'timer' at the finishing line downstream by waving or blowing a whistle.
5. On a sheet such as that in Figure 50, record the time taken for the floats to cover the chosen distance.

Figure 50 Table for recording the speed of flow of a river. Adapt your table according to the way you take your measurements.

Table for recording speed of flow at: *(name of fieldwork location)*		
Left-bank float (blue paint)	Midstream float (red paint)	Right-bank float (no paint)

Floats measure the speed of flow of the **surface** of the river. Geographers and hydrologists have calculated that, to give a truer estimate of the average speed of the whole river, the results for the surface speed should be multiplied by 0.8.

To make sure that your results are as accurate as possible, repeat the measuring procedure at least three times. Record each of these and when analysing your data calculate the average. Explain why you have done this in your final report.

Method using a flow-meter

Follow steps 1–3 described above and then:

(a) Use the metre rule to measure the depth of water.

(b) Adjust the depth of the vane on the flow-meter so that it will measure the speed of flow at 0.4 of the depth from the bed (Figure 48).

(c) Take your measurements and write them on a recording sheet adapted from the one in Figure 50.

It is interesting at each measuring point to also take the speed of flow of the water at the surface. Compare the two sets of measurements later and in your **final report** give your views on what they show. This would be a useful piece of ***interpretation*** and ***evaluation*** of the method.

How to recognise constructive and destructive waves

Waves are generated by the wind. In deep water only the wave, and not the water, moves forward. You can test this by sending a wave along a rope or by watching a brightly painted cork dropped from a pier into deep water.

A wave breaking on a beach is made up of two parts: the part moving forward onto the beach is called the **swash** and the part that runs back to the sea down the beach is called the **backwash** (see Figure 51).

Figure 51 The swash and backwash of a wave.

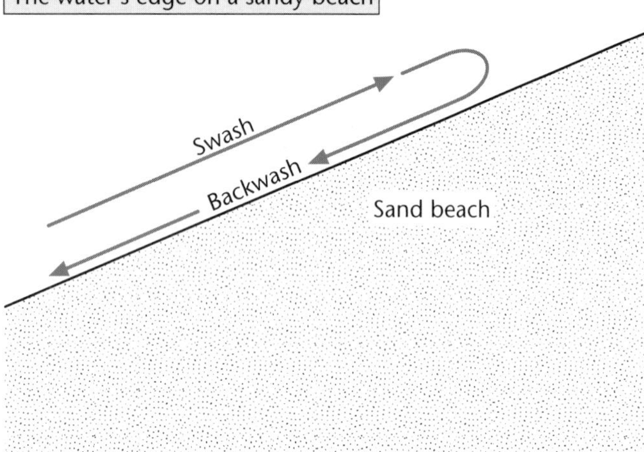

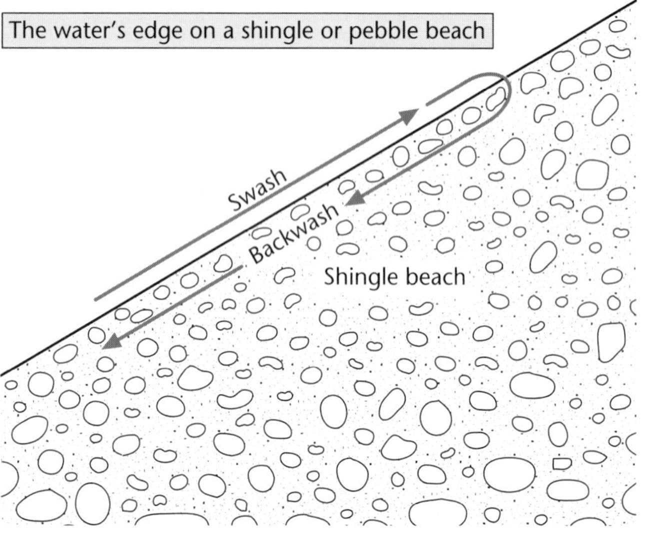

If the swash is stronger than the backwash the wave builds up the beach and is known as a **constructive wave**. Constructive waves break on the beach every 9 or 10 seconds. In waves that break more frequently, reaching the beach every 4 or 5 seconds, the backwash of one wave interferes with the swash of the following wave and spoils its forward movement. It is rather like people walking in a line and unexpectedly tripping over the person in front! In this way the swash loses much of its up-building power. These waves are called **destructive waves** because the effect is for material to be lost from the beach.

In your **final report** describe how you counted the *average* number of waves per minute, and then identified them as constructive (beach-building) waves or destructive (non-beach-building) waves. Try to link the wave type to the features of the beach during your fieldwork. Count the number of breakers arriving on the beach for a period of three minutes and calculate the average per minute. If the average number of breakers is 6 or 7 per minute then class them as constructive waves. If an average of 12 to 14 breakers arrive within one minute, class them as destructive waves. Calculate the average of several measurements per day during your fieldwork.

Record the wave frequency in your field notebook, identify the type of wave and explain in your **final report** how you timed and classified them.

Measuring the movement of material by longshore drift

Along a straight stretch of coastline where the waves approach from an oblique angle, longshore drift may be taking place. At low tide collect a sample of beach material from the foreshore, which is the zone between the high tide mark and the low tide level. Use a small-sized **quadrat** to help you to choose the material without bias. How to make a quadrat is explained on page 14.

Take a selection of beach material of different ***particle*** sizes and shapes and, using spray paint, mark them in easily seen colours. Now return them to the beach, putting them down at a recognisable location on the foreshore, e.g. in the lee of a groyne or beside a boathouse. Return to the beach at low tide once or twice daily for the next week or ten days and look for your painted beach material. Each time you find a particle, pace out or use a tape measure to record the distance it has been transported. Record also the length of time taken for the particle to move.

Does there seem to be a relationship between the distance moved and the size, weight and shape of the pebbles/shingle? Could the weather conditions and the state of the sea (the size of breakers and the height of the tide) have affected the movement of your materials? If all or most of one group has disappeared, can you suggest reasons why this could have occurred?

For greater detail you may decide to investigate the weight, shape and size of different beach materials. Ways of measuring these are described below. Obviously this will have to be done before you return your sample to the beach.

Measuring the size and shape of particles

Measurements can be made of ***particles*** collected from beaches, river deposits, glacial deposits and weathered rocks.

A particle has three axes (see Figure 52). The most important ones to measure are the long axis and the short axis. The axis ratio may be calculated as shown on pages 175–6. When deposited by water or wind, particles usually lie with their short axis projecting upwards and their long axis pointing in the direction of flow of the water or wind.

Particles can be classified into the following shapes: (a) a **sphere**, like a ball; (b) a **rod**, like a torpedo or cigar; and (c) a **disc**, like a coin.

Figure 52 The dimensions of a pebble.

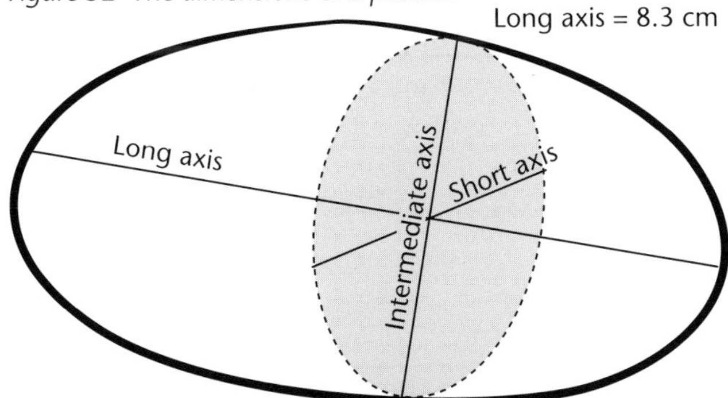

It is difficult to take measurements of particles whose long axis is shorter than 1 cm. Both the particles and a ruler may be viewed through a magnifying glass. See p174 in Coasts

Dividing your sample into particle sizes

Divide your sample into three classes: coarse, medium and fine. Read on and decide how to make your classification. Describe in your **final report** how you have done this and weigh up the accuracy of your classification. This will be an important part of your ***evaluation***

Begin by sieving your sample to divide it into particle sizes. Use a riddle or sieve. Fine material may be divided by using a set of laboratory sieves or kitchen sieves (see Figure 53).

Particles should be dry when they are weighed. They can be left on a radiator or placed in a cool oven to dry out.

To describe the proportions of your sample that are coarse, medium and fine, place each in a separate bag and weigh it. Record the weight. Add up the

Figure 53 Using kitchen sieves to divide fine particles into three sizes.

Flour sieve
Metal sieves hold particles of 2 mm diameter and larger.
Plastic sieves hold particles of 1 mm diameter and larger
= **large particles**

Coffee sieve
Holds particles of 0.5 mm and more
= **medium particles**

Paper
Collects particles of less than 0.5 mm diameter
= **small particles**

total of all three and then calculate each as a **percentage** (see page 86) of the total weight.

For each, or for a ***sample*** of the larger particles, use a ruler or a pebble-measure to classify each into the following recognisable categories:

Particle size	Longest axis (in mm)
boulder	over 200
cobble	60–200
pebble	5–59
shingle	2–4
sand	0.5–1.9
fine sand	less than 0.5

To take a sample, lay the particles in a line irrespective of their size or shape. Choose sample particles at a regular interval, at a random interval, or as a stratified sample. For more detail on sampling methods, see pages 16–18.

Figure 54 shows a pebble-measure that is easy to make. Glue a square of centimetre graph paper 30 cm × 30 cm onto 4-mm-thick plywood or onto very strong card. Cover it with transparent adhesive so that it can be wiped clean. Measure the pebble by placing it on the pebble-measure. Use a set-square to ensure that your measurements are accurate. Record your results on a recording sheet along the lines of the one in Figure 55. Do this recording immediately after you have weighed and measured your particles. Another type of pebble measure is given in the Coasts Investigation (see Figure 145 on page 172).

Figure 54 How to make a pebble-measure.

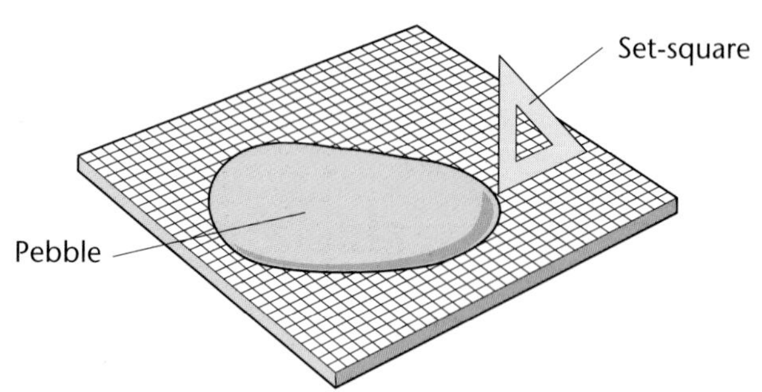

Figure 55 Table for recording particle size and shape.

Location at which sample was collected: (*give details*)______					
	% weight of total	Average short axis (in mm)	Average long axis (in mm)	Shape	Description (colour, rock type, etc.)
Dry weight of coarse material					
Dry weight of medium material					
Dry weight of fine material					
Dry weight of total sample					

Techniques for Towns and Traffic

Parking availability survey

Many car parks and streets have parking spaces marked by white lines and you can easily count these. In order to make a good estimate of the capacity of an **unmarked car park** you should know the size of space needed for different types of vehicles. There may be marked spaces for a car and a minibus at school and it would be sensible to **pace** these out or to measure them. Make a note of the size in your field notebook.

If a parking attendant is on duty, ask the capacity of the park and the average length of time for which vehicles usually park. Explain why you want this information. The car park may be managed by remote control, so write a letter or telephone to ask for the same information.

The cost of parking may be linked to the length of stay and the location of the car park, so make a note of this. Town centre car parks are often more expensive than ones further out. Do people park in streets near to the car park to avoid paying the charge?

Investigate the **restrictions to parking** in streets. Are there time limits between which parking is not allowed? Record the presence of single yellow lines, double yellow lines, and notices that indicate 'waiting times' and 'delivery times'. Car, coach and lorry parks and their use can be illustrated effectively on graph paper. You could easily record your information straight onto graph paper, and then make a neat copy later (see Figure 56). Devise a colour code for different types of vehicles or use letters such as C = car, M = minibus, O = coach.

Figure 56 Graph paper shaded to show how a car park is used.

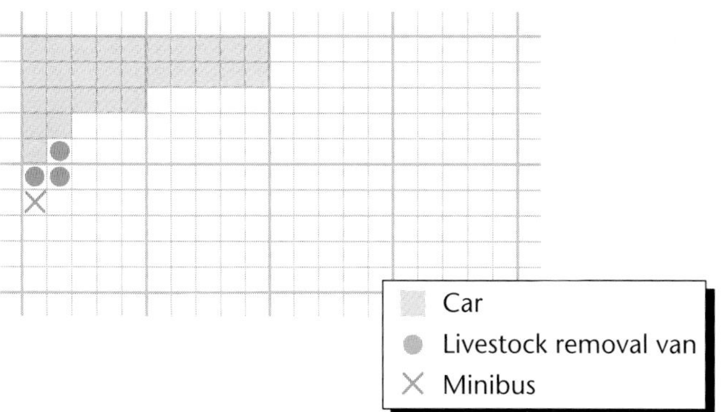

If you compare the layout of different car parks you will be able to discover what you consider to be the most efficient way of using space. Would you mark a car park or street with individual 'boxes' or mark it simply with lines or leave it bare? Do you think that 'Pay and Display' is a good idea? Do you approve of constructing new buildings on stilts to provide parking at ground level? If you were an architect or town planner how would you cater for parking?

The recommended size of a car parking space in Britain is 5 m × 2.5 m. For parking of cars by disabled people a greater width is advised.

Parked vehicle survey

It would be obvious to conduct this survey at the same time as investigating the availability of parking (see above). Count the numbers of different types of vehicles occupying the parking areas.

Use a tally sheet such as that in Figure 60 (page 59) with columns for different types of vehicles. Note the date, day and time of your survey. Walk systematically around the parking area and put strokes for the different types of vehicle in the appropriate columns on your tally chart.

If you are investigating the **places from which cars have come** to a leisure area or stretch of coastline, look at the road tax disc displayed on the windscreen. Many people pay road tax at a Post Office close to their home so this is a reliable

Figure 57 A car tax disc

method of investigation. For those owners who pay their tax directly to the Drivers and Vehicles Licensing Centre in Swansea, devise a symbol or use the abbreviation DVLC. Alternatively you can look at garage label addresses usually found on the back windows of cars.

If a parking attendant or traffic warden is on duty, explain that you are taking a survey of parked vehicles for your geography project and reassure him/her that you will not touch any of the vehicles. Offer to explain this also to any vehicle owners or passengers who are present.

You may discover variations in the numbers of vehicles parked at different times of the day – mid-morning, lunchtime and mid-afternoon – and on different days of the week. Weekends should show a different pattern from weekdays. Public holidays can make a difference too.

If there is a vast number of vehicles it may be sensible to use a ***systematic sample***. Decide upon a workable interval, such as every third or fifth vehicle, and keep to it accurately. A random sample would also work. Note the reason for using a sampling method, and include this in your **final report**.

Where vehicles have come from can be invaluable in showing the catchment area of where you are conducting your survey. This can be extremely important evidence if your aims include the distance travelled or the place of origin of visitors to a shopping centre, sports venue, country park or other leisure area. The importance of this is explained under 'Catchment area/market area/sphere of influence/interaction' on page 110. Lorries, vans, coaches and minibuses often have their address, or at least a telephone number, printed on the vehicle. Make a list of the places of origin and, if a place occurs more than once, put a tick beside it each extra time.

Counting moving pedestrians and vehicles

A simple method of observing moving objects, including pedestrians, is to choose a line: it may be an imaginary one, such as between where you are standing at the back of a pavement, and a lamp standard or a telephone box on the opposite side of the road. Keep your eyes firmly fixed on the position of the line, and count the numbers of people or vehicles crossing it. If you are working with a friend you can decide to count the objects moving in different directions. Record the objects on a tally chart: 𝍸| = 6. A survey sheet for counting pedestrians is given in Figure 58, and one for recording various types of traffic is given in Figure 60.

Consider carefully what evidence you need for your particular aims. This will help you to choose the best location for the count. If one of your aims is to investigate the 'wear and tear' on a footpath in a Country Park, you would probably be best to locate your count on the approach to a marked viewpoint. If your aim is to investigate the effectiveness of

Figure 58 Tally chart for pedestrian surveys.

Location of count: outside Betta shoes	Time: 1100h – 11.10	
Pedestrians moving: towards the post office 𝍸 𝍸 𝍸 𝍸 |||	Pedestrians moving: towards the bus station 𝍸 𝍸 ||	Total in both directions
Total: 23	Total: 12	35
Location of count:	Time:	
Pedestrians moving:	Pedestrians moving:	Total in both directions
Total:	Total:	

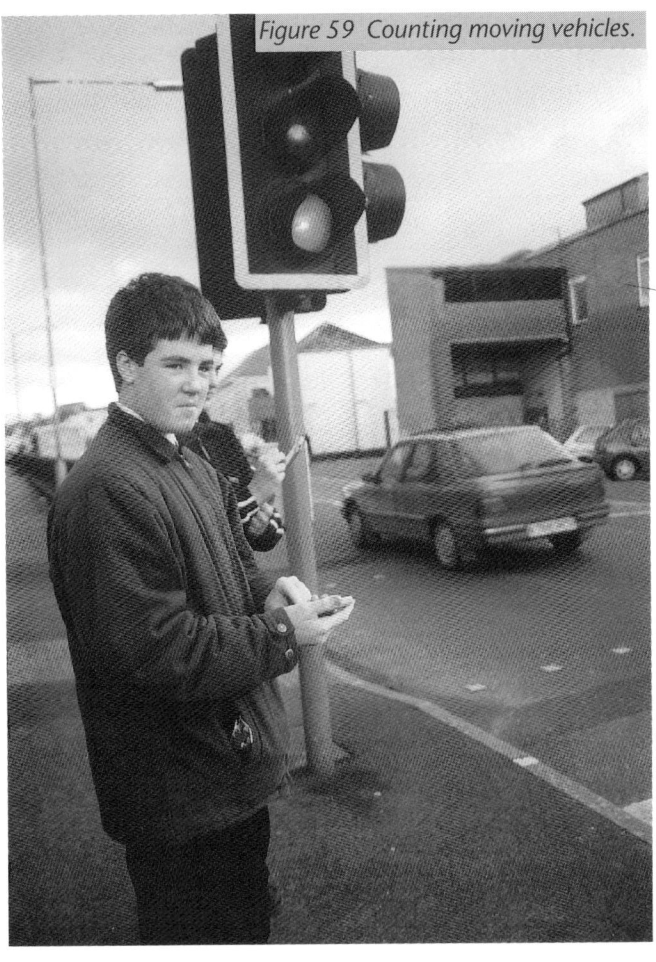

Figure 59 Counting moving vehicles.

traffic-calming measures in a residential part of a town, you could conduct your vehicle count at points on the access roads to the area.

Counts carried out at different times on the same day and on different days of the week, or in different weather conditions, help to produce important and interesting data.

Traffic and vehicle survey tally sheets

Do a quick reconnaissance survey to decide on the number of types of vehicle you wish to include. The greater the number of different types, the more difficult recording becomes, particularly at busy times when a lot of traffic is passing. If you practise before your fieldwork you will become quick and accurate.

How to investigate town development through time

Even an outline knowledge of the history of architecture and building materials, and of street planning, can help you to discover a lot about the development of a town, village or other built environment. You may need to use all three to help you to piece together the jigsaw of urban

Figure 60 Traffic survey sheet.

TRAFFIC SURVEY **Survey site:** **Date and time:**

Investigation being carried out as part of a geographical investigation at

____ School/College

for ____ examination

Vehicles travelling along ________________________________

(DETR road number) in the direction of ________________________

Synchronise your watch with the person counting on the opposite side of the road and signal to each other when to begin. Count for 10 minutes only.

***CAUTION:** Keep well back on the pavement.*

Count only the vehicles on your side of the road.

CAR	LORRY (HGV)	LIGHT VAN	CONTAINER (record sep. from lorry)	DOUBLE-DECKER BUS	SINGLE-DECKER BUS OR COACH	MINIBUS	MOTORCYCLE	BICYCLE
卌 卌 卌 III	*III*	*I*	*II*					

development. As you investigate your fieldwork area, record your observations on a Building Recording Sheet.

BUILDING RECORDING SHEET

Remember to mark your base-map so that you will be able to identify the location of each building.

Address: ____________________

Architectural style: ____________________

Materials used in:

Walls: ____________________

Architraves (surrounding windows and doors): ____________________

Roof: ____________________

Width of street : ____________________
(estimate this from the number of car lanes)

Extra details: ____________________

In each of your streets, take a ***systematic sample*** of buildings such as every fifth or tenth building on both sides of the street.

Investigating town development through time would make a very good project on its own for Geography, or as joint coursework for both Geography and History.

Architectural styles

Date stones are the most reliable evidence of the age of a building in the field, but names can reveal quite a lot: 'Jubilee Terrace' probably refers to buildings constructed close to the date of Queen Victoria's Diamond Jubilee in 1897; 'Waterloo Farm' is likely to have been built close to the Battle of Waterloo in 1815.

The architectural style of people's homes is closely linked to the building materials available at the time, but the following is a guide to use.

Old buildings may be assumed to be **pre-Georgian**, which may approximately be taken as being built before 1700. Old houses often have half-timbered upper storeys which sometimes project outwards over the ground floor. There was great competition for urban land in those times too!

Figure 61 Pre-Georgian buildings

Georgian town houses. Simplicity and elegance of design were important to the Georgians: the rectangular windows and doors give the impression that all of the houses are mirror-images of one another. The homes of wealthy people often had wrought iron railings separating the basement from the street, and some have iron balconies. Few had their own garden but there may have been a garden of grass and trees in a square for the use of all the residents. Houses of wealthy people had coach houses and stables known as 'mews'. Streets were usually wide enough to allow turning space for a carriage drawn by two or more pairs of horses.

Figure 62 Georgian town houses.

Victorian houses. The Victorians liked elaborate ornamentation and wealthy people's homes often had turrets and windows of coloured glass. Slate roofs were topped by cast-iron grills. Houses were often surrounded by large gardens, sometimes with a lodge.

Figure 63 Late Victorian Terraced houses.

Terraced houses were built close to factories because most people had to walk to work. After the Public Health Act of 1875 many houses were built from shiny red Accrington bricks and tiles because smoke did not stick to shiny surfaces. Few houses had gardens. Public parks in towns were important in providing 'a garden for the gardenless'.

Inter-war houses. Inter-war houses were built mainly in the 1920s and 1930s. Many of these are semi-detached with bay windows and gardens at the front and back. Few families owned a car, and a garage built separately distinguishes inter-war houses from those built at a later date. Pebble-dash was a fashionable decoration.

Figure 64 Inter-war houses

Late 20th-century houses. Slate had become expensive by the middle of the 20th century so houses built more recently have tiled roofs. Windows became large and are often double-glazed and have UPVC frames. Most houses have garages; many have car-ports and conservatories.

Figure 65 Late 20th- century houses

Building materials

Until the middle of the 20th century most buildings were constructed from materials that were available locally. The transport of heavy and bulky building materials took too long and cost too much for most people to use. Only important buildings such as cathedrals and town halls had stone brought from far away.

The following are some distinguishing features to look for when investigating the age of buildings.

Old buildings (before 1700). Only very well-built houses remain and these probably indicate the early centre of a village or town. In lowland areas many were built with a timber frame infilled with brick and plastered over for protection from the weather. In upland areas where stone was found close to the surface, many houses and farm buildings were constructed from stone; the same type of stone was used for drystone walls.

Georgian (18th century). Glass was more widely available than before and large sash windows, which move up and down, were invented at this time. Most windows have nine or twelve panes. Bricks may have been used, but to preserve a simple appearance houses were, for the first time, built in terraces. Iron was more readily available, and the houses of wealthy people in the Regency period (late Georgian) were decorated with balconies and had railings between the street and the entrance to the basement.

Victorian (19th century). The Industrial Revolution brought mass production of bricks of uniform quality. Improved transport facilities enabled them to be distributed widely. Victorians liked to make patterns in the walls with bricks of different colours such as yellow and red, in diamond shapes, squares and stripes. Highly glazed bricks such as those from Accrington in Lancashire were used because smoke particles from the many chimneys did not stick to their surface. Slate became used widely as a roofing material because it could be split into fine sheets which weighed less than the flagstones used earlier. The pitch of roof became steeper.

20th century. Reinforced concrete was developed. Bricks became more uniform in size. Artificial roof tiles became widely used because they are very much cheaper than slate. UPVC was developed for use in doors and window frames. The use of steel frames in large buildings enabled them to be built upwards for many storeys. Stone cladding about 1 cm in thickness began to be used frequently on important buildings from the 1980s. Protective varnish for stone cladding was developed in the 1990s.

Street planning and patterns

Street patterns are often more easily distinguished from a map or aerial photograph than in the field. Street planning in towns was not widespread before Victorian times. At that time, rapid growth of population and of urban areas saw the development of networks for the supply of water, drainage, gas, electricity and telephone. Underground pipes were laid beneath the streets near to the buildings they would serve. This is one reason why the line of the streets tends to continue unchanged for hundreds of years.

The width of streets often indicates their age and the social environment in which they were planned. Old streets were often very narrow and winding, such as the Shambles in York or those leading to the Royal Mile in Edinburgh.

In contrast, the streets developed in Georgian and Victorian times had to be wide enough to allow a carriage drawn by two or more pairs of horses to turn around. You may have noticed this if you have visited Bath, Cheltenham, the Regent's Park area of London or the New Town in Edinburgh.

Victorian streets were planned in a grid-iron pattern of straight streets meeting at right-angles. The streets of terraced houses near to the factories are narrow by comparison with the tree-lined avenues enjoyed by the wealthy people.

Town planning in the first half of the 20th century often included curved streets in residential areas. Privet hedges were widespread as garden boundaries, and the density of housing was at its lowest in the 1930s, with only 30 houses per hectare. The second half of the 20th century saw the predominance of housing estates.

Ordnance Survey maps of the present day can give many clues to development through time. Street patterns often reflect the period of history in which they were laid out. Canals and railways were usually built on land that could be bought cheaply because it was not being used for anything particularly important at the time. They can indicate the edge of town at the time of building. Most canals were constructed in the late 18th century – so much so that the 1790s are sometimes referred to as the years of 'canal mania'.

Railway stations built in Victorian times (1837–1901) were located as close to the town centre as space allowed. Railways served as links between the town centre and the middle-class residential areas, and electric trams which began running in the 1890s linked working-class residential areas with the centre of town.

Public parks and botanical gardens played an important role in social life in Victorian and Edwardian times (1901–1910). They often have names such as Victoria Park or Alexandra Park, or the name of the founder whose statue, if one was erected, may be dated.

Figure 66 Aerial view of Manchester city centre showing street patterns

Analysing Data in the Form of Maps and Graphs

Annotation of maps and pictures

Annotation means 'adding notes' to a picture, map or diagram to emphasise or to add to the amount of detail shown. There are three ways of doing this:

1. Writing on the picture, map or diagram.
2. Using arrows to link notes written in the margin to the feature on the picture, map or diagram.
3. Writing on tracing paper which covers the picture, map or diagram.

Look at the illustrations in this book to see how they have been annotated (see Figure 4 on page 13).

Draw maps and diagrams in pencil first so that you can easily alter any mistakes. Check to make sure whether or not you have to acknowledge any computer software used.

Figure 67 How to make a tracing overlay.

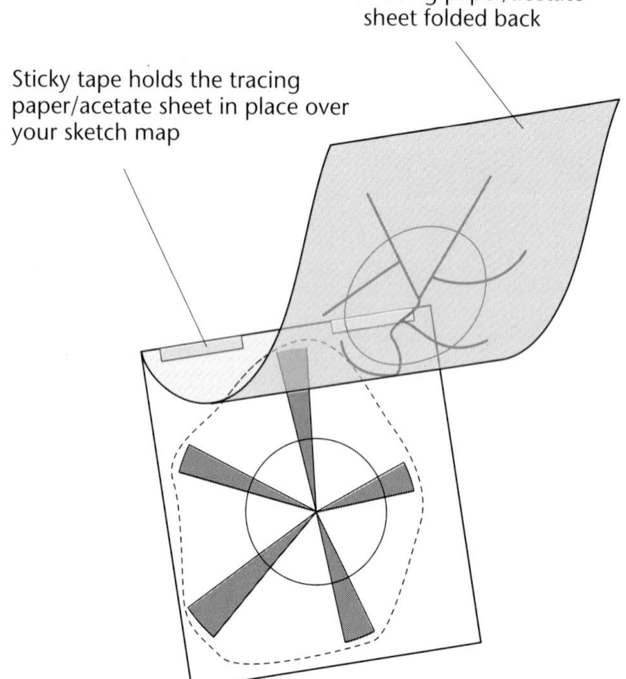
Tracing paper/acetate sheet folded back
Sticky tape holds the tracing paper/acetate sheet in place over your sketch map

Tracing overlays

Layers of tracing paper or acetate sheets are laid over the base-map and held in place by sticky tape along one edge (see Figure 67). This technique is successful for showing areas at different dates in time, or for showing different features at the present time. Examples are the ***sphere of influence/catchment area*** for different shopping and professional services in a town, and the flow of different types of vehicles along a road.

Information can be 'built up' layer by layer and, in this way, tracing overlays produce a result similar to that of a Geographical Information System generated by a computer.

Try not to show too much complicated detail because the result could become confusing. Take care in choosing colours and types of shading to produce the desired end result.

Trial Run 4

Here are the results of a traffic count on the A5103 in Hulme, 3 minutes from Manchester city centre.

Day and time of the count: Wednesday 10 June 1998 between 4.50 and 5.00 pm

	Car	Van	Bus	Lorry	Motorcycle	Bicycle
Towards the city centre	66	10	9	12	0	2
Outwards	223	15	16	3	16	8

Draw a flow-line map to represent the above data, using a different tracing overlay for each type of vehicle. Obviously, the scale must be the same for each overlay.

Isopleths

Isopleth is the Greek word for 'equal quantity'. Isopleths are lines drawn on a map to join points of equal value. Contour lines on a map are isopleths drawn at a particular height above mean sea level.

The skill in drawing isopleths comes from interpreting the map to decide exactly where the line should run between any two dots of equal value.

You will know that lines along which the temperature is equal are **isotherms**, lines along which the rainfall is equal are **isohyets**, and lines on a map along which the atmospheric pressure is equal are **isobars**. Look for these isopleths on the climate maps in your atlas or geography textbook. Isopleths are sometimes known as 'isolines'.

Isochrones

Lines joining points of equal time are called **isochrones**, i.e. the time taken to travel between particular points. Look at the Towns Extra Investigation on the Website.

Choropleth maps

When the area between boundaries such as fields on the map of a farm or between isopleths on a map is shaded in different colours or densities of lines or dots, the map is known as a ***choropleth map***. For example, a lake may be shaded in blue, whilst purple may be used for the highest land, brown for land of intermediate height and green for low land. Atlases contain choropleth maps.

Line shading and dot shading of different densities may be used to show different values. Look at Figure 68 and experiment before beginning. Lines or dots can be drawn over areas of solid-colour shading to show a second set of data. Both lines and dots can be used in combination on the same map or diagram. **Remember to give your map a key**.

Figure 68 Different densities of line or dot shading can represent different values.

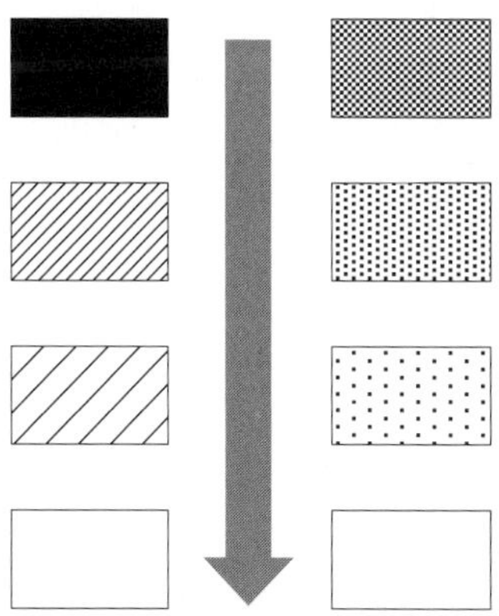

Topological maps

Topological maps are neither drawn to scale nor do they have a compass direction. But they have two great strengths:

1. for people who want to find their way on a journey, particularly when using public transport, and
2. for simplifying the analysis of a route network.

The first ***topological map*** in the world to be widely used was the London Underground map, which was produced in the 1930s by Howard Beck.

Figure 69 Maps to show access by road to Lacock Abbey (National Trust), Wiltshire.

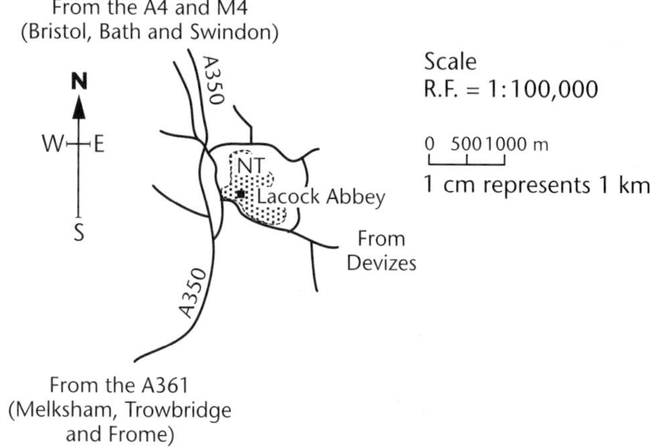

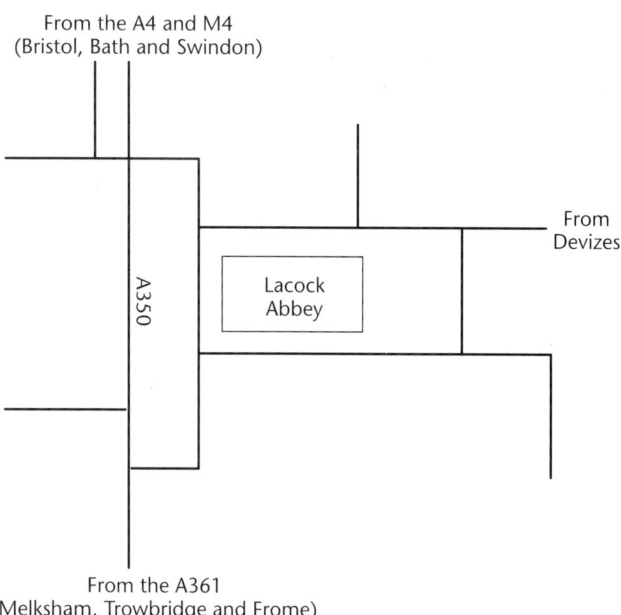

From your knowledge of the London Underground map and of similar maps of bus and train services in your local area, you will realise that neither the compass direction nor the distance is of great importance to the people who use these maps: London tube passengers are often to be seen silently counting the stops before 'their' station is reached!

Topology is a type of geometry. On topological maps the routes are often shown as straight lines. Where two or more routes meet, this is often marked as a dot, and the junction itself is termed a 'node'. The lines between nodes are termed 'edges' or 'arcs'. From the maps in Figure 69 work out how to convert a geographical map into a topological map.

TRIAL RUN 5

1 Redraw the map in Figure 70 as a topological map to show access by road to Alnwick Castle in Northumberland.

2 Describe the route for someone arriving from Berwick-upon-Tweed.

Figure 70 Geographical map to show access by road to Alnwick Castle in Northumberland.

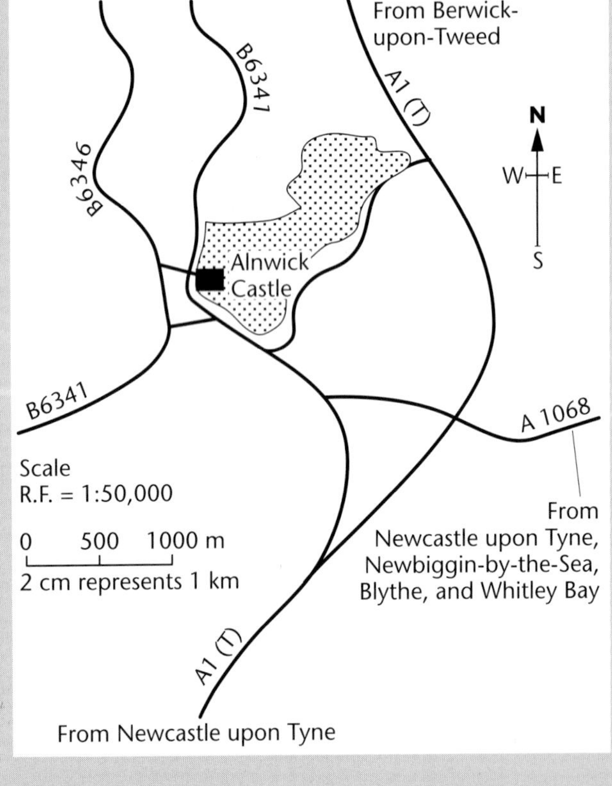

Evaluation

Describe separately the strengths of topological maps and their weaknesses. When would you recommend using **a** a geographical map, and **b** a topological map?

Desire-line maps

Desire-lines are drawn on a map to show the movement of people from their homes to particular destinations such as schools, workplaces, shopping centres, places of entertainment, and holiday resorts.

Desire-lines are drawn as straight lines or arrows between, for example, your home and school. Figure 71 presents two desire-line maps. These show very clearly the difference between people's journeys for Christmas shopping and visits to their doctor. Desire-line maps also emphasise the importance of different service centres, and are helpful when calculating the ***sphere of influence/catchment area/trade area*** of a service centre. This is done in the same way as the delimiting of a drainage basin or water catchment area (see Rivers Trial Run, page 128).

TRIAL RUN 6

On tracings of Figure 71:

1 Instead of arrows draw the desire-lines as separate lines, each of which represents 10 people.

2 Draw dashed lines around the places of origin of the desire-lines for Bangor to show its sphere of influence/catchment area for Christmas shopping and then for the doctor. Remember to include the Bangor residents who use Bangor's services, i.e. the proportional circles. Describe the contrasts in the area. You could calculate the area in square kilometres for each catchment area following the method explained on page 128.

Evaluation

a Describe which method of drawing desire-lines you consider to be the most accurate and visually effective.

b Describe your views on the accuracy of calculating the area of the sphere of influence in this way.

Figure 71 Desire-line maps to show where people in north Wales go (a) for Christmas shopping and (b) to visit their doctor.

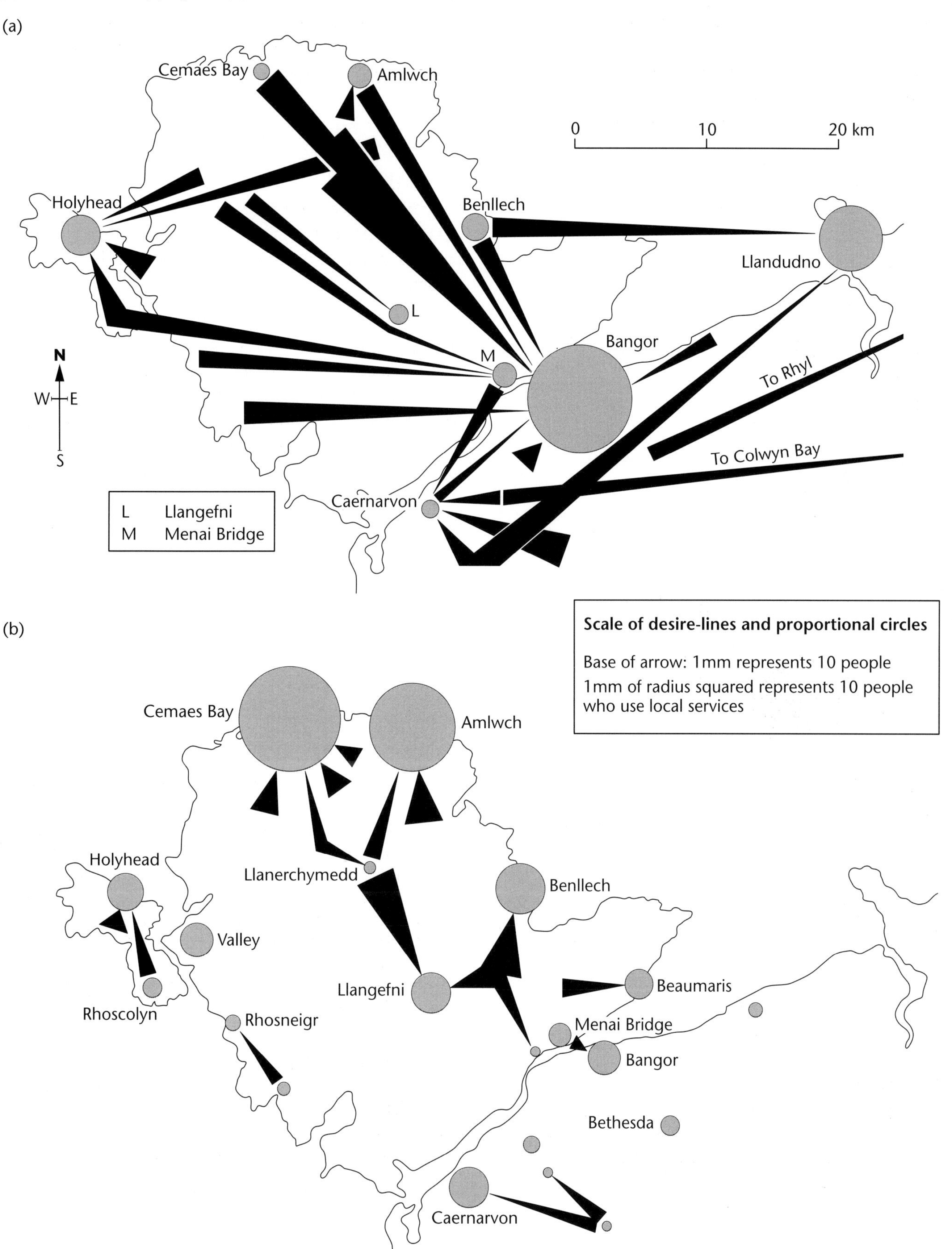

How to describe the distribution of features on a map

It may be sufficiently accurate for you to divide the map into quarters, and then to identify the particular quarter (e.g. the south-western quarter) in which most of the features occur. Obviously you could subdivide the map into smaller sections.

The accuracy and ***objectivity*** are increased if you count the total number of times a feature such as buildings or postboxes occur in particular parts of the map, or if you calculate the area of different parts of the map that are covered by a feature such as a type of farm land use. Now you will be able to calculate the percentage of the total that is located in any one of the quarters of the map.

Centre of a distribution on a map

Place tracing paper over the area of distribution you wish to describe. Mark as dots all of the features whose distribution you want to describe. Choose a system for this such as numbers so that you will be able to identify each feature with its dot. The middle of each field in a farm, or the centre of a shop frontage on a street, would make sensible locations for your dots.

Count all of the dots, working across the map from east to west. Use a ruler to draw a line down the map so that there is an equal number of dots on both sides. Do the same thing from north to south. Where the lines intersect is the central point. You will recognise that this is, in fact, the **median centre**.

Adjacency matrix

If you suspect that particular types of land use in a town are influenced in their location by what is next door, an interesting method of analysis is to complete an **adjacency matrix**.

Figure 73 shows an extract from *Kelly's Trades Directory* for part of Market Street in Manchester in 1961. Market Street has been one of the main shopping streets in the CBD (Central Business District) of Manchester for a long time.

Beside each is the building number on Market Street. Your grandparents may recognise some of the names from your own town centre!

TRIAL RUN 7

Figure 72 shows 1 km^2 of Kendal in Cumbria. The grey-shaded buildings all have listed status. Analyse their distribution on the map in terms of the median centre. The western half of the square has been done for you.

1. On a piece of tracing paper place a dot in the centre of each building's position on the street.
2. Count the total number of dots.
3. Rule a line from north to south where there is an equal number of dots on either side. Rule a line from east to west in the same way.
4. Whereabouts in the square kilometre of Kendal is the median centre? Describe its location in relation to the larger streets.

Evaluation

Would your calculation of the median centre have been more accurate if you had taken into account the area covered by the listed buildings? In other words, does the placing of a dot on each building distort the calculation?

Figure 72 The listed buildings in 1 km^2 of Kendal, Cumbria.

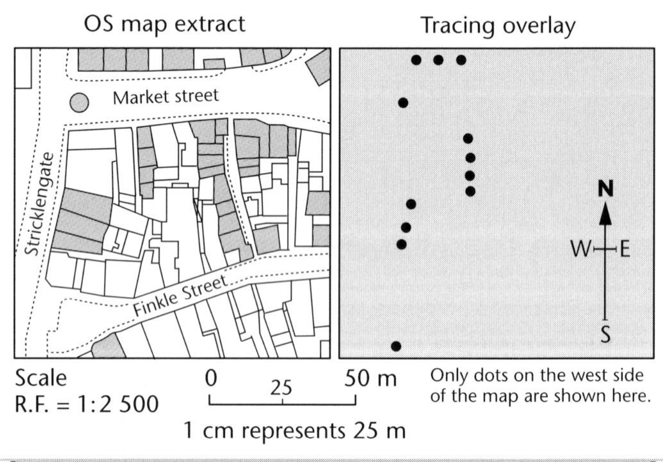

Figure 73 Ground-level land use in Market Street, Manchester in 1961. Source: Kelly's Trades Directory.

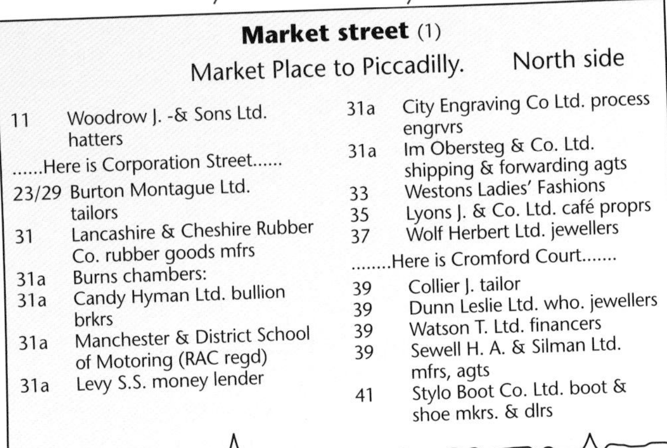

Market street (1)

Market Place to Piccadilly. North side

11 Woodrow J. -& Sons Ltd. hatters
......Here is Corporation Street......
23/29 Burton Montague Ltd. tailors
31 Lancashire & Cheshire Rubber Co. rubber goods mfrs
31a Burns chambers:
31a Candy Hyman Ltd. bullion brkrs
31a Manchester & District School of Motoring (RAC regd)
31a Levy S.S. money lender
31a City Engraving Co Ltd. process engrvrs
31a Im Obersteg & Co. Ltd. shipping & forwarding agts
33 Westons Ladies' Fashions
35 Lyons J. & Co. Ltd. café proprs
37 Wolf Herbert Ltd. jewellers
........Here is Cromford Court.......
39 Collier J. tailor
39 Dunn Leslie Ltd. who. jewellers
39 Watson T. Ltd. financers
39 Sewell H. A. & Silman Ltd. mfrs, agts
41 Stylo Boot Co. Ltd. boot & shoe mkrs. & dlrs

Market Street

23–29	tailor	Burtons Montague Ltd
31	rubber goods	Lancashire & Cheshire Rubber Co.
33	ladies' fashions	Westons Ladies' Fashions
35	café	J. Lyons & Co. Ltd
37	jeweller	Herbert Wolf Ltd
39	jeweller	Leslie Dunn Ltd
41	boot and shoemaker	Stylo Boot Co. Ltd
43–45	house furnishers	Campbell's
47	estate agent and valuer	Isaac Neild & Co. Ltd
49	jeweller	Wilkins
51	boot maker	True Form Boot Co. Ltd
53	ladies' fashions	Etam Ltd
55	estate agent	Thorpe, Robinson & Sons Ltd
57–61	hatter	G. A. Dunn & Co. Ltd
63- 67	tailor	Alexandre Ltd
69	shoes	Wm Timpson Ltd
71	tailor	J. Collier
75 77	tailor	Hepworths Ltd
79	travel agent	Cook, Thos & Son Ltd
83–85	tailor	Boydell Brothers Ltd
87	wines and spirits	Yates, Bros & Co.
89	tailor	Arthur H Martin
93	cinema	Cinephone
95–101	department store	Henry's Stores Ltd
105	jeweller	H. Samuel Ltd
107	furrier	Manchester Fur Co.
Rylands Building	department store	Pauldens Ltd
111–117	department store	Marks and Spencer Ltd
119	restaurant	UCP
121	jeweller	H. Samuel Ltd
125	costumier	Wallis and Co.
127	shoes	Dolcis Ltd

The procedure for completing an adjacency matrix is as follows:

1. Classify the ***functions*** into different types: clothes shops and jewellers, etc.
2. Use graph paper to draw a grid with the classes of function in the same order along the rows and down the columns. You will realise that this enables clothes shops which are adjacent to other clothes shops to be marked on the grid.

	Clothes shop	Jeweller	Café	Others →
Clothes shop			|	|
Jeweller		|		
Café		|		
Others ↓	|			

3. The first shops (Numbers 23–39 Market Street) have been completed to show you how to do it. Start at one end of the street and note the function of each unit of premises and that of the next one in the street. For example, 23–29 Market Street is a clothes shop. It is next to the Lancashire and Cheshire Rubber Co Ltd so a mark is put into the box at the intersection of row 'Clothes shop' and column 'Others'.
4. After completing your grid, add up the total in each box and then calculate each as a percentage of the total for that particular function. The answer will provide you with an objective indicator of the percentage of adjacency.

TRIAL RUN 8

Draw your own adjacency matrix for Market Street, and complete the calculations. Finally, describe any patterns you pick out, and suggest reasons for them. In the example of Market Street, out of a total of 14 clothes shops, 7 are next to other clothes shops. This indicates that, in this particular street, 50% of the clothes shops are located next to other clothes shops. Use your knowledge of geography to suggest reasons why this is not surprising.

Part of your **evaluation** could be to consider other ways of assessing clustering such as Nearest Neighbour Analysis.

Gradients

A quick method of estimating the gradient by looking at a map of scale 1:25,000 or 1:50,000 is:

- where the contours are 1 mm apart, the gradient is 1 in 5, i.e. 20%
- where the contours are 2 mm apart, the gradient is 1 in 10, i.e. 10%
- where the contours are 0.5 cm apart, the gradient is 1 in 25, i.e. 5%

How to measure distance on a map

The map must be drawn to scale. Use either a map-measuring wheel or the pin-and-string method shown in Figure 74.

TRIAL RUN 9

Figure 123 on page 127 shows a map of the area around the Goyt Valley. Measure the distance of road between Grid References 019773 and 043748.

Figure 74 How to measure distances accurately on a map using pins and string.

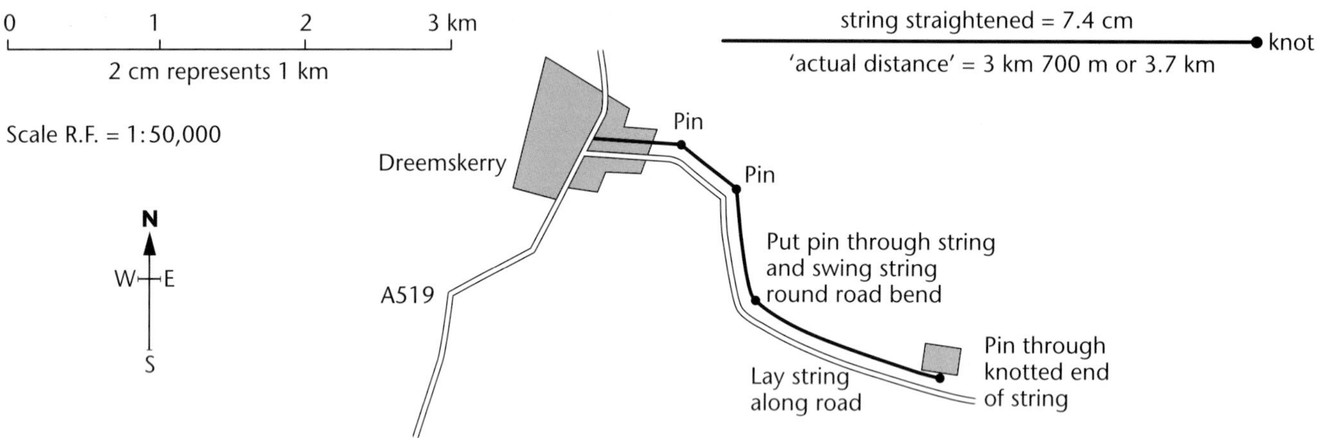

How to measure area on a map or cross-section

Cover the area you wish to measure with tracing paper on which you have drawn a grid of squares to scale. For example, if tracing paper with a grid whose sides are 1 cm in length is placed over a map of scale 1:1000, each square centimetre represents 100 m^2 on the ground. On Ordnance Survey maps of scale 1:50,000, each of the grid squares is 1 km^2 in size. Now count the number of 'complete' squares and those which are 'half or more complete'; ignore the rest. Multiply the number by your scale and this is the area.

TRIAL RUN 10

Figure 75 shows the cross-sectional area of a stream. Calculate the area covered by water.

Figure 75 Calculating the area of a cross-section.

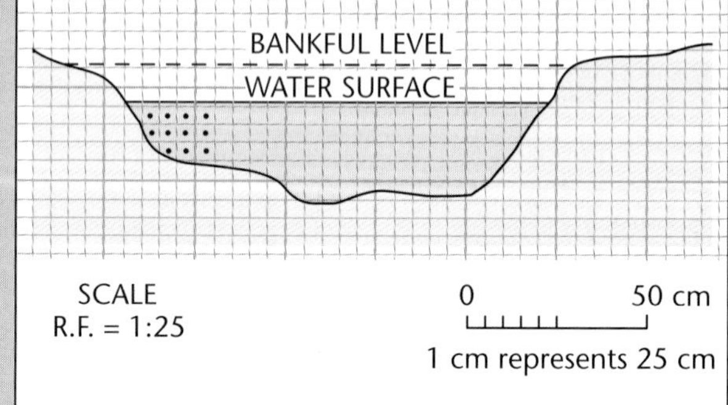

1 Place a dot in each square that is completely covered or more than half covered by water.
2 Count the dots.
3 Measure the scale to calculate the area of each small square.
4 The number of squares you have counted multiplied by the area represented by each square will give you the cross-sectional area of the stream.

An area on a scale map is calculated in the same way.

Cross-sections and profiles to show relief features

Cross-profiles are line graphs drawn between two points to show the height and shape of the land. They may be drawn to illustrate a slope that you have surveyed by using any of the methods described in 'Surveying a slope' (pages 24–27) or to show the cross-section of a stream.

Cross-sections can be drawn from a contour map. First, lay a piece of paper with a straight edge along the ***transect*** you wish to show in the section. Identify it by a six-figure grid reference at each end.

Every time a contour is crossed, mark it on the paper and label the height of the contour. Mark the location of other features that you wish to show, such as rivers, buildings, roads, or the beginning and end of an area of woodland. Next, the information must be transferred from the paper onto graph paper and drawn to scale. In Figure 76, the scale for the distance between X and Y is exactly the same as the distance on the map: 1 cm represents 500 m (1 small square on the graph paper represents 100 m).

In order to see the relief clearly, it is often necessary to use a vertical scale that is bigger than the horizontal scale. The number of times that it is bigger is called the 'vertical exaggeration'. In Figure 76, the vertical scale is 1 cm represents 50 m (i.e. 1 small square represents 10 m). The vertical exaggeration (VE) is ten times that of the horizontal scale, and this is written beside the section as 'VE = × 10'.

To draw the section from the pencil marks on the paper, lay the piece of paper with its straight edge along the horizontal axis of the 'frame'. Use a set-square or ruler to measure vertically upwards to the appropriate height on the vertical scale, and mark this with a dot. Join the dots with a smoothly curving line, so as to avoid cutting off the tops of hills.

The relief may be seen clearly if the cross-section is shaded in brown. Use blue for lakes and reservoirs, and green for woodland where they occur. Describe the different parts of a slope as 'straight = ', 'convex = ' or 'concave = '.

TRIAL RUN 11

Make a copy of Figure 76 and then complete the cross-section using the markings on the paper laid below it.

Evaluation

Would a smaller or larger vertical exaggeration have been more effective for this particular cross-section?

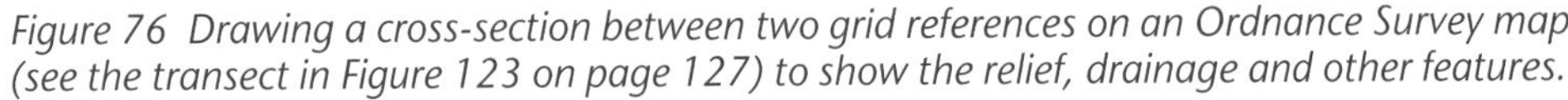

Figure 76 Drawing a cross-section between two grid references on an Ordnance Survey map (see the transect in Figure 123 on page 127) to show the relief, drainage and other features.

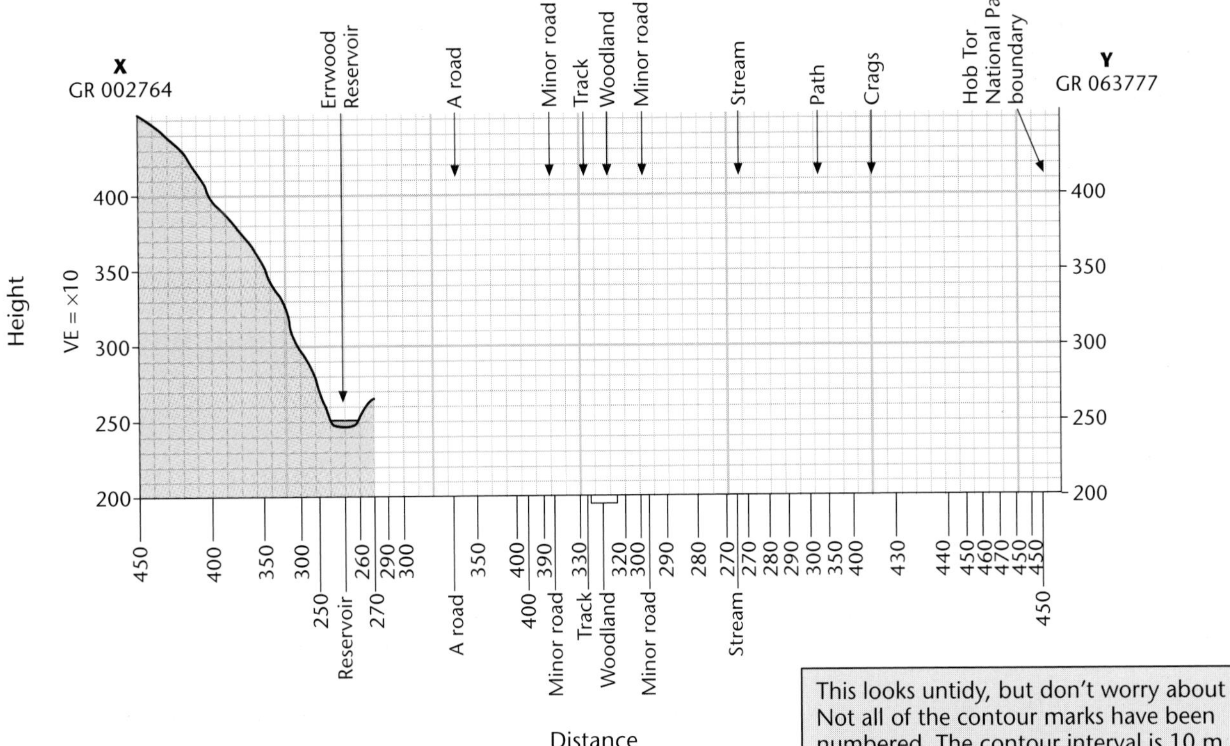

To calculate the vertical exaggeration on the cross-section:

On the horizontal scale, 1 cm represents 5 00m
1 mm represents 50 m

On the vertical scale, 1 cm represents 50 m
1 mm represents 5 m

The vertical scale is, therefore, 10 times bigger than the horizontal scale. This is as VE = × 10.

Graphs

A graph shows the characteristics of a set of variables in the form of a diagram. Variables are sets of numbers whose characteristics vary: rainfall from day to day; slope angle along a transect; pedestrian flow at different times of the day.

In the form of a graph, the data are organised and summarised so that their meaning becomes more obvious.

As you know from mathematics, there are different kinds of graph, so take time and care to choose the type which represents the ***data*** in the way you want the reader to understand it.

Small differences between values in a set of numbers may be important as well as the need to display both large values and small values. For example, if 1 cm represents 10 people, you will still see a difference between 7 and 8 people. If you used a scale of 1 cm to represent 100 people then it would be difficult to pick out the difference between 7 and 8 people. If the range of a data set is very big, the vertical axis may be broken and a zig-zag line drawn across the part where no data are shown (as in Figure 78).

It is a good idea to try out the scale in rough first with a few numbers. Ask yourself whether you can see the data clearly before going ahead with the real thing. Choosing the scale of your graph is important.

Line graphs and bar charts

Line graphs show two sets of data which are related. Sometimes only one set of data varies, and the other remains constant. For example, daily rainfall: the rainfall may vary but the length of day remains constant. The variable data are usually shown on the vertical axis (y-axis) and the horizontal axis (x-axis) is divided into equal intervals.

Multiple line graphs show more data and this helps further to reveal patterns. In the 'weather data section' of an atlas, the maximum, minimum and mean temperatures month by month are often shown in the form of multiple line graphs as three separate lines on the same graph.

On **bar charts**, or bar graphs, the height of the bar is proportional to the number it represents. The other axis is subdivided so that it will give bars of a sensible width. Bar charts look most effective when the bars are shaded in blocks of colour. This enables a second set of information to be added by line-shading or by writing numbers or letters over the shaded bars in black or a distinctive colour. In Figure 79 each wind direction is shaded differently.

The horizontal axis on a graph is often referred to as the x-axis and the vertical axis as the y-axis.

Remember to add a key to the graph.

A **histogram** is drawn in the same way as a bar chart but the bars are proportional to the frequency with which one of the data sets varies. A histogram is often used to illustrate data that have been arranged according to how often a feature occurs, e.g. traffic flow within particular intervals of time, early morning rush hour and mid-morning 'lull'. Figure 77 is a histogram to show the length of French tramway extensions due for completion at different dates (the data is taken from Trial Run 19 on page 84).

Figure 77 Histogram to show the dates of completion of tramway track extensions in France.

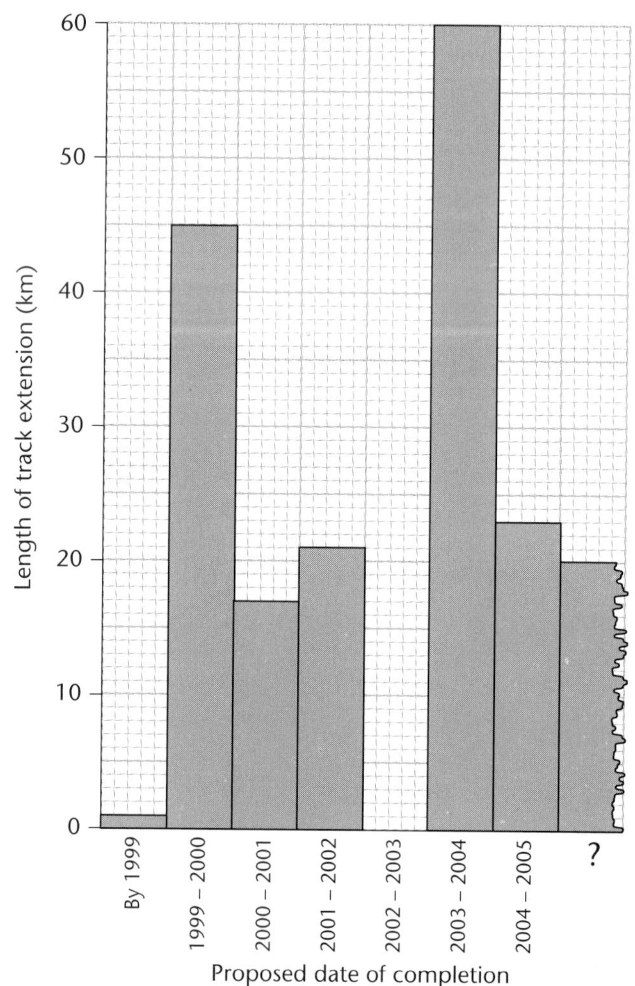

TRIAL RUN 12

1 On a copy of Figure 78 complete the bar chart to illustrate the other figures for French tramway extension projects given on page 84. Would a zig-zag line between the bars for Grenoble and Paris make the information more or less clear? Is a zig-zag line necessary? Give your views.

This is an **evaluation**.

2 Describe the information shown by the bar charts.

3 Describe the information shown by the histogram in Figure 77.

4 On a map of France, locate each of the cities by means of a dot. Place a bar chart beside each dot to represent the tramway project in that city. Describe any pattern which the map and bar charts show.

Evaluation

a Which of the following methods of analysing the data seems to you to be the most effective: bar chart, histogram, or map and bar chart? Explain your reasons.

b If you have also completed Trial Run 19, consider whether the information is easier to understand in the form of calculations or graphs. Write a few sentences to explain your views.

Figure 78 Bar chart to show the proposed extension of tramway track in cities in France.

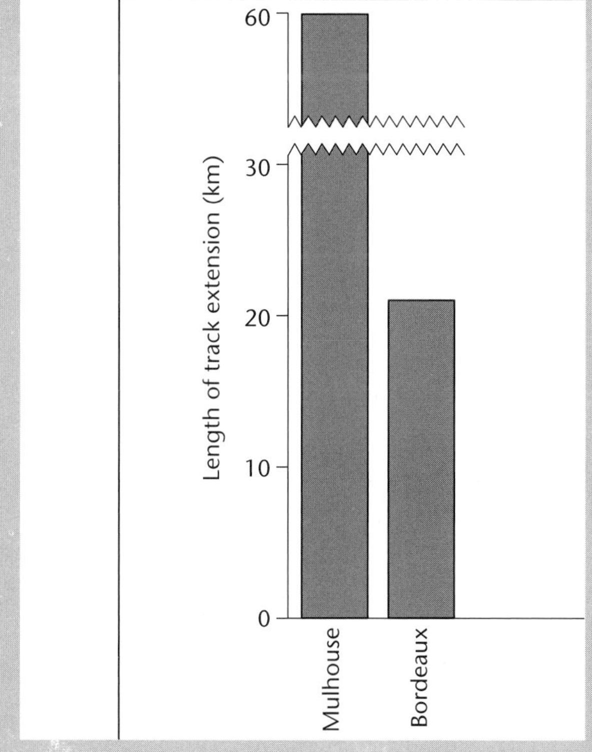

Bar charts for comparison

If two or three different sets of information have been obtained for each location, or the same information has been obtained for two or three different places, these can be compared by placing the bars in groups side by side (as in Figure 81). Avoid showing more than three sets of data in each group because the graph becomes difficult to read.

Alternatively, instead of placing the bars into groups side-by-side, the total length of each bar may be subdivided to show the information. The biggest value in most bars is usually shown at the bottom, with the smallest at the top. It helps the reader if you draw lines between the subdivisions, as shown in Figure 79. These are known as **cumulative bar charts**.

Figure 79 Cumulative bar charts drawn to compare wind directions.

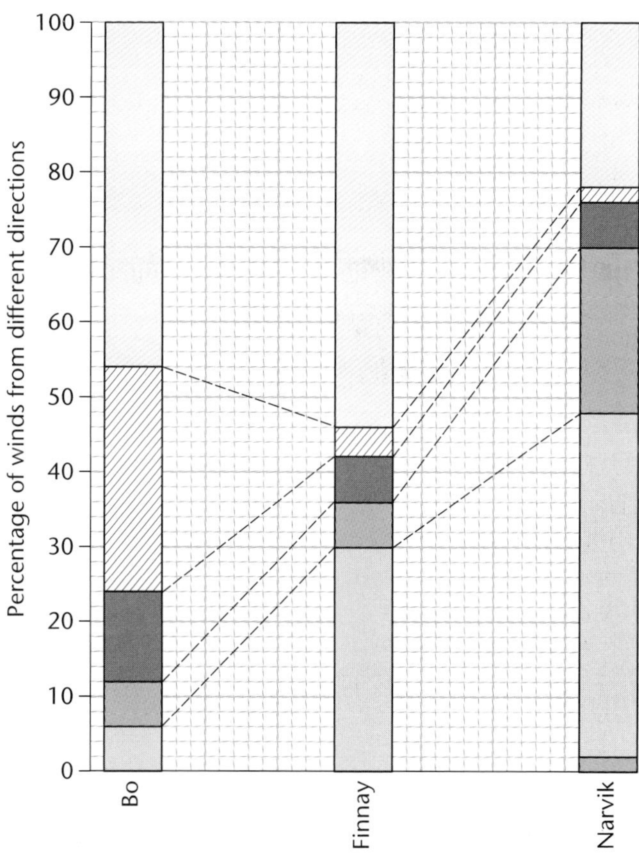

TRIAL RUN 13

Below is a table giving the percentage of winds from the four main directions of the compass and those from all other directions, for three different weather stations in northern Norway for the months of September, October and November 1993. The locations of the three weather stations are shown on Figure 80.

	Bo	Finnay	Narvik
% of winds from the east	6	30	48
% of winds from the west	6	7	22
% of winds from the north	12	6	6
% of winds from the south	30	4	2
% of winds from other directions	46	53	22

1 On a copy of Figure 81, complete the bar charts for the percentage of winds from the north, south and other directions.

2 For each of the three weather stations in turn describe what your graphs show about the wind direction.

3 Look at the map of northern Norway in Figure 80. Explain how the relief affects the wind direction at the different weather stations.

Evaluation

- Do you consider that it would have helped to have had the precise directions of all of the winds?
- Does presenting the data in the form of percentages obscure some of the accuracy?
- Would it have been valuable to have had wind speed as well as direction?

Figure 81 Bar charts grouped to show wind directions at three weather stations in northern Norway.

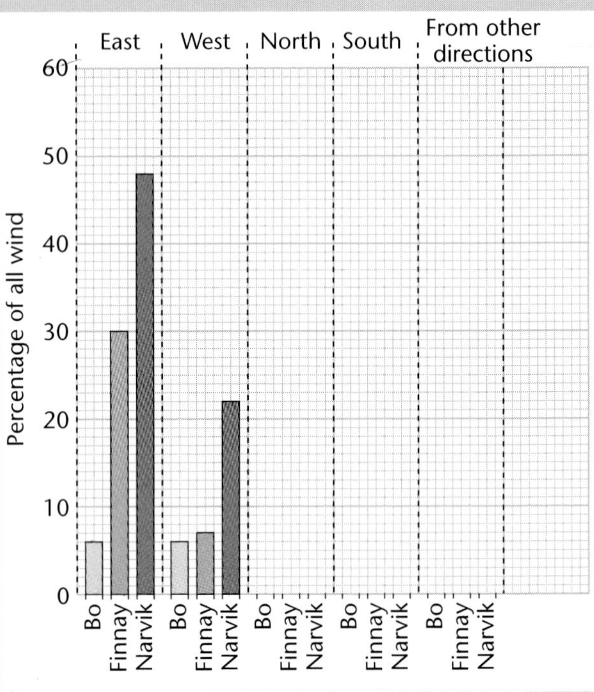

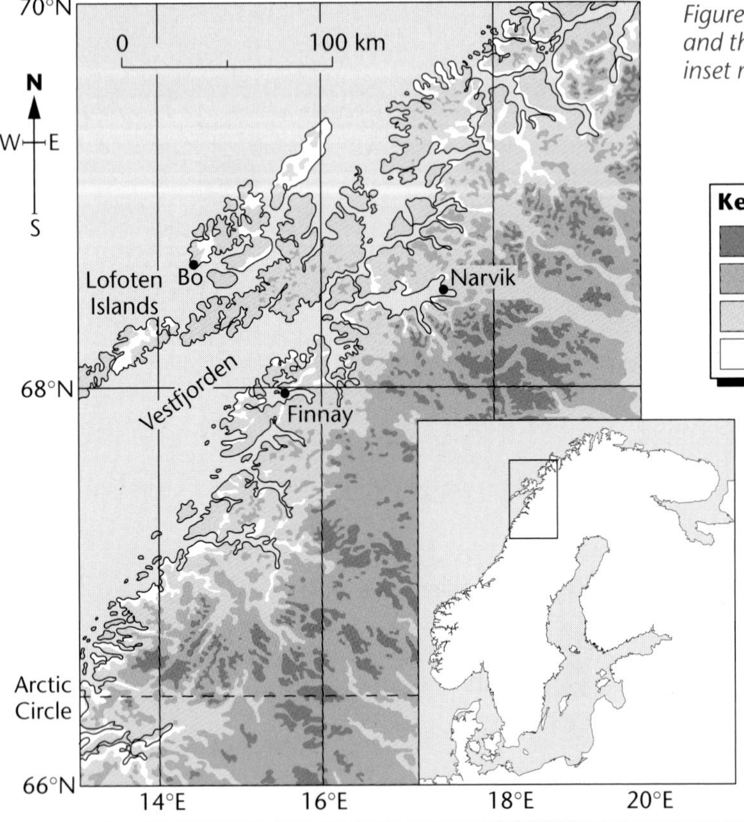

Figure 80 Map to show the relief of northern Norway and the locations of the three weather stations. The inset map shows the location of the study area.

Key

- Land over 2 000 m above sea level (a.s.l.)
- Land between 1 000 m and 2 000 m a.s.l.
- Land between 300 m and 1000 m a.s.l.
- Land below 300 m a.s.l.

Rose diagrams/star diagrams

These are like bar charts but the bars radiate outwards from a circle. They are very useful for showing data that are related to particular compass directions.

> **TRIAL RUN 14**
>
> Draw the data for wind directions in northern Norway (page 74) as rose diagrams. Draw a separate rose diagram for each weather station.
>
> **Evaluation of different types of bar charts**
>
> Compare two or three of the different ways of showing the same data: bar charts for comparison, compound bar charts, and rose diagrams. Describe which you consider to be the most effective method.

Figure 82 Map and rose diagrams to analyse the effect of buildings upon wind direction during two weeks' fieldwork.

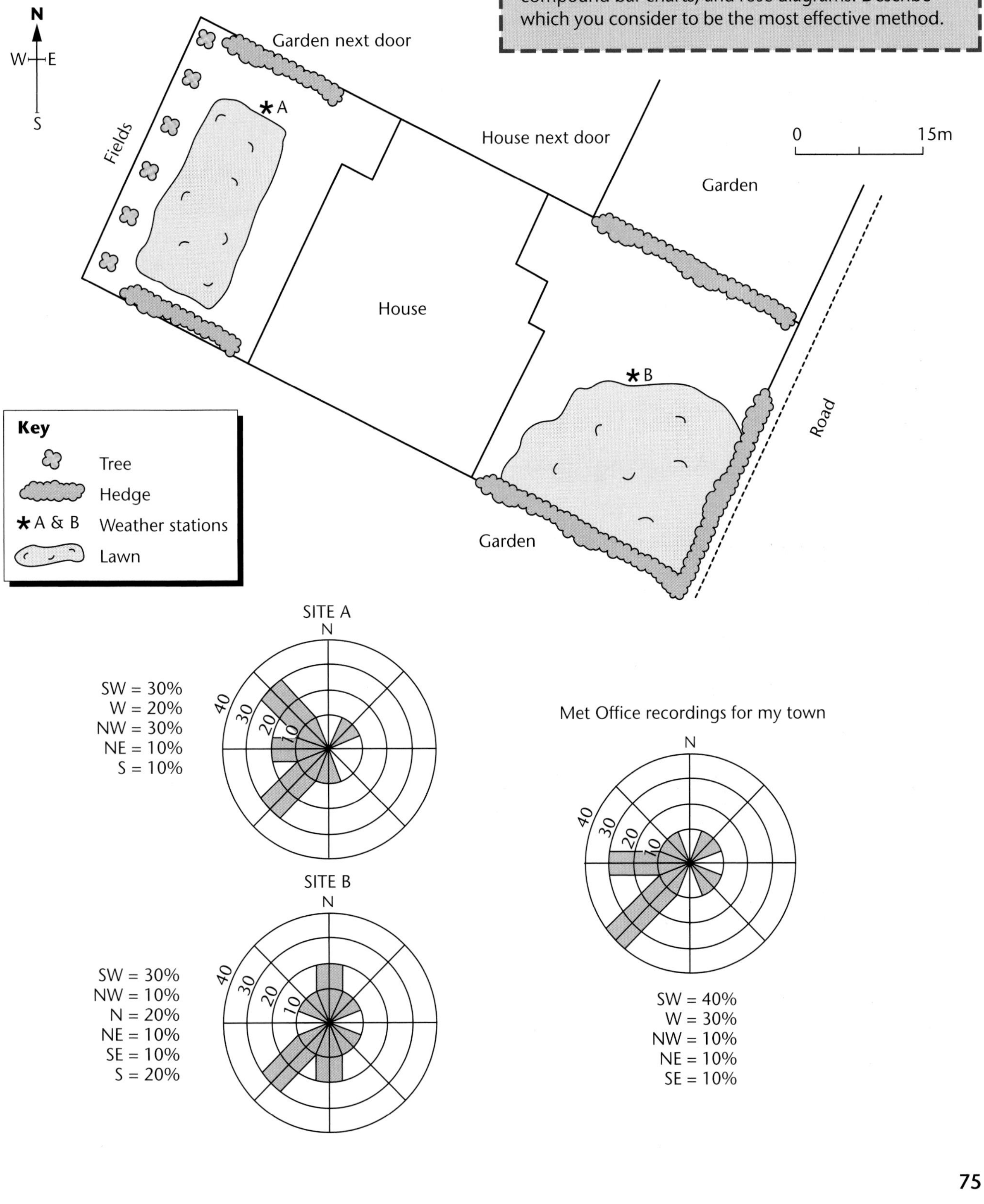

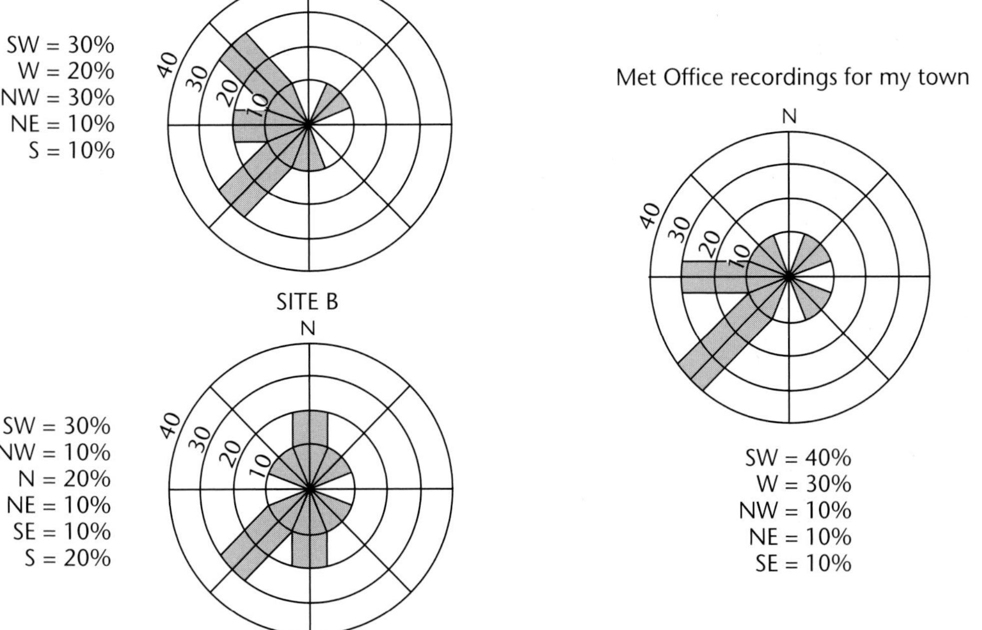

Scattergraphs

Scattergraphs are easy to draw and are particularly helpful when looking for patterns in the ***inter-relationships*** between two sets of data. Plot your results as dots according to their place on the horizontal scale and on the vertical scale.

There are two ways of looking for patterns in the data on a scattergraph:

1. Identifying groupings or clusters

Look for groupings or clusters within the dots and draw a dashed line around each group. You will have to think carefully about this, and be able to justify the classifications you have made. Look at Figures 83 and 84 which show the settlements of Anglesey and the adjacent mainland of North Wales placed in ***order of importance***. The map in Figure 84 was based on the interpretation of the scattergraph in Figure 83.

Interpretation of Figure 83

- Settlements of high importance have more than 750 dwellings and 35 or more shops and services.
- Settlements of moderate importance have between 250 and 750 dwellings and 10 or more shops and services.
- Settlements of low importance have neither of these combinations.

Interpretation of Figure 84

- All settlements of high importance, except Llangefni, are coastal. Llangefni has been the administrative centre for Anglesey since 1881.
- All settlements of moderate importance, except Llanfairpwll, are also coastal. Llanfairpwll is developing as a commuter settlement for Bangor.
- All settlements of less importance have inland locations.

Figure 84 Map to show a hierarchy of settlements of North Wales based upon the interpretation of the scattergraph in Figure 83.

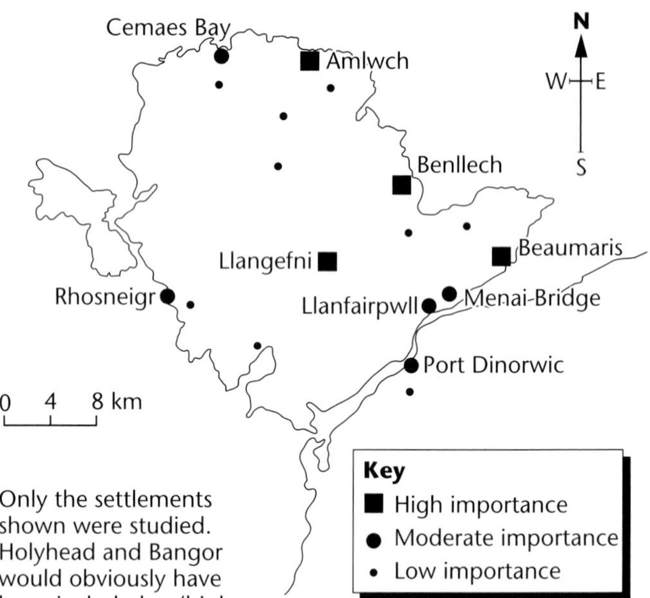

Figure 83 How to identify orders of importance by picking out groupings on a scattergraph.

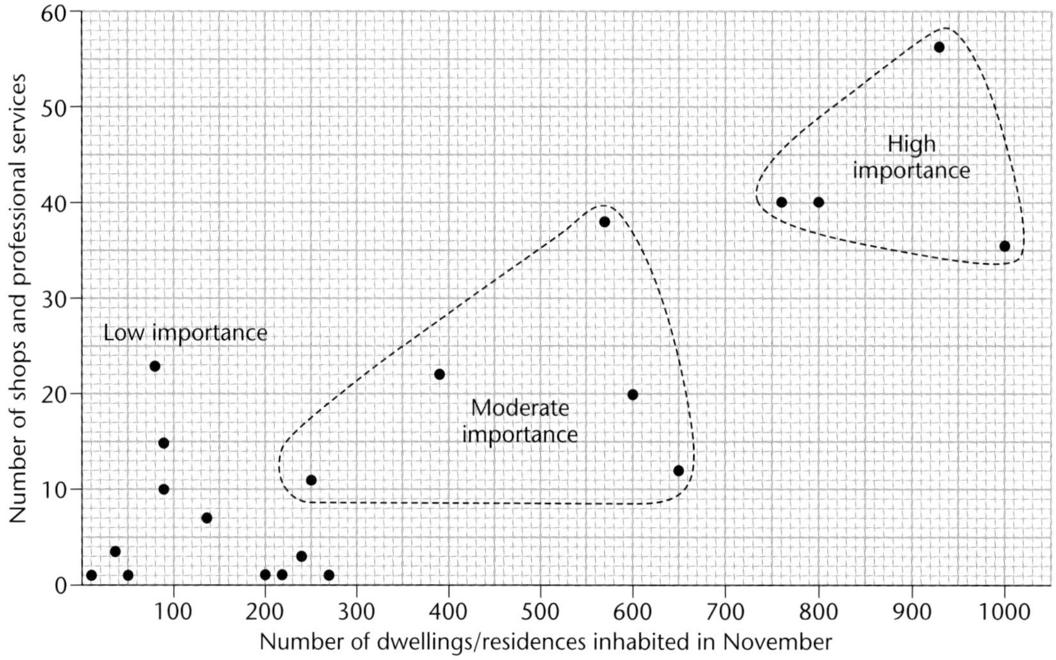

EVALUATION

Do you consider that the two 'high importance' settlements with 800 and 756 inhabited dwellings should have been placed in the 'moderate importance' category? Explain your reasons.

2. Drawing a trend line on a scattergraph

Calculate the mean value of the dots on the horizontal axis and then on the vertical axis. Mark the point on the graph where the mean values intersect. Use this symbol: ⚠.

Draw a **trend line** through the mean point ⚠. There are two types of trend line, so consider which one will be the most helpful for interpreting *your* data:

1. **Line of best-fit**: this is a straight line and, when it passes through the mean point, there should be a similar number of dots above and below the line (see Figure 85).
2. **Line of regression**: this is drawn when one set of data is dependent upon the other. For example:
   - driving rain is dependent on the direction of the wind
   - the number of visits per month to a particular shop is dependent on the distance travelled to the shop.

   In these cases, the driving rain and the number of visits to the shop are the dependent variable, and the wind direction and the distance travelled are the independent variables. On the graph, the dependent data are plotted on the vertical axis and the independent data are plotted on the horizontal axis, as in Figure 86. The regression line is drawn between the two extremes: the Post Office and the furniture shop in Lymm and the Post Office and Christmas shopping in Clitheroe.

On your graph, there may be items which are very far from the values for most of the features which you have investigated. These are known as **residuals**. The supermarket is a residual on the Lymm graph (in Figure 86). You may be able to account quite easily for why they occur, or you may question the accuracy with which you have collected your data. In either case, they may be worth including in your ***evaluation***

Figure 85 Scattergraph with a line of best-fit to show the relationship between the length of street frontage and the rateable value.

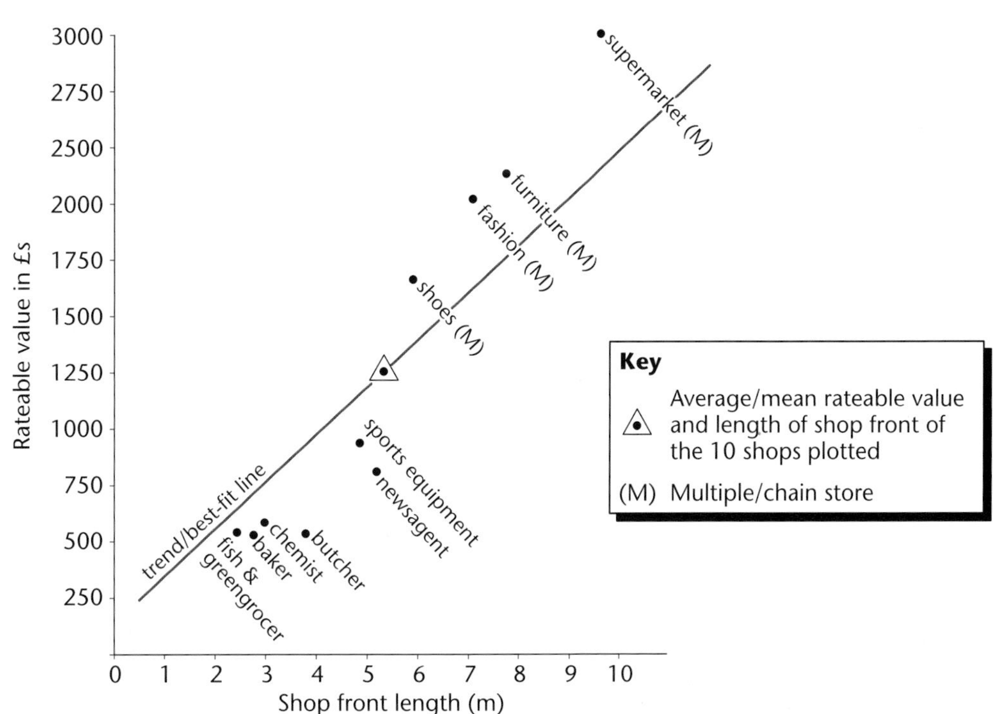

Figure 86 Pictorial scattergraphs with regression lines to show the relationship between distance travelled for goods and services and the frequency of purchase.

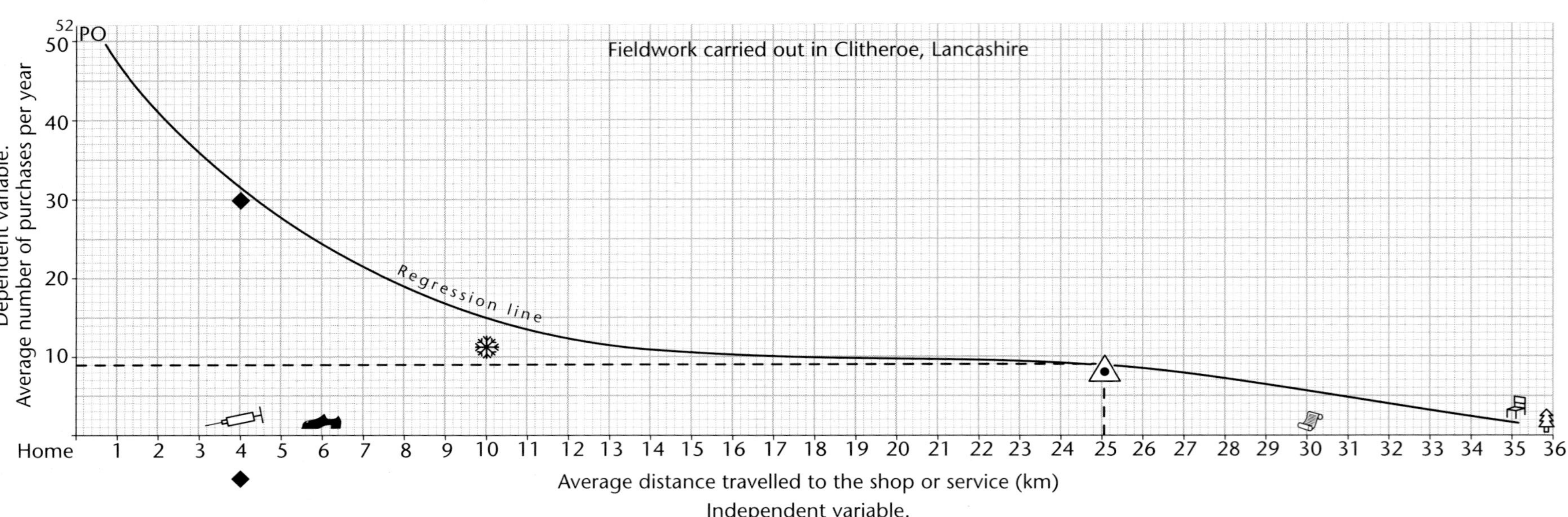

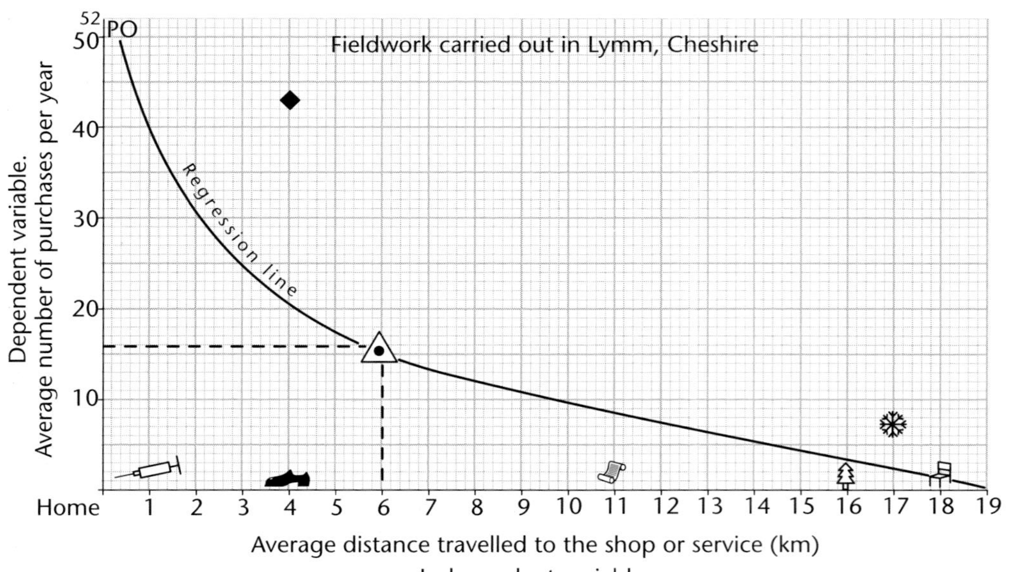

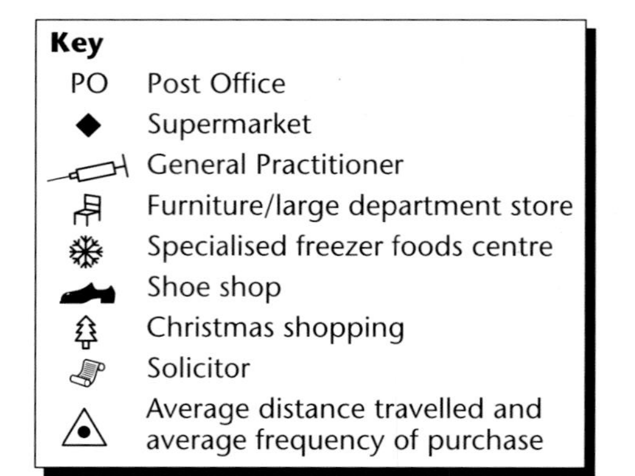

TRIAL RUN 15

Here are the results of some fieldwork on buildings: the age of the buildings, the main materials from which they were constructed, and the degree to which the material is weathered, on a scale of 1–5. The data are ranked according to the age of the building:

Age of building	Index of the severity of weathering (5 = badly damaged, 1 = hardly weathered at all)	Building material
200 years	1	granite
170 years	1	slate
160 years	1	slate
150 years	5	Portland limestone
120 years	5	Portland limestone
120 years	2	sandstone
110 years	1	Accrington brick
110 years	5	marble
110 years	2	London brick
100 years	5	marble
90 years	5	marble
90 years	2	London brick
80 years	1	Accrington brick
50 years	3	marble
50 years	2	Portland limestone
40 years	2	concrete
30 years	1	concrete
20 years	1	sandstone
10 years	1	brick

1 Draw a frame for the scattergraph with sensible scales on the horizontal and vertical axes.

2 Calculate the mean of the age of buildings and then calculate the mean of the index of the severity of weathering. Mark the intersection of these as '⨺'.

3 Devise a key to the building material – perhaps the first letter of the type of material – and plot the data on your graph.

4 Look carefully for groupings, and consider whether it would be wise to draw a line of best-fit. Would regression apply in this case? Another way of asking this would be, is the severity of weathering dependent on the age of the building?

5 Describe what your scattergraph shows. What are the main influences on the degree of weathering? Is the degree of weathering related to the age of the building? Is the degree of weathering related to the type of building material? Which inter-relationship – time or building material – is more important?

What other factors could affect the degree of weathering and how could they be investigated?

Pie charts

Pie charts, or pie graphs, can be drawn to help in the ***interpretation*** of data which can be subdivided into groups, classes or categories. In this way pie charts are similar to divided bar charts. Some people find them easier to understand than bar charts.

Pie charts are circles divided into sectors called **pie sectors**. Each sector is proportional to the value it represents.

They are simple to draw. The total amount of your data is represented by 360°. Here is an example: an investigation into the shape of pebbles in a 1 m^2

quadrat on the highest ridge (the storm beach) on a pebble beach showed the pebbles to be:

29 disc-shaped
24 rod-shaped
13 spherical
66

On the pie chart, the 360° of the circle represent the total number of pebbles, which is 66. To subdivide the circle proportionally to the three groups of pebbles, divide 360° by the total number of pebbles (66) and then multiply this by the number in each class:

The 'disc-shaped' pie sector

$$= \frac{360}{66} \times 29 = 5.45 \times 29 = 158^\circ$$

The 'rod-shaped' pie sector

$$= \frac{360}{66} \times 24 = 131^\circ$$

The 'spherical' pie sector

$$= \frac{360}{66} \times 13 = 71^\circ$$

To draw in the pie sectors, begin at 'midnight' on the circle and work clockwise, starting with the biggest group (see Figure 87).

Figure 87 Pie chart to show the shapes of pebbles in a sample from a beach.

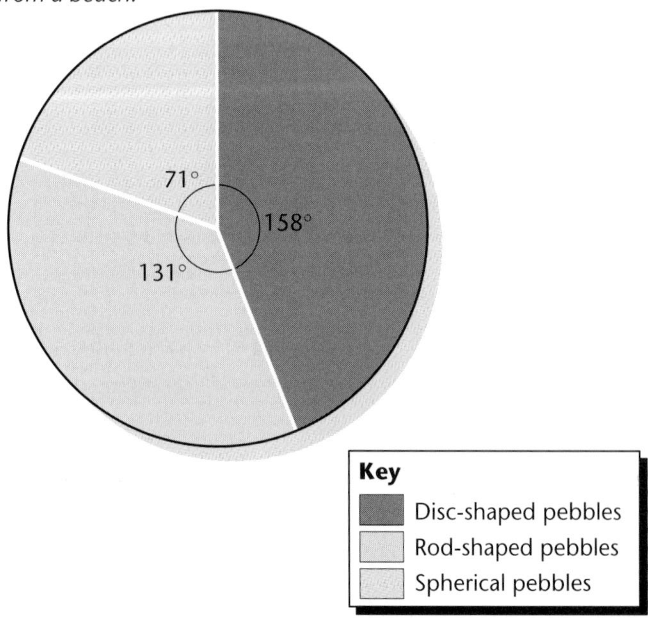

Data to be represented as pie sectors may first be converted into percentages: 1% is represented by 3.6° of the circle.

TRIAL RUN 16

Figure 88 is a tally chart showing the numbers of people of different age groups in a Country Park enjoying organised activities with rules.

Figure 88 Tally chart.

Types of outdoor leisure activity	Under 12 years	13–20 years	21–30 years	31–60 years	Over 60
Formal, e.g. tennis, golf	𝍸 |	||	𝍸 𝍸 𝍸	𝍸 |	||||

1 Add up the number of people in each age group. What is the total of all the people recorded? This is represented by the whole of the circle (360°).
2 Rank the figures for each age group.
3 Calculate the angle of the pie sector of each.
4 Draw a pie chart showing the age groups. Begin clockwise from 'midnight' with the biggest, followed by the second biggest, and so on.
5 Choose a colour or type of shading for each of the four age groups. Complete a key.

Evaluation

Would the pie chart have looked more effective if you had begun with the youngest age group?

Consider other ways in which you could have shown these data:

- bar charts grouped for comparison
- a cumulative bar chart
- proportional circles or squares, subdivided into a pie chart
- a proportional circle divided into pie sectors.

Draw two of these and then write a few sentences to explain which one is best and why.

Venn diagrams

A Venn diagram is made up of overlapping circles. Each circle contains classes of data with characteristics in common. In Figure 89, outdoor leisure activities are grouped into 'informal' such as picnicking, and 'formal' such as golf and other games which have rules. However, some leisure activities such as walking and sailing could be placed in either category, and are illustrated within the overlapping parts of the circles.

Figure 89 Venn diagram used to classify some outdoor leisure activities.

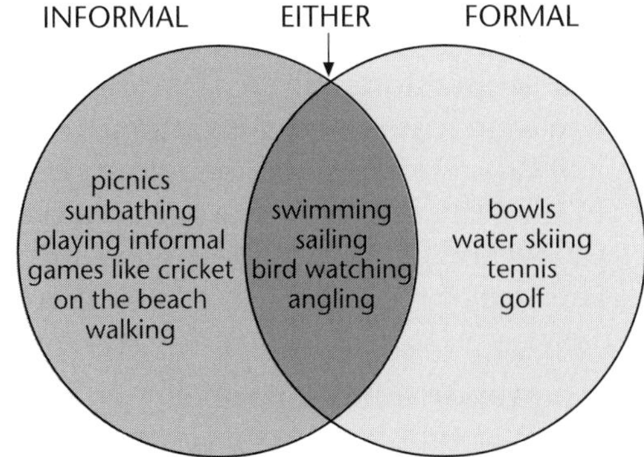

Formal activities tend to be organised and need rules and equipment.

TRIAL RUN 17

Below is a list of service functions.

theatre	medical centre
nursery school	cathedral
church	town hall
post office	university
take-away food service	wine bar
hospital	building society
council offices	stockbroker
bank	village hall
primary school	public house

Some cost a lot of money and are not used every day by most people whereas others cost less and are used frequently. They may be classed respectively as 'high-order services' and 'low-order services'.

A town that has high-order services may be classed as a high-order service centre whilst a town that does not have high-order services is of lower order as a service centre.

1 Classify the service functions listed below into:
- high-order services and low-order services
- these found in big towns of high importance, those found in smaller towns of less importance and
- those that are found in both.

2 Draw a Venn diagram to show the service functions in different-order service centres.

Evaluation

How many functions does each of the circles contain? Should there be fewer in the high-order circle than in either the low-order circle or the overlapping segment? It is worth considering that W. Christaller's theory considers that the number should change by 3, or by a factor of 3, from one order to the next.

Flow-lines

Flow-line diagrams are very useful when ***interpreting*** information that moves, e.g. pedestrians walking up a street, or traffic moving along a road. Flow-lines are arrows drawn on a map pointing in the direction in which the data collected were moving during fieldwork. The width of the lines is drawn to scale so that they represent

Figure 90 Two different methods of drawing flow-lines on a map.

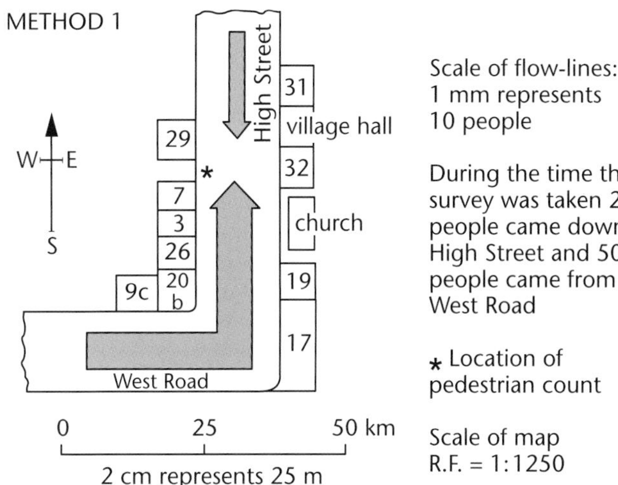

Key to shops

3	bread and cakes
7	chemist
9c	children's wear
17	fish-and-chips
19	flowers
26	hairdresser
29	knitting wools etc.
31	off-licence
32	Post Office
20b	small supermarket

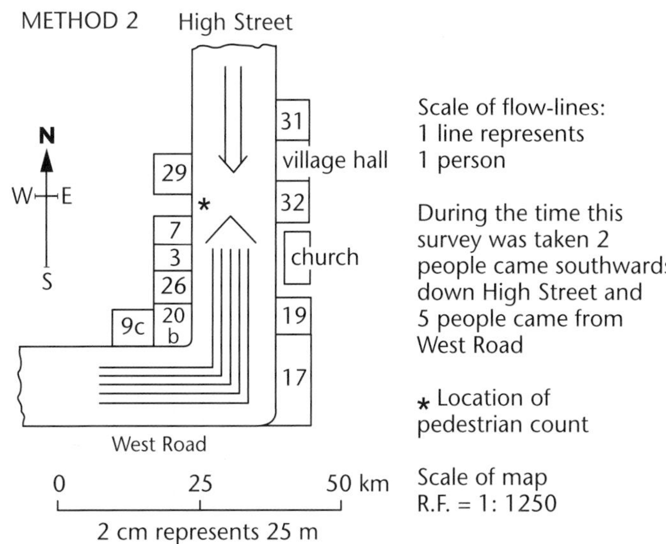

the number counted. Figure 90 shows two methods that are often used to draw flow-lines. Flow-lines may be stuck to a map, and if they are very wide they may be folded like a concertina.

TRIAL RUN 18

Here are ten destinations outside the European Union to which UK residents travelled by air in 1996. (For the purpose of this survey, the countries of the Caribbean are classed together.)

	Thousands
USA	3066
Canada	506
Australia	290
New Zealand	90
Japan	100
South Africa	204
The Russian Federation	123
Hong Kong	154
Israel	147
Caribbean	534

1 **Rank** the figures to help you to decide which scale to use (see page 84). Experiment first with 1 mm represents 100,000, or 1 mm represents 50,000. This could be shown as the width of the flow-line in Method 1 or the width of each individual line in Method 2 of Figure 90.

2 On an outline map of the world, draw flow-lines to show the number of UK residents who flew to the destinations in the list. Label the United Kingdom and each of the destinations on the map. Add the scale of the flow-lines.

Evaluation

Would flow-lines attached separately to the map as concertinas be visually as effective as drawing them on the map? Would a **topological map** represent the data better? See pages 65–66.

Proportional circles and squares

Information measured in square metres, square kilometres or other forms of area, is best illustrated as proportional circles or squares. Large numbers such as population figures for towns can be shown compactly in this way, too. Proportional circles or squares can be drawn on maps to show where the ***data*** are located.

The area of the circle or square is proportional to that of the data it represents. First, find the square root of the data.

- **To draw a proportional circle**. You know that the area of a circle is $\pi r2$. As π is constant, draw the area of each circle proportional to r^2. Do this by calculating the square root of the area you wish to show and use this as the radius of the circle. The area of the circle will be proportional to the data represented.
- **To draw a proportional square**. The sides will be proportional to the square root of the data.

Displaying information from your weather log

Map

Most people find it easier to understand a visual display than to have to interpret, in their mind's eye, a set of ***tabulated*** results in the form of your weather log. A visual display can be made in the form of a large-scale map of your fieldwork area: your home and garden; school grounds; a valley or hill. An example of what your map could look like is shown in Figure 91.

You may want to make a display on felt or on a blackboard or whiteboard for others to see, but keep your own record on A4-sized paper so that you can include it in your **final report**. Add a key to explain the meaning of the symbols and the map for non-geographers. Date the map, and use different colours to indicate measurements taken at different times within the day.

You will know the official meteorological symbols that are used on **synoptic charts**, and as these are given in most specialist books on weather, you can easily check on them. Use these symbols as far as possible and **do not forget to include the key**.

Graph

Graphs can provide a useful summary, as Figure 92 illustrates.

As on the map, use different colours to represent measurements taken at different times of the day, or you may feel that separate graphs placed side by side are simpler to read. Whichever you choose, remember to give your reasons in the data analysis section of your **final report**.

Figure 91 Map to show and explain variations in weather conditions in the school grounds.

20th June
1300h
No rain recorded
Shaded from strong sun by three-storey building = lower temperature. Shape of buildings causes eddying and a strong SW wind. Wind sock halfway up.
23°
N
W
E
S
Scale
R.F. = 1:1250
0
25 m
1 cm represents 12.5 m
Trees
No shading = high temperature
26°
Trees to west reduce wind force
26°
High fence gives shelter and reduces wind force to 'calm' (Beaufort scale 1)

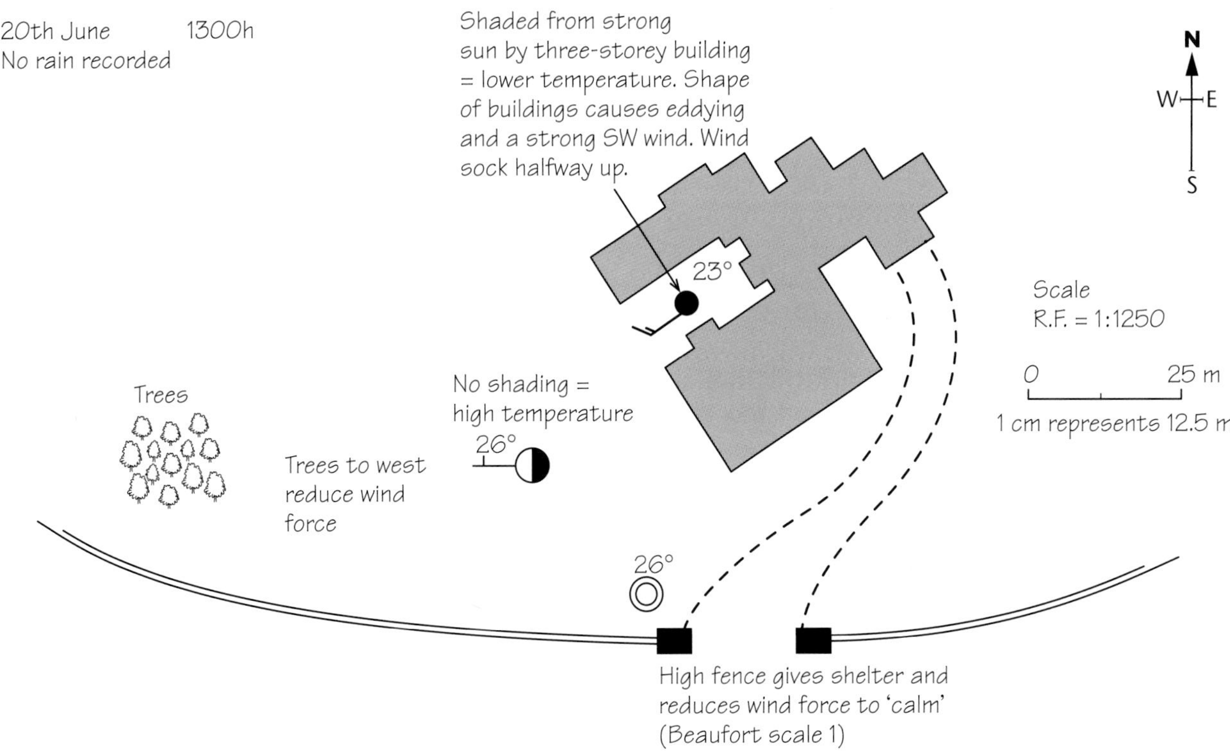

Figure 92 Graph to summarise recordings of the weather elements.

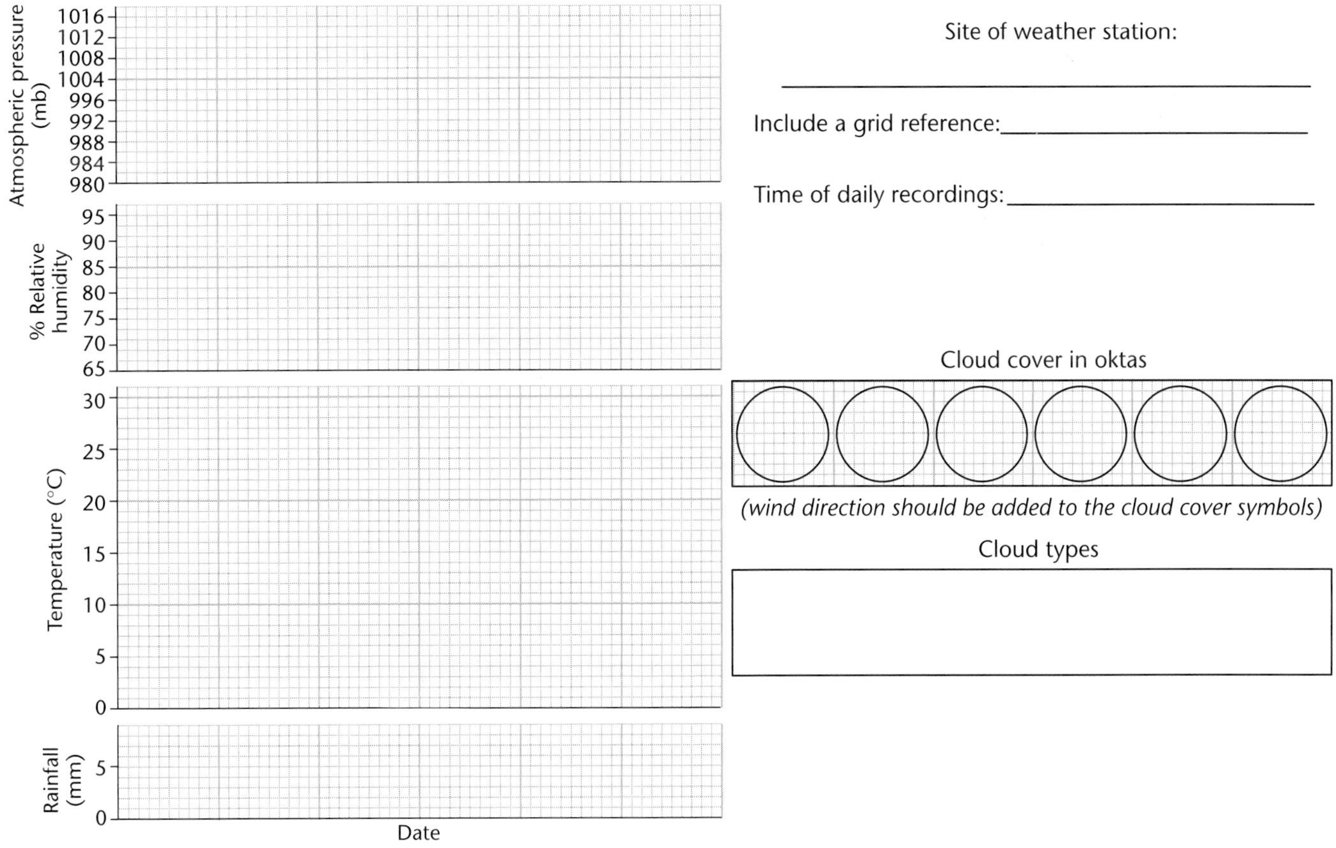

Atmospheric pressure (mb)
1016
1012
1008
1004
996
992
988
984
980
% Relative humidity
95
90
85
80
75
70
65
Temperature (°C)
30
25
20
15
10
5
0
Rainfall (mm)
5
0
Date
Site of weather station:
Include a grid reference:
Time of daily recordings:
Cloud cover in oktas
(wind direction should be added to the cloud cover symbols)
Cloud types

Analysing Data in the Form of Numbers

Mean, median, mode and frequency

For any set of number data begin by listing the ***data*** in the order in which they were collected. A list of this sort is called **raw data** because the data have not been processed in any way. It is difficult to pick out patterns from raw data so first pick out the biggest and the smallest numbers. The difference between the biggest and the smallest numbers is known as the range of the data.

If you decide to draw a graph of the data, the range will influence the scale you use.

Patterns in the numbers begin to appear when you **rank the data in order from the biggest to the smallest.** You will then be able to pick out the following:

1. The **median** number, which is the middle number. By ranking the extended lengths in kilometres from the French tramway project in Trial Run 12 as follows:

   60, 21, 20, 18, 15, 12, 12, 11, 11, 6, 1

   you can pick out that the median is 12 km because the middle number is 12.
2. The **mode**, which is the number that occurs most frequently within the set of data. Looking at the extended lengths again, 12 km and 11 km are both modal values. All of the other values occur only once.
3. The **frequency**, which is the number of times that a particular number occurs within your set of data. Therefore, 12 km and 11 km both have a frequency of 2 whereas all of the others have a frequency of 1.

The **mean** or **average** is calculated by adding up the total of the list of numbers to find the sum and then dividing the sum by the number of values in the list (n).

$$\frac{\text{the sum of the tramway extensions}}{n} = \frac{187}{11} = 17$$

Trial Run 19

The following data on some of the tramway projects in France are given in alphabetical order of the city involved. The extended length of track and the proposed date of completion are given.

City	Extended length (in km)	Proposed date of completion
Bordeaux	21	2002
Dunkerque	20	?
Grenoble	1	1999
Lyon	18	2000
Marseille	12	2005
Montpellier	15	2000
Mulhouse	60	2004
Nantes (extensions to existing system)	12	2000
Paris (extensions to existing system)	6	2001
Toulon	11	2005
Valenciennes	11	2001

1 Rank the figures in the order of the length of track extension.

2 Which do you consider tells the reader most about the proposed extension of the work in progress: the median, the mean or the range of the track extensions? Write one or two sentences to explain what each of them means and then give your views as a conclusion.

Evaluation

Which do you think **summarises** most accurately the French tramway extension project: the mean or the median? What do the proposed dates of completion tell us about the project?

Dispersion diagrams

Patterns in sets of ***data*** become more visible when you draw them as dispersion diagrams. You can see this following if you look first at the following sets of monthly rainfall figures and then at the same information in Figure 93. All geographers know that rainfall tends to be higher in western Britain than in eastern Britain but it is quite difficult to pick this out simply from sets of numbers.

In dispersion diagrams the data can be analysed further by dividing the dots into four equal sets to show the degree of clustering or dispersion around the **median**. The dots in the quarters on either side of the median are termed the **inter-quartile range**.

Average monthly rainfall (in mm)

	Birkenhead	Renfrew	Durham	London
January	80	111	59	54
February	52	85	51	40
March	50	69	38	37
April	48	67	38	37
May	52	63	51	46
June	68	70	49	45
July	94	97	61	57
August	77	93	67	59
September	80	102	60	49
October	83	119	63	57
November	72	106	66	64
December	90	127	55	48

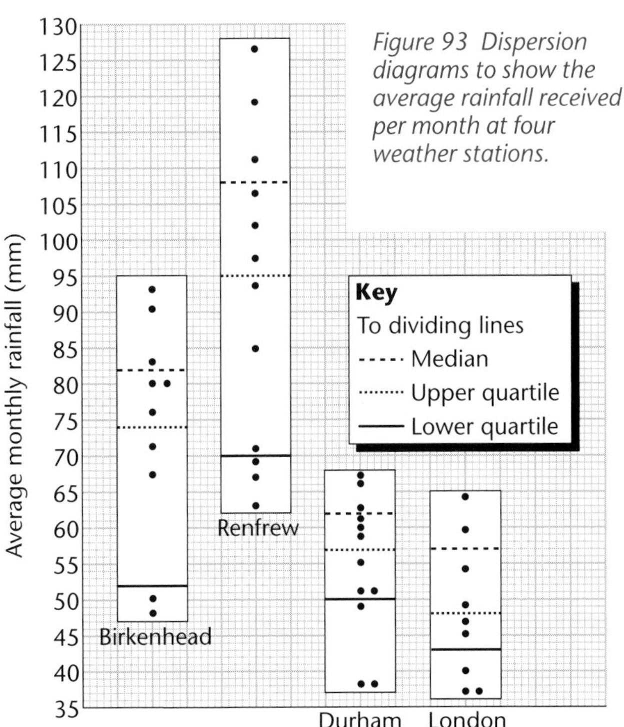

Figure 93 Dispersion diagrams to show the average rainfall received per month at four weather stations.

TRIAL RUN 20

1 Quoting the rainfall figures in both the highest and the lowest quarter from the diagrams in Figure 93, explain how much higher the rainfall is in the west than in the east. Does the median line on the diagrams explain this adequately?

2 Write one or two sentences to describe the contrast between the inter-quartile range of rainfall in Durham and that of Renfrew.

TRIAL RUN 21

Here are data from a fieldwork investigation into the pattern of land use in the area around Abergavenny in Gwent.

The data were collected at sample points using a **table of random numbers**. At each point the type of land use and the height of the land above sea level were recorded and then the data were ***tabulated*** as follows:

Type of land use	Height above sea level (in m)		
Coniferous woodland	225	265	50
	160	260	60
	90	250	
	330	175	
Cereal crops	50	75	120
	30	80	125
	25	100	45
Rough pasture	180	280	150
	175	447	155
	170	420	300
	220	400	325
	225	75	320
	265	125	

1 Using graph paper draw a dispersion diagram for each set of data.

2 Write a few sentences to explain whether the dispersion diagrams suggest that the type of land use could be related to the height of the land.

3 **a** Draw a line through the median value on each of your dispersion diagrams.

b Write a sentence to say whether you feel that it helps in showing the relationship between land use and altitude.

c Draw the upper quartile and lower quartile on each diagram.

d Write a few sentences to explain whether you feel that these clarify the inter-relationship between the data or obscure it.

How to calculate percentages

To calculate what percentage of buildings in a town are of a certain type, divide the smaller number by the total and then multiply this by 100. For example, in a town of 764 buildings, where 53 are shops, divide 53 by 764 and multiply the answer by 100, which equals 5.9%.

$$\frac{53}{764} \times 100 = 5.9\% \text{ of all the buildings are shops}$$

How to calculate percentage change

First, note from the original two numbers whether there is an increase or a decrease. Next, subtract the smaller number from the larger number. This is the **difference** or change. Finally, calculate the difference as a percentage of the original/first number.

For example, according to the UK population census, the population of Jersey in 1901 was 52,576 and in 1991 it was 84,082. The difference equals an increase of 31,506. The percentage change is 31,506 divided by 52,576 and multiplied by 100. The answer is an increase of 59.9%.

TRIAL RUN 22

Locations of the world's longest suspension bridges:

	Length (in m)
Akashi-Kaikyo, Shikoku, Japan	1990
Store Baelt East Bridge, Denmark	1624
Humber Estuary, UK	1410
Jiangyin, Yangtze Kiang, China	1385
Verrazano Narrows, Brooklyn, Staten Island, USA	1298
Golden Gate, San Francisco Bay, USA	1280
Mackinac Straits, Michigan, USA	1158
Minami Bisan-Seto, Japan	1100
Bosporus I, Istanbul, Turkey	1089
Bosporus II, Istanbul, Turkey	1074
George Washington, Hudson River, New York City, USA	1067
Ponte 25 de Abril, River Tagus, Lisbon, Portugal	1013
Firth of Forth (road) near Edinburgh, UK	1006
Severn Estuary, UK	988

What percentages of the world's longest suspension bridges are in each of the following continents: North America, Europe, and Asia?

TRIAL RUN 23

Here are some population figures obtained from Census returns.
They are given in millions. Calculate the percentage change in each country.

	1811	1901	% change (note whether it is an increase or decrease)	1901	1991
England & Wales	10,165	32,528		32,528	49,890
Scotland	1,806	4,472		4,472	4,999
Northern Ireland	1,649* (1841 Census)	1,237		1,237	1,587
UK	13,368	38,237		38,237	56,467

* 1841 was the first year in which a population Census was conducted in Northern Ireland.

1 Calculate the percentage change for both of the 90-year periods for each of the four areas.

2 Compare the percentage change between the 90-year periods. Briefly describe these.

3 Describe the patterns (or trends) shown by the figures above.

4 **Evaluation**: What comments would you make about the earlier figure for Northern Ireland?

Correlation

A ***correlation*** is a relationship between two sets of data. The relationship between the data – the correlation – may be directly proportional (positive) or inversely proportional (negative). Temperature increasing as the length of daylight increases is an example of **positive** correlation; the temperature decreasing as the height above sea level increases is an example of **negative** correlation.

The extent to which two sets of variable numbers are related to one another is usually seen clearly by plotting the data on a **scattergraph** (see page 76 and Figures 83, 85 and 86). A special type of positive correlation is seen in **regression** where one variable is dependent on another (see page 77 and Figure 86).

Spearman's Rank Correlation Coefficient

A statistical method that provides additional evidence of correlation is the calculation of Spearman's Rank Correlation Coefficient, sometimes called 'Spearman's r'. It is based on the ***rank orders*** of the individual sets of variables rather than on the values themselves.

Look at the example in figure 94 below.

You would expect that the number of journeys to work by car would correlate positively with car ownership per thousand of the population. If the correlation were perfect it would be termed 'perfect positive correlation'.

Method for Spearman's r

1. Put the two sets of data into seven columns as in Figure 95. You will see that in column 2 the data are ***ranked*** according to car ownership and in column 5 they are ranked in order of journeys to work by car.
2. Subtract column 5 from column 3 to complete column 6: the difference between the rank orders.
3. Square the difference of each: d^2. This means multiplying the number by itself to remove the negative numbers, e.g. $-1 \times -1 = 1$.
4. Add all the numbers in the d^2 column to give the sum of d^2. This is written as $\sum d^2$ (sigma d^2).
5. Next, put your numbers into this formula:

$$r = 1 - \frac{6\sum d^2}{(n^3 - n)}$$

where

r = the correlation coefficient

$\sum d^2$ = sum of the square of the differences in rank order

n = the number of data used (7 in this case, but it may be more or fewer)

$n^3 = 7 \times 7 \times 7 = 343$

Figure 94 Car ownership and types of journey in the metropolitan areas of England in the autumn of 1994.

Area	Car ownership (per thousand of the population)	Bus journeys (in millions)	Journeys to work by car
Greater London	337	1112	1353
Greater Manchester	344	249	683
Merseyside	284	198	297
South Yorkshire	332	175	307
Tyne and Wear	264	192	259
West Yorkshire	321	234	594
West Midlands	403	366	757

6. For this example:

$$r = 1 - \frac{6 \times 8}{343 - 7}$$

$$= 1 - \frac{48}{336}$$

$$= 1 - 0.14$$

$$= 0.86$$

The result of Spearman's Rank Correlation Coefficient may be +1 or –1 or anywhere in between. +1 shows a perfect positive correlation between the data sets, and –1 a perfect negative correlation. The closer ***r*** is to 1, the more certain you may be of the correlation. In the example, there is an 86% correlation between the data sets, and this shows the original expectation to have been correct.

TRIAL RUN 24

What degree of correlation would you expect between car ownership per thousand and bus journeys in millions (see Figure 94)? Calculate Spearman's Rank Correlation Coefficient for these two sets of data. Comment on the extent to which this confirms your expectations.

Evaluation

Does the calculation of Spearman's r replace the need to draw a scattergraph of the data? Which do you consider to be the better method for a geography project?

Figure 95 Table used for the calculation of Spearman's Rank Correlation Coefficient

1	2	3	4	5	6	7
Area	**Car ownership (per thousand)**	**Rank order of car ownership**	**Journeys to work by car (in thousands)**	**Rank order of 'car journeys'**	**Difference between the rank orders, *d***	d^2
West Midlands	403	1	757	2	–1	1
Greater Manchester	344	2	683	3	–1	1
Greater London	337	3	1353	1	2	4
South Yorkshire	332	4	307	5	–1	1
West Yorkshire	321	5	594	4	1	1
Merseyside	284	6	297	6	0	0
Tyne and Wear	264	7	259	7	0	0
						$\Sigma d^2 = 8$

Other fieldwork and data analysis techniques

These additional fieldwork and data analysis techniques are not covered in Section 2 but are explained where they are used during Investigations in Section 3 and on the Website. If these techniques might be helpful for your fieldwork project, you should look at the relevant page numbers provided here to see how these techniques can be used in the field.

Fieldwork

Technique	Where to find it
Measuring the size of raindrops	Weather Investigation, page 92
What is stream ***discharge***?	Rivers Investigation, page 124
How to measure the volume of a river	Rivers Extra Investigation, Website
How to measure the cross-sectional area of a channel and a river	Rivers Extra Investigation, Website
How to test the rate of evaporation	Weather Project Suggestion 5, page 91
How to measure the reflectivity/albedo of a surface	Weather Investigation, pages 103–4
How to record land use in a town	Towns Investigation, page 118
How to record the use made of buildings above ground level	Towns Investigation, page 118
Value-numbers for assessing landscape features/landscape evaluation	Towns Extra Investigation, Website Leisure Extra Investigation, Website
Making a noise meter	Transport Investigation, page 151
How to find the centre of a town:	
peak land value point	Towns Investigation, pages 117, 121
peak pedestrian flow point	Towns Investigation, pages 117,118,121
How to investigate the ways in which traffic flow is regulated	Towns Extra Investigation, Website
Assessing the impact of the public on an area	Leisure Extra Investigation, Website
How to measure wear and tear on footpaths and other surfaces	Leisure Extra Investigation, Website
How to measure the ***infiltration rate*** of a soil	Coasts Trial Run, page 162 Leisure Extra Investigation, Website
Making an infiltration can	Coasts Trial Run, page 162
How to measure soil depth	Leisure Extra Investigation, Website
Where to find tide tables	Coasts Investigation, page 159
A guide to investigating an ***ecosystem***	Coasts Trial Run, pages 161–2
Making a hypsometer to measure the height of landscape features and objects	Coasts Investigation, pages 173–4
How to measure the height of cliffs and other features	Coasts Investigation, pages 173–4

Data analysis

Technique	Where to find it
How to assess accessibility by measuring the map	Towns Extra Investigation, Website
How to assess accessibility within a transport network	Transport Extra Investigation, Website
Calculating channel efficiency:	
width:depth ratio	Rivers Extra Investigation, Website
hydraulic radius	Rivers Extra Investigation, Website
Assessing the connectivity of a route network:	
alpha index	Transport Extra Investigation, Website
beta index	Transport Extra Investigation, Website
How to calculate from a map the potential number of visitors in a ***catchment area***	Leisure Investigation, pages 178, 188–9

Weather

Weather has a great effect upon our lives, and we, in turn, affect the weather. When 'not on top of the world' people sometimes describe themselves as being 'under the weather'. Do they mean that they are feeling the rapid changes in weather which take place as a ***depression*** passes over? Rapid pressure changes are known to cause headaches. Do you think that low pressure systems are well named as depressions?

Until we developed accurate weather instruments in the 1600s, weather sayings and weather predictions were based on people's observations. Many of these were handed down from generation to generation. Here are two accurate forecasts:

'Clear moon, frost soon.'

'One swallow does not make a summer.'

How many others can you think of?

So what is weather? The dictionary tells us that it is 'the state of atmospheric conditions including temperature, sunshine, wind, clouds and ***precipitation***, at a particular place and time'.

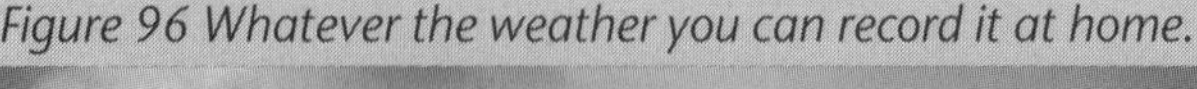

Figure 96 Whatever the weather you can record it at home.

This sounds very dull! You only really discover the fascination of the weather and of all its changing patterns when you measure and record its different aspects. This is easy and fun to do, and most of the equipment needed can be made simply and cheaply at home.

When you keep records of your measurements you begin to notice how the weather 'behaves'. It is by doing just this that our forecasters are able to predict the weather to come. An investigation into weather can be of real practical value. *It can also be a good link with Science*, because meteorology is concerned with the physics of atmosphere. Don't be put off if physics is not your favourite subject. As you watch the weather and develop a 'weather eye', this in turn will help you to understand physics better. You could also use your data in mathematics.

In Section 2, each of the weather elements is explained:

- Their importance is described on pages 28–37.
- The equipment needed for measuring each is explained on pages 28–37.
- Ways of displaying the information are given on pages 82–3.

Look through the following pages and decide which aspects of the weather interest you most. Then consider how you could plan your project around them. The Trial Run, Short Project and Investigation in this chapter are intended to give you some ideas. There is also an Extra Investigation on the Website.

Project suggestions

1. In what ways, and for what reasons, does the weather affect the outside of buildings? Buildings are most likely to be affected by rain, wind, frost, high temperatures, a high range of temperatures, air-borne ***pollution***, and by the growth of crystals of salts such as sodium chloride. Measure two or three aspects of the weather and the amount of ***weathering*** on the building.

   Where to find help:

   Buildings and air pollution, 41–5

   Weather aspects and how to measure them, 28–36

   Ways of displaying information, 82–83

2. Are there differences between the weather at home and at school? Keep weather records at home and at school over a period of two or more weeks and then compare them. Choose sites for your instruments that are as similar as possible to the site at school. Try to account for any differences you find.

   Where to find help:

   How to make and keep a weather log, 28

   Weather elements and how to record them, 28–36

   For sites, see Weather Investigation on 100–106

3. Investigate the relationship between two or more of the following pairs of weather elements from recordings kept over two weeks or longer. Are there links between different weather elements? Choose two or more of the following pairs and base your investigation on recordings kept over two weeks or longer:

   wind direction and wind speed

   wind direction and rainfall

   wind direction and relative humidity

   wind direction and visibility

   atmospheric pressure and rainfall

   wind speed and minimum temperature

   cloud cover and the daily range of temperature

   Try to give reasons for any links that you find.

   Where to find help:

   How to make and keep a weather log, 28

   How to record the weather elements, 28–36

4. Does the weather vary upwards? In a building with several floors, record the temperature four or more times every day for at least two weeks. Include measurements close to the ground at about 10 cm and at the official height of a Stevenson screen (1.2 m). Compare the readings, and attempt to give reasons for them. Remember to record the general weather conditions of each day: atmospheric pressure, cloud cover, wind speed and direction. Do these affect your measurements?

   Where to find help:

   Temperature and how to measure it, 31–33

   The effects of buildings on temperature, 103–4

   How to investigate indoor climate – Weather Extra Investigation, Website

5. How does the evaporation rate vary from place to place? Put dishes containing a measured volume of water in different places. The dishes should be of the same size and shape: 250 ml will fit well into a soup plate or a cereal dish. Put the dishes into contrasting environments: out-of-doors at least 1 m away from a wall or building; in an unheated outbuilding; in a room on the sunny side of the building and in a room on the shady side. Take care to find out whether there is a source of heating in these rooms.

   Measure the amount of evaporation that has taken place in successive periods of 2 or 3 hours. Record your measurements and try to explain variations between sites. Are they related to the following:

   temperature

   wind speed

   wind direction

   relative humidity?

   If you repeat this procedure on different days you will see that variations occur according to different weather conditions. Relate these to changes in the amount and type of cloud cover, to differences in temperature, wind speed and direction and to relative humidity.

   Where to find help:

   How to investigate indoor climate – Weather Extra Investigation, Website

   How to measure the relative humidity, 33–4

6. How do variations in the weather affect what we do?

   Where to find help:

   Website weather Investigation

   Secondary Sources – advertised events and weather forecasts and records

7. How do plants alter the ***microclimate*** of the area in which they grow? Your fieldwork area could be your garden at home, a part of the school grounds, farm fields, or a public park.

   Where to find help:

   How to measure weather elements, 28–36

   How to investigate length of shadow, 103

   Interception experiment, 130

8. How do ***aspect*** and exposure affect the use which a farmer makes of his land?

   Where to find help:

   Trial Run 21 on 85

   Farm land use – Project idea 5, Appendix 1, 196

The Royal Meteorological Society recommends a fascinating little investigation into the size of raindrops which you could use for most projects about weather.

1. Make a scale of raindrop size by dropping water drops of known size or volume onto a piece of coloured blotting paper. Draw round the drops with ballpoint pen. Measure the diameter of the drops.
2. When it is raining, put out a new piece of blotting paper. Measure the size of drops immediately.
3. How much smaller are the raindrops in drizzle than in a heavy shower?

Gentle raindrops of small diameter are the most effective for farming and gardening. Large raindrops are the most serious in causing soil erosion. Find out more about these and illustrate your findings by examples from different parts of the world.

The study of weather is known as meteorology. Climatology is the study of climate. Climate is the average weather based on observations and recordings ideally kept continuously for a minimum of 40 years.

Fieldwork area

For a successful project, concentrate on taking measurements and making observations in a small area such as around buildings or in different parts of your school grounds. This will form an investigation of ***local climate***. For a project on ***microclimate*** concentrate on smaller areas still, such as garden flowerbeds, window boxes, lawns, and the effects of shrubs and trees. Caution: It is vital to take readings and to record what you find at the same time every day for a period of time. Record your observations in a 'weather log', either in your field notebook or on computer. Some people like to call it a 'weather diary'. Look at Figure 20 on page 28 in Section 2.

In Canada, Tom Waite of Ranfurly, Alberta, has begun each of 25,000 days by walking 30 m to observe the weather instruments behind his farmhouse. In Canada, there are 2000 unpaid volunteers like Mr Waite who help to record Canada's weather and contribute to weather forecasting by Environment Canada.

Weather Trial Run: Does Manchester produce the effect of a heat island?

FIELDWORK TECHNIQUES

The following techniques were used:

- **Field sketching**
- **How to lay a line of transect**
- **Measuring temperature**
- **Sampling**

The ***data*** were collected during anticyclonic weather in December 1996 as part of a day's fieldwork by students working in groups of three.

Before you begin

1. Find out as much as you can about urban heat islands. Describe them in a summary in your own words.
2. Find out the population of Manchester. Look, on a map (such as Figure 110 on page 110), at the built-up area of the Manchester conurbation. It would be a good idea to include a tracing or sketch map so that someone reading your report will see the location of Manchester, and the location of the ***transect***.

Look at the map in Figure 98 and the data in Figure 99 and work through this as if it were your project.

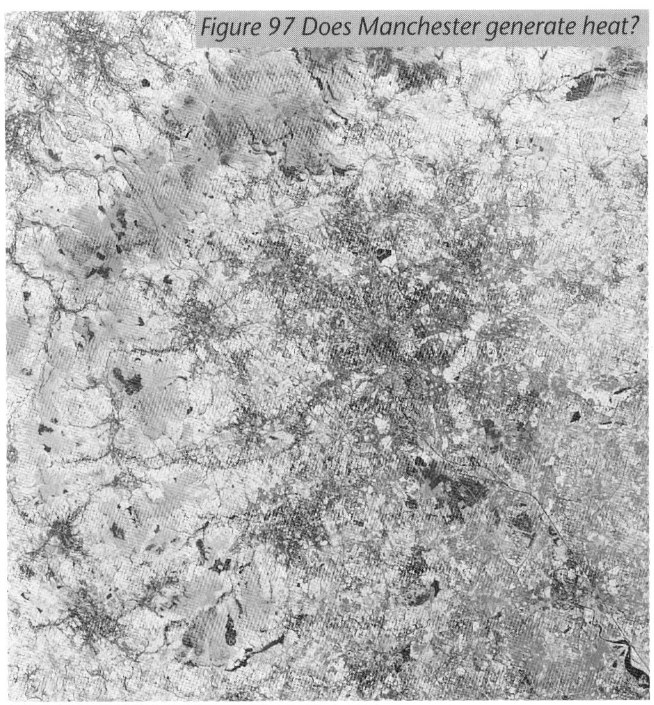

Figure 97 Does Manchester generate heat?

Aims

1. Does the temperature decrease with distance from the city centre?
2. Is the temperature related to the density of building in the local area?

The following equipment was used:

Equipment used by each group:

- Ordnance Survey map of scale 1:50,000 for the fieldwork study area of the whole group.
- Ordnance Survey map of scale 1:10,000 for the local area where small groups were working.
- Two standard household thermometers (one as a spare).
- One thermometer was carried inside a portable thermometer screen on a timber pole 1.2 m high (Figure 27, page 31)
- Temperature recording sheet.

Fieldwork method for Aim 1

Does the temperature decrease with distance from the city centre?

A transect 11 km in length was chosen as a ***sample*** for this investigation. The transect ran from the city centre, which was taken as the main bus station (grid reference 844980), to the suburb of Whitefield (grid reference 805062). Part of this can be seen in Figure 98. A north–south transect was chosen because it was approximately at right angles to the direction of the prevailing wind.

It was decided that a systematic random sample of intervals along the transect would be used, measuring sites as close as possible to 250 m apart.

Each group was responsible for taking measurements at three adjacent sites. At each, the thermometer in its screen was put in place for 15 minutes and the temperature then recorded. The results were ***tabulated*** as in Figure 99.

Figure 98 Map to show the line of transect and the locations of the investigation sites.

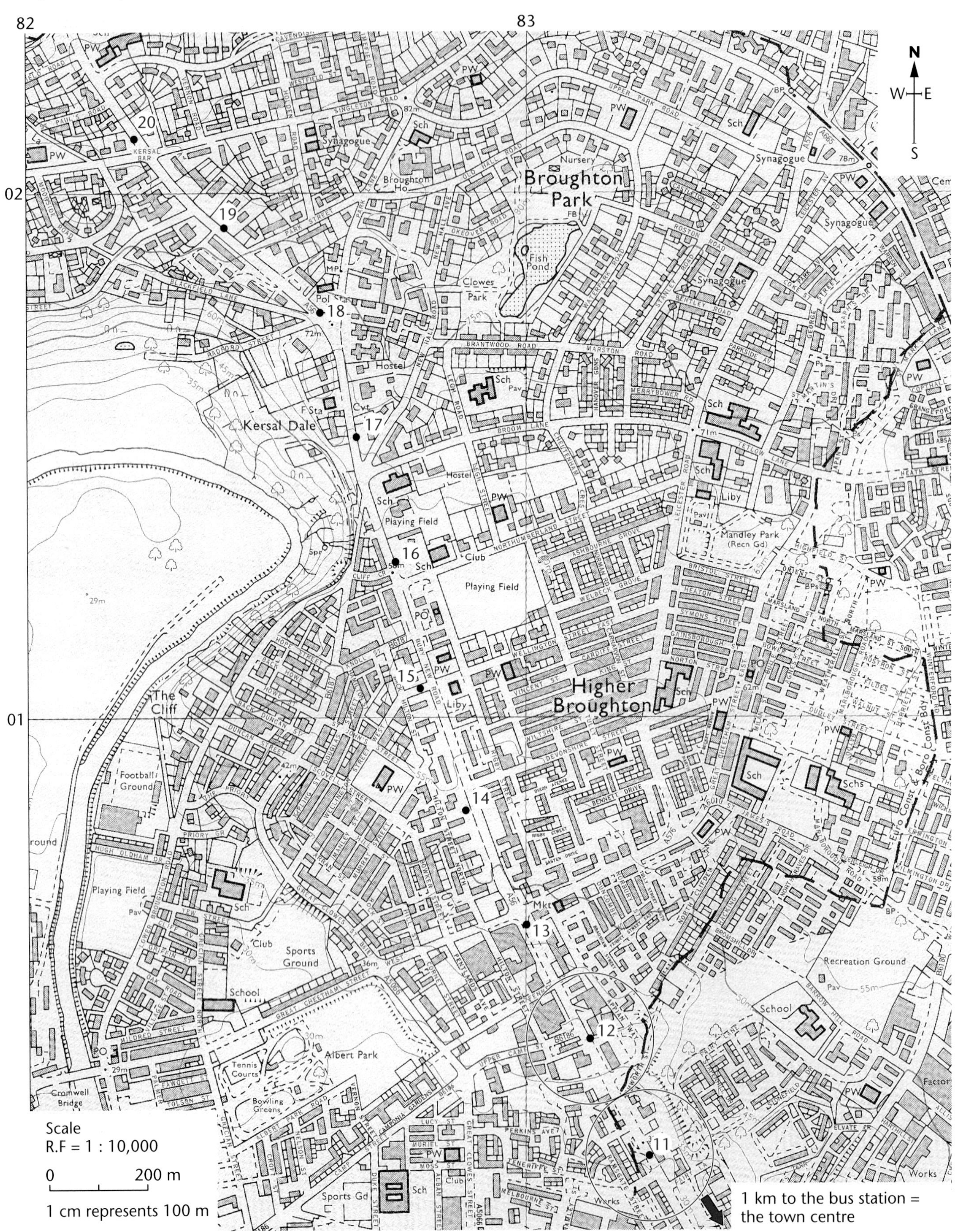

Figure 99 Table of results

Site	Temperature	Building density	Distance from city	Site	Temperature	Building density	Distance from city
no.	(°C)	as % of each circle	centre (km)	no.	(°C)	as % of each circle	centre (km)
NORTH							
44	7	2.3	11	21	8	8.4	5.25
43	7	4.7	10.75	20	8	5	
42	7	5.0	10.5	19	7	4.75	
41	8	5.9	10.25	18	8		
40	8	6.7	10	17	8	4.25	
39	8	15.3	9.75	16	8	4	
38	8	9.2	9.5	15	8	3.75	
37	8	18.9	9.25	14	8	3.5	
36	8	15.9	9	13	8	3.25	
35	9	16.7	8.75	12	8	14.5	3
34	8	12.2	8.5	11	8	15.7	2.75
33	7	17.5	8.25	10	8	26.7	2.5
32	8	17.7	8	9	8	23.6	2.25
31	8	17.5	7.75	8	8	14.3	2
30	8	17.3	7.5	7	8	10.2	1.75
29	8	12.8	7.25	6	9	19.8	1.5
28	8	7.9	7	5	9	15.1	1.25
27	9	10.0	6.75	4	9	16.3	1
26	8	28.3	6.5	3	9	14.9	0.75
25	8	16.9	6.25	2	10	11.6	0.5
24	8	6.9	6	1	10	35.6	0.25
23	8	5.7	5.75	City Centre	10	54.6	0
22	8	9.4	5.5	SOUTH			

Fieldwork method for Aim 2

Investigating the relationship between temperature and building density

This part of the investigation is based on the use of ***secondary data***, the 1:10,000 map published by the Ordnance Survey. On Figure 98 the building density of sites 11 and 12 has been completed. Following the steps given below calculate the building density for sites 13–20.

1. Draw a circle of radius 1.25 cm on the map around each recording site. As the scale of the map is 1:10,000, 1.25 cm represents 125 m on the ground.
2. Calculate the area of the circle.
3. Place tracing paper over Figure 98. Draw a circle of radius 1.25 cm around each of the recording sites. Divide each circle into five equal pie sectors of 75 each. A simple way of doing this is to make a template on acetate or an extra piece of tracing paper. Within each, shade the area that is covered by buildings. Give the result as a percentage of the whole circle.
4. Complete the percentage building density for sites 13–20 in Figure 99.

Analysing and interpreting your data

A line graph to show the relationship between temperature and the distance from the city centre

On graph paper, choose appropriate scales to represent the distance from the city centre on the x-axis (horizontal) and the temperature on the y-axis (vertical). Plot the results from the table in Figure 99. Describe what your graph shows. Can you conclude that it supports Aim 1? Does the temperature decrease with distance from the city centre?

Evaluating your work

Suggest reasons for any unexpected variations. For example,

- a change in wind speed at different sites
- inaccurate reading of instruments or recordings
- a central heating vent in a building

What other reasons could there be?

Calculations of the average percentage building density and its relationship to the temperature

Figure 99 shows that only four different temperature values were recorded whereas many different percentages of building density were measured. For each of the temperature values in turn, add up the total building density in the areas surrounding the sites. Next, divide the total building density by the number of times (frequency) that that particular temperature value occurs.

For example, 10 °C occurs three times. The building density in each of the areas surrounding a 10 °C result is: 11.6%, 35.6% and 54.6%. Added together these total 101.8% and, when divided by 3, the average percentage building density can be calculated: 101.8% = 33.9%.

For each of the other temperature values recorded, calculate the average building density in the surrounding area by using the same method of calculation:

$$\frac{\text{The sum of the building density in the circles}}{\text{Frequency of occurrence of the given temperature}}$$

Make a table of these results, and then choose a technique for illustration which makes the data easy to interpret: a bar chart or a scattergraph. Describe what your results show. Do you draw the conclusion that the temperature is related to the percentage building density of the surrounding area? Do you think it would be helpful to calculate Spearman's Rank Correlation Coefficient (see page 87 in Section 2).

Evaluating the methods of investigation

Give your views on the method of calculating the result. Knowing something about the following may help:

- the use of the buildings
- the height of the buildings
- the amount of traffic

Drawing conclusions

Does Manchester produce an island of heat or not?

1. Summarise your conclusions to both aims.
2. Describe, with reasons, which of the two influences on the temperature you feel to be the more important, or do you feel that they are of equal importance?

Evaluating your work

If you could have planned the investigation yourself would you have altered the procedures? Here are some hints:

- Should the heights of buildings be included?
- Is the type of land use important? Buildings are artificially heated and give off heat in winter, whilst open ground does not.
- Are the building materials important?

Interesting extra ideas

Try this investigation in your home area. It would make a good project.

Weather Short Project: What is the difference in temperature between the different sides of a building or the inside and outside of a building?

Fieldwork area: how to choose your fieldwork sites

On opposite sides of a building, outside or inside, but ideally one facing south and the other facing north, find safe places for your weather instruments. You will have to leave them in place for about 5 or more days. Place them about 5 metres away from the nearest wall. Make sure that they will not be in anybody's way.

Use a compass or an Ordnance Survey map of scale 1:25,000 or bigger to help you to find out which is the north side of the building and which the south side.

You will need the following equipment:

Two sets of equipment exactly the same. In each set include:

- 1 thermometer. See pages 31–32 for help in choosing the best type for your project.
- 1 thermometer screen. See page 31 for instructions on how to make one
- Recording Sheet/Weather Log to write down your measurements. Make one along the lines of that in Figure 20 on page 28. This one is very detailed. Think carefully about the information you need to record and adapt it.

You may include a camera to take photographs of the sites and of someone taking measurements.

Before you begin

1. For your final report put the heading 'Fieldwork Sites' and then:
   (a) Describe how and why you chose your fieldwork sites and
   (b) Draw a map to show the building and the sites
2. Choose your instruments as follows:
   (a) Find out what types of thermometer you could use. Look at the kinds described on pages 32–33.
   (b) If possible, try out more than one type and then decide on the one you feel most confident with. Practise using it so that you will become quick at reading the temperature. Try it out in the Geography Room, then in a corridor and then outside. Each should have a different temperature.

Each time leave the thermometer in place for 10 minutes or more and then read the temperature and write it down straight away on your Recording Sheet/Weather Log. If your thermometer has a metal indicator (probably it will be coloured) use a magnet to pull it back onto the mercury ready for the next recording.

(c) For the introduction to your final report:

(i) describe how the thermometer works. A drawing with labels will help. Look at Figure 29 and Trial Run 2 on page 32 for examples.

(iii) explain why you chose this particular type of thermometer. Hints: Can you see the line of mercury or coloured alcohol clearly? Does it record both the maximum and the minimum temperature? If it was the only type of thermometer available, say so.

(d) Why do you think a thermometer screen is important in helping you to gain more accurate and reliable results? Explain this in your final report. You can read about thermometer screens on page 31.

3. In your final report describe, step by step, the preparations you have made.

Fieldwork method

1. Measure the temperature three times a day on five or more days. Take your measurements at the same time each day e.g. 9 am, midday and late afternoon or in the evening. Record the temperature each time on your Recording Sheet/Weather Log.

2. In your final report describe how you carried out your fieldwork.

Analysing and interpreting your data

1. Draw a line-graph of the temperature like the one in Figure 100. On the graph plot as a dot or a cross each of your temperature recordings in turn. Next, join up the dots or crosses to make a line-graph. Use different colours for your recordings at the different sites. Add a key to show the colour representing each site.

2. In your final report describe what your graph shows:

(a) about the temperature from day-to-day on the south side of the building

(b) about the temperature from day-to-day on the north side of the building

Either (a) or (b) could be an inside temperature reading.

(c) about the difference between the two sets of temperature readings

Figure 100 Line graph to show temperature differences on different walls of a building

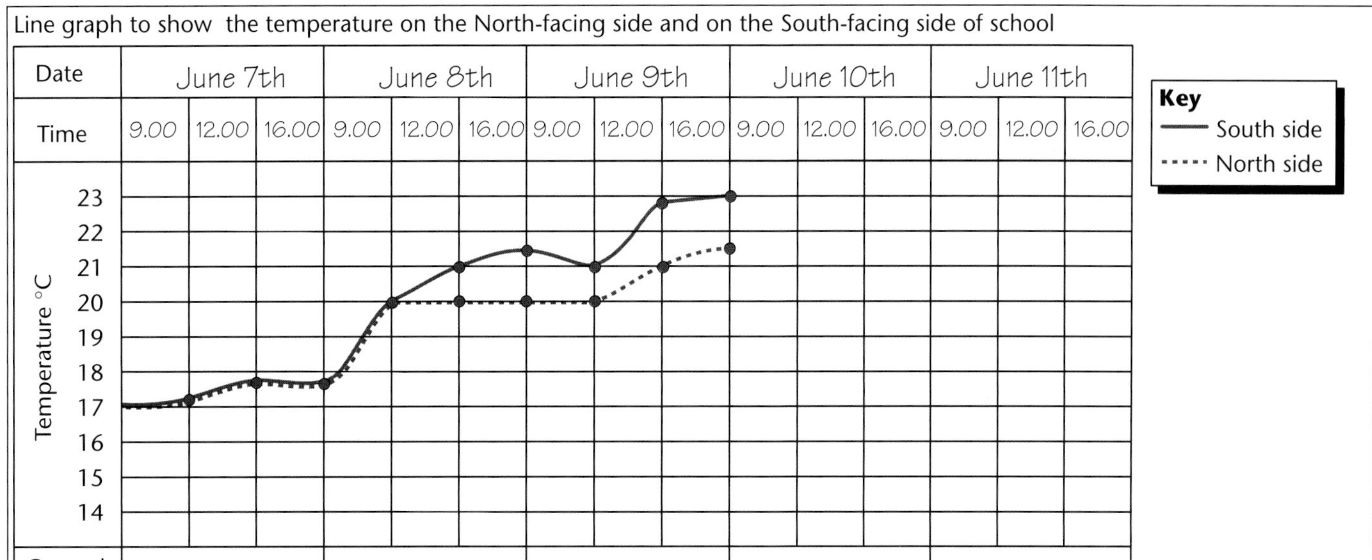

Drawing conclusions

1. Write a paragraph as a summary of the differences in the temperature between the two sites.
2. Is the difference greater on a sunny day than on a dull day?

Evaluating your work

1. Does your line graph look complicated because you have plotted 3 readings per day? Would it have been simpler to have worked out the average of the 3 daily readings (see page 84) and plotted this on your line graph? Try it and see.
2. Would a separate graph for each site have been better? What are the advantages and disadvantages of this method?
3. If your temperature readings were all taken outside:
   (a) Could your measurements of the temperature have been affected by heating from the building?
   (b) Was the building high enough or big enough to make a difference to your results?

Interesting extra ideas

- Repeat your fieldwork in different weather conditions such as a spell of settled weather or a spell of changeable weather. Do the different types of weather make bigger or smaller differences between your sets of temperature recordings?
- In countries such as Great Britain and New Zealand which are a long way from the Equator, shadows are very much longer in winter than in summer (see Figure 105 on page 103). It would be interesting to repeat your fieldwork to see whether the temperature on the north side of the building is linked to the length of shadow. Use a tape measure to measure the length of shadow.

Weather Investigation: How do buildings affect the area surrounding them?

FIELDWORK TECHNIQUES

You will use the following techniques:

- **Sampling**
- **Measuring the weather**
- **Identifying inter-relationships**

This is an investigation of ***local climate***. The whole point of constructing a building is to modify the environment, and to give protection from the weather.

Fieldwork area

Your investigation will be more interesting if you include two or more different kinds of building from a range such as these:

- main school building
- single-storey classroom
- unheated sports pavilion
- greenhouse
- tunnel or cantilever-type bus shelter
- your home

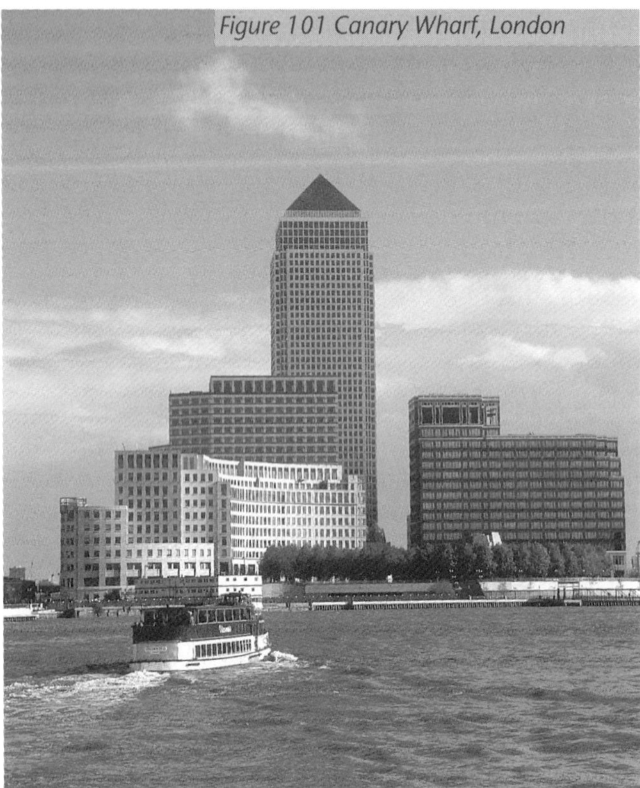

Figure 101 Canary Wharf, London

In order to assess the effects of the buildings take an extra set of measurements well away from buildings and out in the open. This will act as a control for your investigations, in the same way as a control is sometimes necessary in experiments in Science lessons. Call your control the 'open-space measurements'.

Consider carefully which aspects of the weather are affected by buildings and then choose which instruments to use and where to site them.

Four sites in addition to your open-space control site should give sufficient results to complete a good project. Place your instruments close together at each site. Look at the map in Figure 102 for ideas. Your instruments will have to be left in place for several days and read on a daily or twice-daily basis. If your sites are on private land make sure that you obtain permission in advance. Help for writing a letter is given on pages 18–20.

Before you begin

Here are some of the ways in which buildings modify the weather around them. Your investigation will reveal exactly how your buildings affect the local weather.

Buildings are constructed to be efficient in removing rain

Gutters and downpipes on a building, and gutters in the impermeable macadam and concrete surfaces which surround them, are intended to remove water to the drains as quickly as possible. The gutters and downpipes form the local drainage system. After it has been raining, go around at 15 minute intervals with your map and field notebook to write down the areas that have dried. Are the wet patches related to the surface materials, to the aspect, or to their angle of slope?

To assess the efficiency of the local drainage system (gutters and downpipes):

1. measure the area which it serves;
2. multiply this by the amount of rain collected in your rain gauge during the rainy spell;
3. see how quickly the water disappears.

Figure 102 Map to show the location of sites for investigating the influence of buildings upon local climate.

N
W E
S

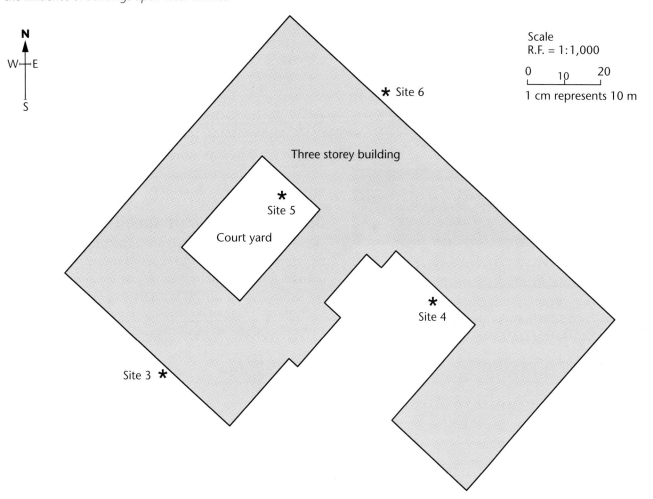

Scale
R.F. = 1:1,000
0 10 20
1 cm represents 10 m

* Site 6

Three storey building

*
Site 5

Court yard

*
Site 4

Site 3 *

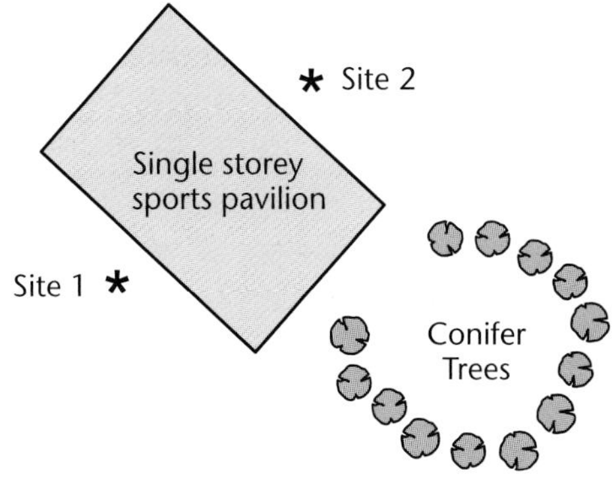

* 'Control site' as far from buildings and windbreaks as possible

A gutter on a building needs a gradient of only 1 in 360 or 0.5° to be considered efficient.

You could conduct your own experiments by pouring a measured volume of water from a watering can fitted with a fine rose onto paving slabs or slates set at different angles. Does gentle rain disperse more quickly than heavy rain? Try putting driving rain gauges facing in opposite directions to see whether they collect different amounts of rainfall.

IMPORTANT: Remember to write down your measurements before emptying rain gauges, resetting thermometer indices and putting instruments back in place.

The advantages of choosing the sites shown in Figure 102 for your instruments are that the main winds in Britain come from the south-west. Also, sites 1 and 2 and sites 3 and 4 should provide interesting contrasts: sites 1 and 2 are beside a single-storey building whereas 3 and 4 are close to a much taller and bigger building.

The control site is as far away as possible from the influence of buildings, but is not obstructing school activities.

The amount of rain that falls per hour or per day is called the rainfall intensity. In Britain, the Meteorological Office classes a 'rain day' as any 24-hour period, beginning at 9 o'clock in the morning in which 0.2 mm or more of rain is received. Gutters and downpipes are designed to cope with a rainfall intensity of 75 mm per hour.

Buildings affect wind speed and direction

Wind speed and direction are particularly affected by large buildings. Wind speed is increased at the corners and channelled along narrow streets and passageways. Gustiness is increased, but there is shelter in the lee of a building. Figures 103 and 104 show the effects of buildings.

Figure 103 A diagram to how wind direction and speed are altered by a high building.

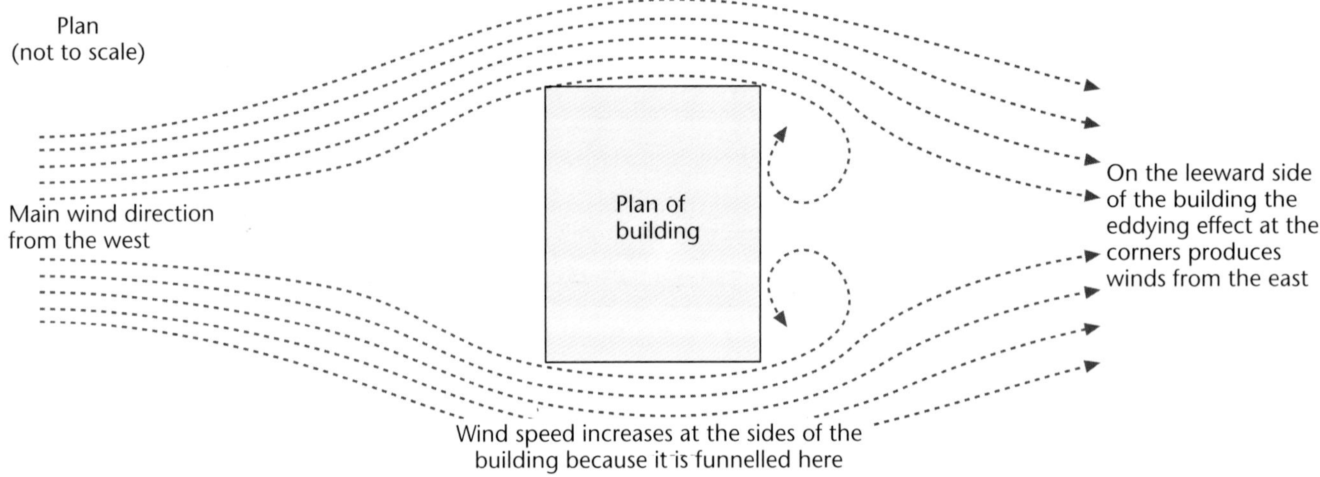

Figure 104 A diagram to show how buildings produce turbulence in wind flow.

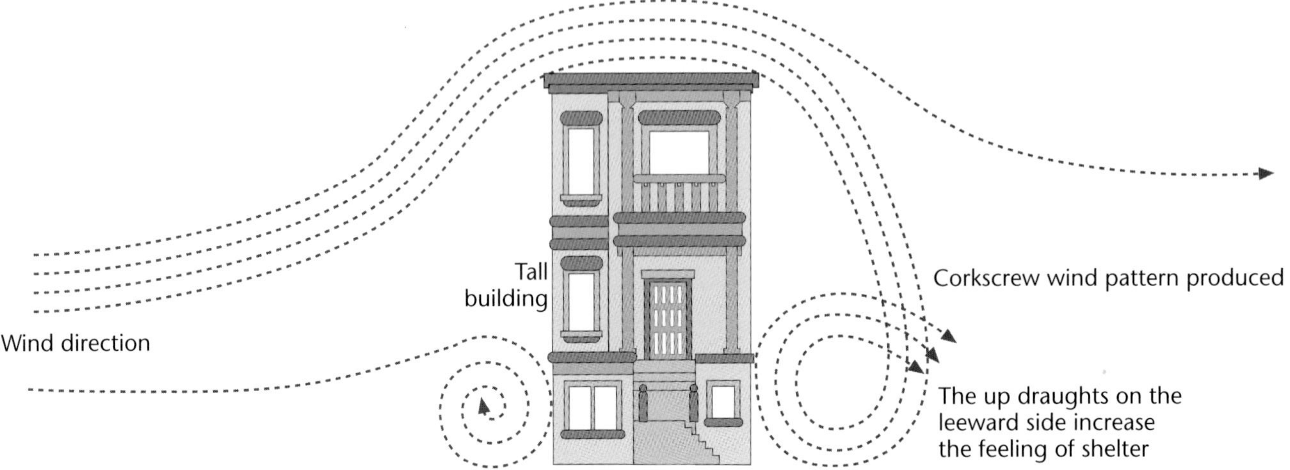

Buildings affect the temperature close to them

They do this by a combination of:

- shadow: the sun is the main source of heat, and shade reduces the sun's heating;
- shelter: this reduces the wind-chill factor (see page 36) and makes the temperature more comfortable for people and animals, and protects plants;
- heating: heat loss from a building, as shown in Figure 106, may be thought of as a heat gain to the surrounding air.

Shadow is produced particularly in winter when the sun appears to be low in the sky (see Figure 105). Use a tape measure to measure the length of shadow in the same place at the same time each day. Take temperature measurements on the sunny side of a building and in the shade.

The heating effect of buildings is demonstrated in Figure 106. If you have a diagram from Design and Technology or from Science which you prefer, then use that one or draw your own. Measure the temperature indoors, then reduce this by the percentage shown in Figure 106 to estimate the amount of heating to the air immediately outside.

Figure 105 How to measure the effects of buildings upon shadow at different times of the year.

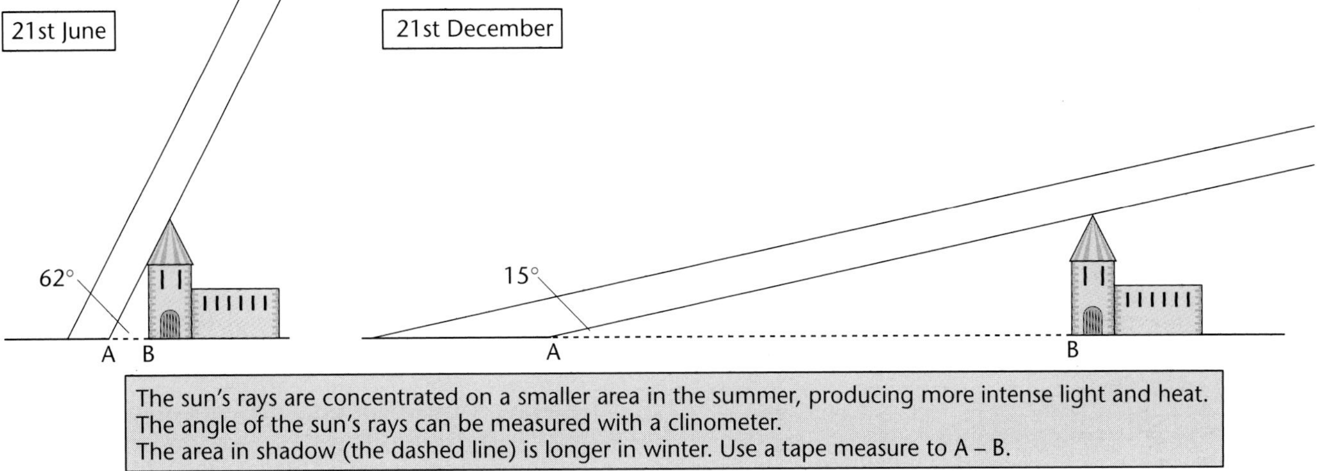

21st June
62°
A B
21st December
15°
A
B
The sun's rays are concentrated on a smaller area in the summer, producing more intense light and heat.
The angle of the sun's rays can be measured with a clinometer.
The area in shadow (the dashed line) is longer in winter. Use a tape measure to A – B.

Figure 106 Diagram to show the estimated heat loss from a building.

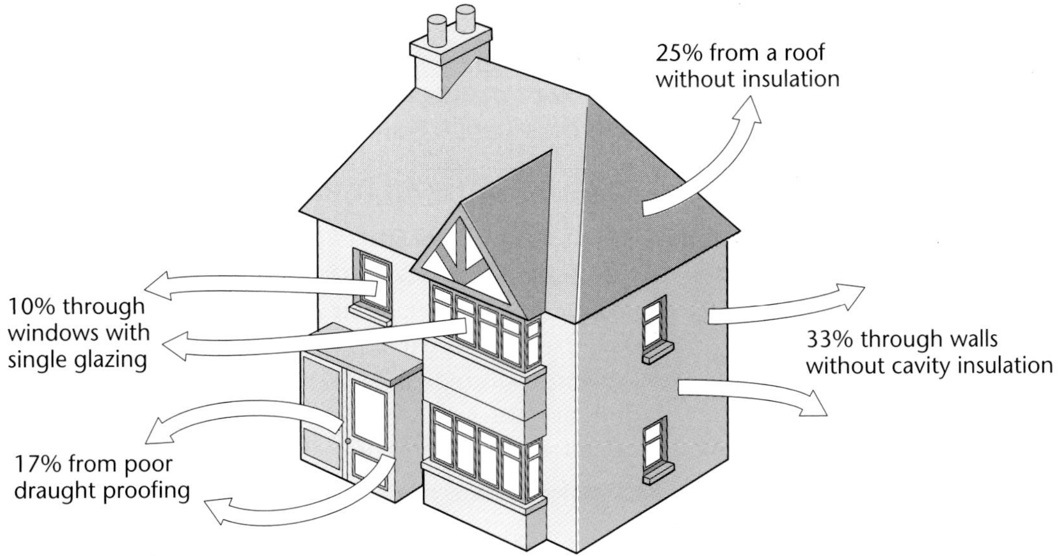

Buildings affect light intensity

First, measure the light intensity of the sky, pointing a Luxmeter or photographic exposure meter vertically upwards. Next, take measurements on different sides of the building. The type of building material can also affect light intensity by its degree of reflectivity. This is known as the **albedo**. Try pointing your meter to a shiny surface and then to a matt surface; to a light surface and then to a dark one. To see whether the albedo affects the temperature, take measurements where your light meter shows a difference in intensity. See pages 36–7 in Section 2.

Our eyes very easily adapt to different intensities of light, so it is wise to use a Luxmeter or photographic exposure meter if possible. These are reliable and give better recordings than what we think we see as bright or dull.

Relative humidity is another interesting aspect of the weather that can be affected, though less obviously, by buildings. Temperature and wind particularly influence the relative humidity.

You will need the following equipment:

- Basic fieldkit
- Pocket compass
- Weather log for recording your results
- Equipment to measure your chosen aspects of the weather

  See pages 28–37.

Carry a magnet with you to reset the metal indicators in the thermometers (the automatic gadget for this does not always work). Your ***reconnaissance visit*** will have helped you to decide how many sets of instruments you need.

Tiles covered in adhesive plastic may be left with the sticky side up to see how many solid particles from the atmosphere will stick within a given time such as a week. You could compare the results under different weather conditions, such as when a depression is passing over and during a spell of anticyclonic weather (high pressure).

Fieldwork method

Safety is more important than anything else. Make sure that your instruments will not be in anyone's way.

You will have to leave your instruments in place for two weeks or more. Choose places where they will not be disturbed. If you have to site some of them in less than ideal places then explain your reasons in the ***evaluation*** section of your final report.

Take measurements at least once a day, and preferably twice a day, for a minimum of five consecutive days. Write down each measurement on your weather log as soon as you have read it. Keep your measurements carefully.

CAUTION: Never trick yourself into thinking that you will remember the measurements 'for later'.

Analysing and interpreting your data

Graphs of your measurements

Draw graphs of your recordings of temperature and rainfall (see Figure 107). Temperature is shown as a line graph and rainfall as a bar chart. If you use a particular colour for each site, this will help to make the differences clear.

Additional measurements can be included on your graph by using either diagonal line shading or **dots** in black on top of solid colour or a **tracing overlay**. Avoid graphs that are too crowded with information. Place them side by side if you feel that the information would be clearer that way.

Evaluating the graphs

Do you think this information would be easier to read if a separate graph were drawn for each site?

Maps annotated to show cloud cover, wind direction and speed

Use the same colours for your different sites as you used on the graphs. Draw a separate map for each day. Use an arrow to show the direction from which the wind was blowing. Add feathers to the wind direction arrows to show the wind speed (in knots, in metres per second or as Beaufort force).

Figure 107 Graph to show temperature and rainfall measurements for the sites shown in Figure 102.

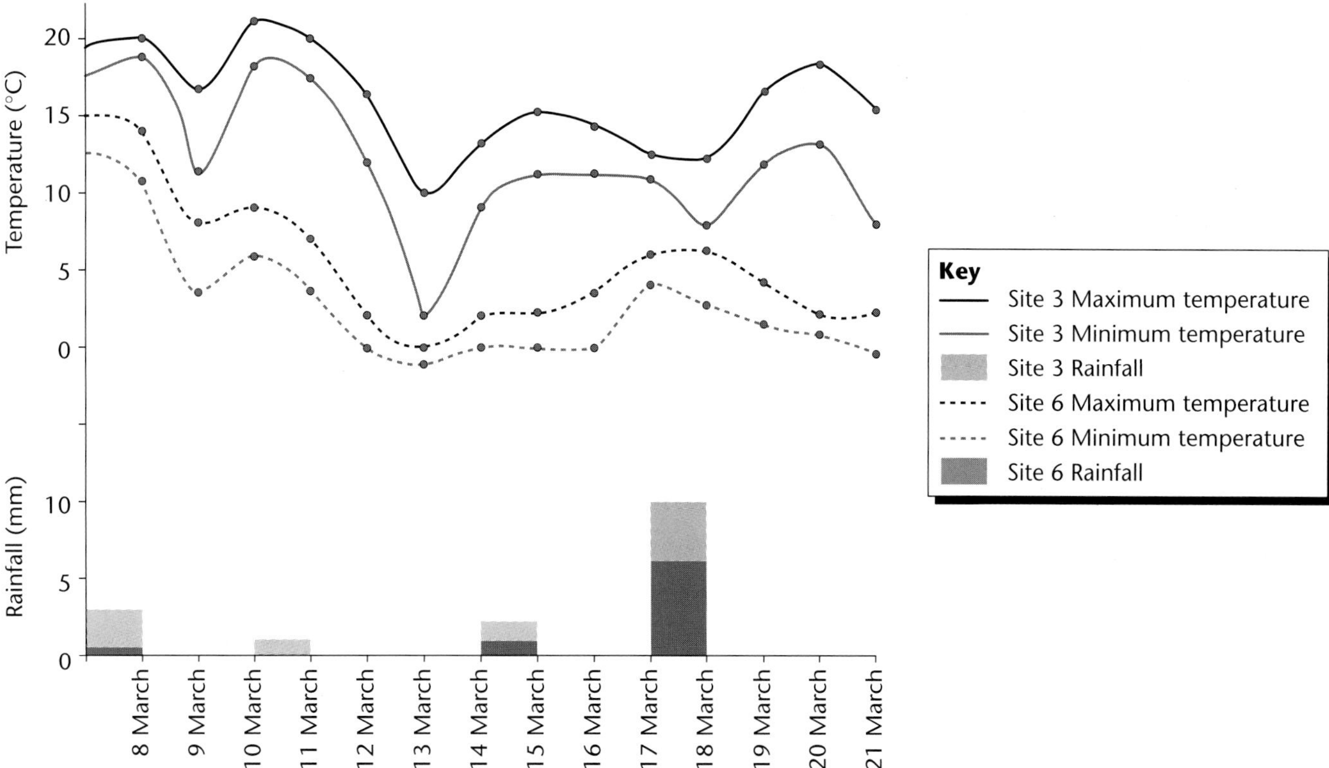

Remember to give the key clearly on at least one of your maps; on all the other maps, print 'Key as on Map x'. ***Annotate*** your map to explain any unusual features. See Figure 108 on page 106 for an example.

Drawing conclusions

Describe your results site by site and day by day. Can you see any patterns between the sets of data shown on your graph? Describe these in detail in your own words. Next look at your map and describe this in detail. Does the map help to explain any of the patterns shown on your graph?

You could extend your study by obtaining weather data from your local Weather Centre or from the Meteorological Office at Bracknell (see Appendix 2 and Website for addresses). You could then compare your results with the published ones. To what extent are they similar? Remember that your results are for a small local area.

Evaluating your work

- Do you consider your buildings to have been big enough and high enough to affect the weather?
- Considering the number of aspects of the weather you have investigated, would it have been better to have investigated more or concentrated on fewer?
- Did you put your instruments in the best places?

Interesting extra ideas

1. Measure the 'weather' inside a building and compare it with that outside. You could make a transect by putting instruments inside a room, attached to a window sill, immediately outside, and several metres away from the building.
2. What would be the effects of installing double or triple glazing to a single-glazed building? Are patio doors a good thing in terms of heat conservation inside a house?
3. In a building with several storeys, attach weather instruments to window sills facing in the same direction at different heights. It is interesting to do this inside the building too. Place instruments on different landings as you go upstairs. Take care not to interfere with people's movement upstairs or downstairs.
4. Give your estimation of the efficiency of the building's design for the distribution of heat, light, relative humidity and draught-proofing.

Figure 108 Map to show cloud cover, wind direction and wind speed with annotations.

N
W E
S

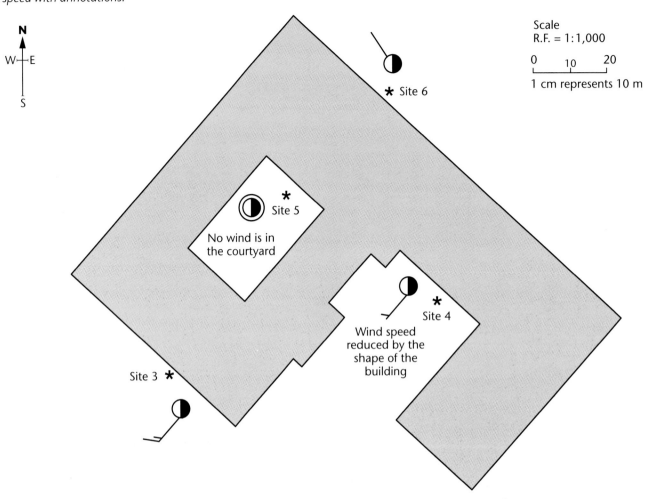

Scale
R.F. = 1:1,000
0 10 20
1 cm represents 10 m

* Site 6

* Site 5
No wind is in the courtyard

* Site 4
Wind speed reduced by the shape of the building

Site 3 *

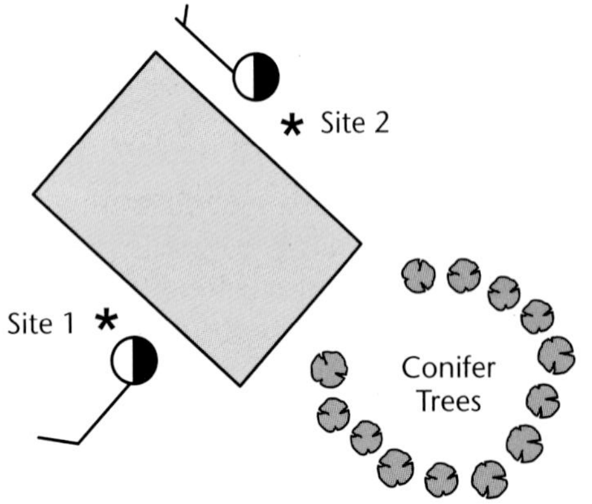

Beaufort Scale (wind speed)			Cloud cover	
0		Calm		clear sky
1		Light air movement		1/8 covered
2		Light breeze		2/8 covered
3		Gentle breeze		3/8 covered
4		Moderate breeze		4/8 covered
5		Fresh breeze		5/8 covered
6		Strong breeze		6/8 covered
7		Near gale		7/8 covered
8		Gale		8/8 covered (complete cloud cover)
9		Strong gale		
10		Storm	=	sky obscured by mist (= is the symbol for mist)

A large cumulus cloud covered the sky as the cloud cover measurement was taken.

* Control site

Towns

The fieldwork investigations suggested in this chapter focus on a group of buildings in an urban area which, for convenience, we have termed 'towns'.

Most of us are familiar with life in towns but what is a town? Put simply, towns are groups of buildings that provide homes, services and employment. The purpose for which a building is used is termed its ***'function'***: homes have a residential function, and shops, banks and schools have a service function. Many people work in service functions but others work in warehouses and factories whose function is 'industry'.

The functions of a town are reflected in the patterns made by its streets, buildings and open spaces. These patterns give the town a form or layout, and the study of form is called **morphology**.

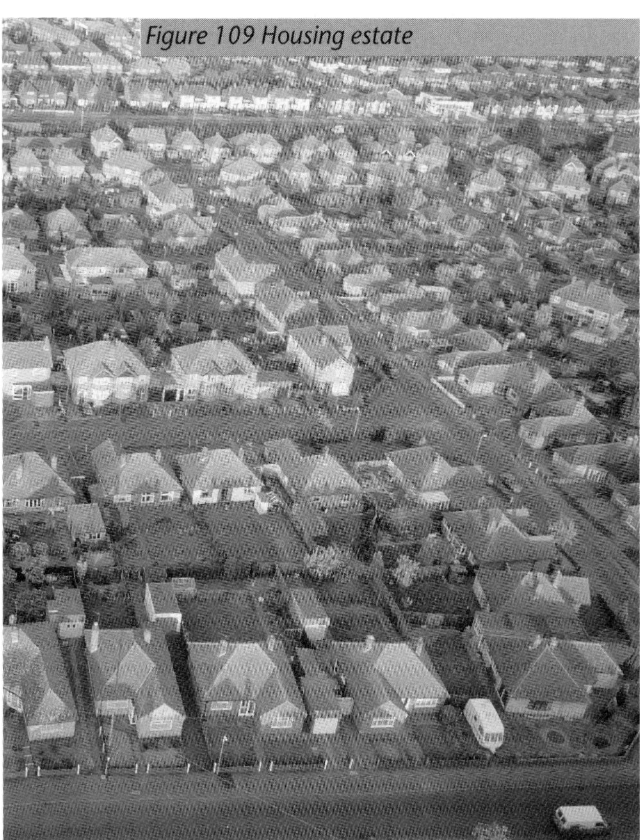

Figure 109 Housing estate

You will know that a town is just one of a ***hierarchy*** of settlements of different sizes and importance. A settlement may be defined as 'any building made by people upon the land', so settlements range from isolated farmsteads and tiny villages to enormous conurbations. Each of these is an environment dominated by buildings.

Most towns in Britain are at least several hundred years old: 90% of all the towns now in England and Wales were recorded in the Domesday Survey of 1086. A similar proportion of those of Scotland and Ireland can be found on maps dating from the Middle Ages. *A project that investigates changes through time can be an interesting link with your work in history.*

Towns offer so many possibilities for project topics that it is easy to be spoilt for choice. First, decide which aspects of the geography of towns interest you most. This chapter gives detailed guidance on how to discover the following aspects of towns:

a the ***order of importance/hierarchy*** of settlements

b the ***sphere of influence*** of a town

c whether ***functional zones*** exist in a town

d similarities and differences between residential areas

You can find **a** and **b** in the Trial Run, and **c** and **d** in the Short Project and Investigations. You can also find **c** and **d** in the Extra Investigation on the Website.

Project suggestions

1. Can zones of land use/functional zones be recognised in your town ? Does the layout of your town appear similar to the theoretical town plans of Burgess and other geographers?

   Where to find help:

   Land use recording as explained in each Investigation in this chapter and in the Towns Extra Investigation on the Website

   Street planning and patterns, 62

2. Does your town have a distinctive Central Business District and are there distinctive areas within that Central Business District?

   Where to find help:

   Land use recording as explained in each Investigation in this chapter and in the Towns Extra Investigation on the Website

   Identifying the peak pedestrian and peak land value points, 117

3. In the Central Business District do certain types of shops cluster together? If so, why?

   Where to find help:

   Land use recording as explained in each Investigation in this chapter and in the Towns Extra Investigation on the Website

   Secondary sources – Goad plans and Valuation office, 109

   Adjacency matrix and distribution on a map, 68–9

4. Compare two different types of residential area, such as:
   - an area of terraced houses built in Victorian or Edwardian times
   - a suburban housing area built between 1920 and 1970
   - an edge-of-town residential estate
   - a housing estate in a rural area

   In your project try to answer the following questions, giving reasons where possible:

   a Do newer areas of housing have better facilities for (i) shopping and (ii) recreation than older areas of housing?

   b Are different street patterns reflected in the quality of the environment?

   c Are house types related to the ***socio-economic status*** of their inhabitants?

   d Is the residential area well provided with two or more of the following:

   shopping facilities

   churches or other places of worship

   postal services, e. g. post office, pillar boxes and postal deliveries

   schools

   recreational facilities, both outdoor and indoor

   Where to find help:

   Towns Extra Investigation, Website

   Architectural style and street patterns, 60–62

   Secondary sources – Census, 109

5. How and why has an area changed through time?
   - Are the changes reflected in the population structure (proportions in different age groups), and the socio-economic status of the parish or the ward?
   - Have there been phases of rapid growth during the town's history? Have these affected the layout of the town today?
   - Bringing new life to old areas? What effects has this had?

   Where to find help:

   Public Library – Local History section

   Secondary sources, 109

'Social' means how people behave, and 'economic' is the way in which people earn their living. The two are closely related, hence the term socio-economic.

Three ways of planning lead to successful projects:

a Along ***transects*** such as roads leading outwards from the centre of a town. Are you able to pick out particular zones such as the Central Business District, the zone in transition and residential zones?

b Focusing upon concentrated areas, e. g.
- an investigation into the similarities and contrasts between different residential areas
- an investigation of land use and services within the Central Business District
- discovering the way in which the area has changed through time

c Studies of the ***distribution*** of facilities, e. g. where within a town are one or more of the following located and why?

public gardens and public open spaces

churches

schools

pillar boxes and public telephone boxes

bus stops

listed buildings

Street patterns are a good clue to the age and type of functional area. The line of a street tends to remain long after it was first laid out. This is usually because services such as water, electricity and telecommunications cables have often been laid below the surface of the street.

Fieldwork area

As a geographer, you are looking for patterns and for the reasons why they have developed. It may be difficult to see patterns clearly in a town which has a population of less than 5,000, but two small towns can provide interesting similarities and contrasts.

You may decide to concentrate on particular areas in a larger town:

- two contrasting residential areas such as a housing estate on the edge of town and an area of Victorian housing;

- the core of the shopping and service area of the town – you probably know this as the Central Business District or CBD;
- a street near the town centre or a Census ward or parish and how it has changed through time. Change in a parish can be an interesting study.

As a rough guide, two people can make an interesting investigation of about 1,000 buildings.

Reconnaissance for your project

Begin by looking at the Ordnance Survey map of scale 1:25,000 or 1:50,000. Is there enough scope for a project? Look at the street patterns, the open spaces, churches with a tower or spire, the focus of routes. Ask yourself:

- Where would I place land-use ***transects*** so that they would represent the whole town?
- Which residential areas would provide interesting contrasts or similarities?
- Where does the edge of the CBD appear to be?
- Which area looks as if it has a long history?

Secondary data can be helpful in giving information on the reasons for many of the patterns you discover in your fieldwork.

The Small Area Statistics of the Census of Population are available in public libraries. They give a detailed picture of the ***socio-economic status*** of the people living in the area at a particular time. You can see an example of this in Appendix 2 in Figure 159.

Most public libraries also have **trades directories** from the past for their town. *Kelly's Trade Directory* is probably the most famous. It was first published in 1845. Trades directories are listed street by street, building by building, giving the occupant and occupation. More recent sources of similar information are the *Yellow Pages* **telephone directories** which are available at the BT Technology Museum in London. **Goad Plans** have been published since 1966 for towns in the United Kingdom with a population of over 50,000 and for larger towns in Europe. Back issues may be bought from the address given in Sources of Information on the Website.

Parish registers of baptisms and burials are kept by churches. These are particularly useful because the parish of the established church was at one time the same as the civil parish used for the census. Take care to remember that baptisms are not the same as births, and funerals are not the same as deaths. Each practising religious group keeps similar records, and these will be available from the person in charge.

Early editions of the Ordnance Survey maps are now available for many places, and these provide very good evidence for what the town was like in the past.

The Valuation Office of the local authority keeps records of each valuation carried out, such as the ones in 1993 and 1973. These records are kept for each building in every street. They are easy to use and form an excellent record of building use through time. You will need to telephone or write a letter to make an appointment to use them.

Towns Trial Run: What are the order of importance and the sphere of influence of Alderley Edge in Cheshire?

FIELDWORK TECHNIQUES

The following techniques were used:

- **Questionnaires and interviews**
- **Classifying information**
- **Using desire-line maps**
- **Recording land use**

'Sphere of influence', 'catchment area', 'market area' and 'trade area' all mean more or less the same thing. 'Service centre' and 'central place' mean the same thing. Choose whichever term you feel happiest with. The terms used in this Trial Run are 'sphere of influence' and 'service centre'.

Before you begin

The size of the ***sphere of influence*** reflects the distance from which people from the surrounding area are attracted to the service centre to use its shops and professional services.

The ***order of importance*** can be based on the number and types of ***function***. Specialist shops such as jewellers and designer clothes shops are high order shopping functions. A newsagent is a low order shopping function.

You will know that all shops and services need a threshold of population to support them. For example, fieldwork in Anglesey has shown that a population of 2,500 or 700 houses are needed to support 40 or more shops and services.

As the introduction to your Trial Run report:

- Describe the meaning of 'order of importance' and 'sphere of influence'
- Describe 'high order functions'
- Describe the meaning of 'threshold of population'

The location of Alderley Edge

As can be seen from the map in Figure 110, Alderley Edge is located 25 km from the centre of Manchester and 12 km from the centre of Stockport. It lies on the A34, the road which runs from Manchester to Stoke-on-Trent. There is also a frequent train service to both Stockport and Manchester.

The following equipment was used:

- Base-map, i. e. Ordnance Survey map of scale 1:2,500 (Landplan Series)
- Land use recording scheme (see page 119)
- Questionnaires – 50 copies (see page 21)

Figure 110 Map to show the location of the study area.

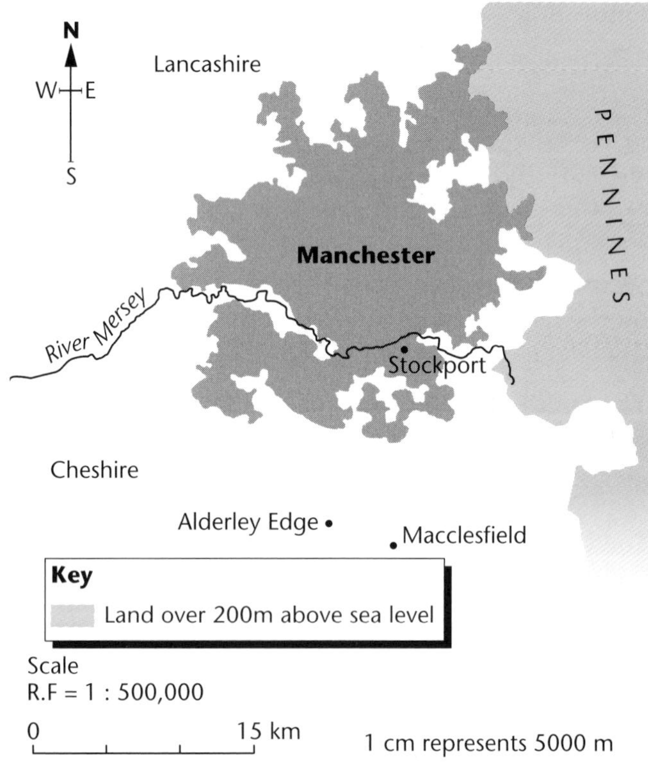

Fieldwork method

The fieldwork was carried out by one person on Saturday 11 February 1996 between 10.30 am and 2.30 pm. It concentrated on two aspects:

1. The ability of a service centre to attract custom depends mainly upon the number and types of its shops and professional services. The functions of all the buildings along the shopping streets were recorded, using the Scheme for Recording Amenities given in the Towns Extra Investigation on the Website. Anything else related to the topic, such as the car parks and railway station, were also recorded. The results are shown in Figure 111.

Figure 111 A list of shops and professional services surveyed in Alderley Edge.

	Shops and services	Number counted
S10	Clothes shop	8
	Other non-food shops	8
S7	Furniture/Carpets	6
P6	Restaurant	6
P2	Bank or Building Society	5
S8	Chemist	4
P5	Estate Agent	4
P7	Hairdresser	4
S4	Butcher	2
S20	Newsagent	4
S21	Off Licence	4
	Vacant	4
S3	Baker/Confectioner	3
P10	Launderette and Drycleaner	3
P21	Solicitor	3
S6	Car/Motorcycle showroom	2
S15	Greengrocer	2
S19	Jewellery/Clocks	2
P3	Place of Worship	2
P24	Travel Agent	2
	Car Park beside supermarket No. of spaces =	1
P4	Dentist	1
P12	Doctor's Surgery	1
S4	Fishmonger	1
S16	Grocer	1
S12	Hardware/DIY	1
P9	Insurance	1
P14	Optician	1
P17	Police Station	1
P18	Post Office	1
	Public Car Park	1
S26	Radio/TV/Electrical	1
	Railway Station	1
S23	Shoe shop	1
SS6	Supermarket	1
S2	Stationery	1

The code letters are from the Scheme for Recording Amenities in the Towns Extra Investigation on the Website

2. A questionnaire was designed to discover the distances from which customers come to use Alderley Edge as a service centre. This included questions about where people came from and how often they came to use shops and services of different orders of importance.

As the main streets of Alderley Edge were crowded with people, it was decided to interview every fifth person who passed a particular point: an estate agent's shop in the centre. This formed a systematic, random ***sample***. The answers to the questions on distance travelled are shown in Figure 112. Most people gave the distance in miles and many answers were only approximate. To ensure greater accuracy the distances were all measured as straight-line distances on the map.

Analysing and interpreting your data

1. A large sphere of influence shows that a service centre is important. Look at the results of the land use survey in Figure 111. Classify the functions into categories as explained in Section 2. See page 15.

Figure 112 Distances travelled to Alderley Edge.

Visitor's place of origin	Distance from Alderley Edge (in km)	No. of people
Adlington	7	1
Bramhall	7	2
Disley	15	1
Knutsford	8	4
Local	–	25
London	240	1
Macclesfield	7	2
Northwich	20	1
Prestbury	6	1
Sandbach	20	1
Stoke-on-Trent	26	1
Wigan	37.5	1
Wilmslow	2.5	4

Now assess the number and types of functions. Do they suggest to you whether or not Alderley Edge is a high-order service centre and whether it would be likely to have a large sphere of influence? Alderley Edge has a few highly specialised shops. You could only know this if you had visited the town. Two examples are the balloon shop and a shop which specialises in Italian bridal wear.

2. a Use the results in Figure 112 to complete a desire-line map to show where the people interviewed came from (see page 66 for the method). You could use Figure 113 as your base-map. Draw a proportional circle (see page 82) centred on Alderley Edge to represent the number of local people interviewed who used the local shops and services.

   b Draw a dashed line around the places of origin of the desire-lines and then calculate the area of the sphere of influence. See page 66.

   Describe what your map shows.

Figure 113 Map for use in analysing the data in the Trial Run.

• Wigan

• Manchester

• Sandbach

• Stoke - on - Trent

To London

Scale
R.F = 1: 500,000

5 $2\frac{1}{2}$ 0 5 10 km

1 cm represents 5 km

3. The Small Area Statistics from the returns of the 1991 Census of Population gave the following information:

The population of Alderley Edge	= 4,285
The number of households in Alderley Edge	= 1,923
The number of households in Alderley Edge with no car	= 330
The number of households in Alderley Edge with 1 car	= 801
The number of households in Alderley Edge with 2 or more cars	= 792

   a Calculate the threshold of population for Alderley Edge's shops and other services and compare it with Anglesey.

   b What proportion of Alderley Edge's households have two or more cars per household?

   c Alderley Edge is on a commuter railway line. Look again at the map which shows the location of Alderley Edge. Give your views on whether Alderley Edge is itself likely to be within the sphere of influence of a larger town. You could discover the population of other towns on the map by using the census returns in your local library.

Drawing conclusions

1. Describe what your analysis of the list of land use shows about the importance of Alderley Edge as a service centre. Add to this the facts about the population and car ownership per household.
2. Again give the result of your calculation of the area of the sphere of influence based on the questionnaire results. In view of the population size, car ownership, commuter railway line, and nearness to large centres of population, describe what you feel about the area of the sphere of influence.

Evaluating your work

Consider the influence of the following on your conclusions:

- use of straight-line distances for calculating the sphere of influence
- the likelihood that the people interviewed from London, Stoke on Trent and Wigan may not be regular shoppers in Alderley Edge. Should their answers have been included in the results?

K. Briggs (1974), in his book *Introducing Towns and Cities*, considered that one professional service was 'worth' four shops. Compare the ratio of shops to professional services in Alderley Edge. Does it support his views?

If you could have planned the investigation yourself, how would you have altered the procedures? Here are some hints:

- Should the amenities recording scheme have been adapted to give prominence to highly specialised shops and services?
- Would your first question on the interview sheet have been: 'Have you come to Alderley Edge today to shop or to use the services?'
- Would you have investigated, for example, public transport services to Alderley Edge, or perhaps parking facilities and cost?

Interesting extra ideas

1. Many towns have a covered shopping area such as a mall. Conduct pedestrian surveys and interviews to see whether it has a wider sphere of influence/catchment area in wet weather in winter than in sunny weather in summer.
2. For a town in a tourist area discover whether the sphere of influence/catchment area increases during the tourist season. Conduct pedestrian surveys and interviews in the same places in different seasons. Do a land use survey out of season to discover if any shops and other functions have closed.

Towns Short Project: Is there a difference in the use of buildings on a street near the centre of town and a street near the edge of town?

For convenience in this project the two different areas will be called 'your streets'.

Fieldwork area

A main road which runs from the centre of town to the outskirts is ideal for this project. However, safety is more important than fieldwork so, if it is a busy road with on-street parking, choose side streets close by.

Ordnance Survey maps of scale 1:25,000 and bigger show individual buildings and gardens. Pick out your fieldwork areas from the map. Choose a length of 100 metres or 25 buildings on both sides of the street: first, near to the centre of town and then on a street near to the edge of town.

In each area, pick out from the map the name of a side street as the place to start your fieldwork.

Before you begin

1. In what ways do you expect the building use to be different in your streets? Find out as much as you can about the different ***zones*** in a town. Zones are usually given names such as the 'Central Business District' and the 'Residential Zone'. They are part of the structure of towns. Your geography textbook may have a diagram showing the zones of a town. Copy it for the introduction to your final report and describe in your own words what you expect your fieldwork zones to be like.
2. The term for the way a building is used is its '***function***'. The function upstairs on the first, second and higher floors may be different from the function at ground level. For this short project keep to the ground level function only. For the introduction to your final report explain what a function is. Suggest a few types of function which you expect to find in your streets.
3. It would be a good idea to make a quick visit to your streets to see what types of functions there are. This is termed 'making a ***reconnaissance visit***'.

You will need the following equipment:

Base-map of your chosen lengths of streets. You will need two copies. On a scale such as the Ordnance Survey map of 1:1,000 or 1:2,500 there will be enough space for you to write over the building on the map. Keep the second copy for your final report.

On page 119 of this book there is a **Land Use Recording Scheme**. The first letters of this tell you what the main category of function is: 'S' means 'shop'; 'Se' means 'Service' and so on. Copy this out and call it your Land Use Recording Scheme.

Fieldwork method

The fieldwork can be done accurately and quickly if two people work together. One can look at the function of the building whilst the other looks up the code letter in the key and writes it down on the building on the map. Take it in turns.

You may have to bring the map up-to-date

1. Walk along both sides of your streets. As you come to each new building look how the ground floor facing the street is used. Look at the Land Use Recording Scheme for the letter which describes it most accurately. Write the letter over the building on your base-map.
2. Explain in detail in your final report how you did your fieldwork. Include a piece of your fieldwork map as proof of the way you recorded the functions. Include the Land Use Recording Scheme. It is the key to your fieldwork map.

Analysing and interpreting your data

1 **a** On the second copy of your base-map colour the function of every building recorded. A colour key is suggested on page 119. Give a reason for using certain colours and remember to add the key.

b Describe what your finished maps show. Are there more shops, offices and services in one area than in the other? Are there more residential buildings in one area than the other? Suggest reasons why.

2 **a** For both of your streets count the number of buildings in each category: shops, public buildings and so on.

b Draw a bar chart (see pages 72–74) for each street to show the number of buildings in each category. Put the different functions in the same order on both bar charts: work across from 'shops' at the left, 'offices' next, ending with 'residential' at the right-hand side.

c Describe the similarities and differences shown by your two bar charts.

Drawing conclusions

1. Are there more shops and offices near the centre of town than the edge of town? Give the numbers in each category.
2. a Are there more public buildings near the centre of town? Give numbers.
   b What types of public buildings are there near the centre?
   c What types of public buildings are there near the edge of town?
3. a How many homes are near the centre of town?
   b What are they like? Look at pages 60–61 for guidance on architectural style and building materials.
   c Describe the homes on the edge of town.
4. a Which area has the most open spaces?
   b Describe the types of open space (i) near the centre and (ii) near the edge of town.
   c Are there gardens attached to people's homes in both areas?

Write one or two paragraphs as a summary of your conclusions. Do the results seem typical of the zones they represent? Do they match your ***expectations*** of the zones?

Evaluating your work

a You have investigated a sample of two different parts of a town with functional zones. A sample should represent the whole functional zone. Did yours? You can read more about ***sampling*** on pages 15–18.

b Did one of your streets contain more buildings than the other? If so, you could have calculated the types of functions as a percentage of the total. The method for calculating percentages is explained on page 86. Would the comparisons between your streets have been more accurate?

Interesting extra ideas

- Is there more traffic on the street near to the town centre? Carry out traffic surveys in both locations. See pages 58–9.
- Are there more bus stops on the street near the centre of town than on the street at the edge of town?
- Are more cars parked on the street near the edge of town?
- Investigate the appearance of the street in both locations:
  - Is the pavement wider at the edge of town?
  - Is there more greenery – trees, shrubs, hanging baskets, grass verges – on the streets at the edge of town?
  - Are there more benches and litter bins in one than in the other?
- Are the building materials – stone, brick, slate, tile – different at the edge of town?
- Investigate the architectural style of the buildings.
- Use the Census of Population of 100 years ago and older and historical sources to discover what the streets were like in the past.

Towns Investigation: Does your town have distinctive functional zones?

> **FIELDWORK TECHNIQUES**
>
> **You will use the following techniques:**
>
> - **Laying a line of transect**
> - **Counting moving pedestrians and vehicles**

This investigation could easily be extended into a comparison of your town with one or more of the theoretical models of towns.

Buildings of one ***function*** are usually built close to others of the same function and/or to those who depend on them. This happens as much for convenience as anything: shops depend upon people and people need access to shops. In this way ***functional zones*** develop, and the zone is recognisable by its main function.

Figure 114 A clear functional zone: an industrial estate

Before you begin

1. In the introduction to your final report explain what a functional zone is and how it develops.
2. Transects are lines drawn on a map to follow during fieldwork. The ***transects*** should be as representative as possible of the whole town. Look at the street patterns on the map of scale 1:50,000. Starting at the town centre, choose transects that cross as many areas of different street patterns as possible. A reconnaissance visit will show whether it would be better to follow transects along main streets or to keep to smaller streets. You will remember that Hoyt considered that main roads distorted the concentric zones of Burgess, turning them into sectors.

   Make sure that you have access along the entire length of your transects, and that it is safe to work in all areas in small groups.
3. If you are in a very large town you may decide to take a systematic random ***sample*** of buildings along your transects. Record the function and other details of every second building, every fifth building and so on.
4. To decide upon the site of the present town centre in most towns requires more skill than many people would think. Here are some suggestions:
   - Until recently the road distance between towns was measured as the distance between the main post office in each. The post office was located in a central position for customers' convenience. The post office was built in what was the centre of town in Victorian times but this is not necessarily the centre of town now.
   - The town centre is supposed to be the most accessible place in the town, and is often at the focus of roads. The bus station was a reliable centre in the mid-20th century, but it may have been moved more recently.
   - The centre of town is in the centre of the shopping and service area (CBD). Some geographers locate this as the place where most pedestrians pass. It is sometimes called the peak pedestrian flow point or PPFP. If you carry out **pedestrian counts** in different parts of the Central Business District you will be able to identify it. See pages 58–9.
   - The prime site for retailing has the highest rateable value, and the prime site is usually the most accessible one. You will find this by looking at the rateable values (non-domestic rate) in the Valuation Office of your local council.

Whichever way you identify the town centre, explain your reasons in your final report.

5. Obtain large-scale maps of your transects to act as base-maps for recording the function of the buildings and any other details, such as the number of storeys. The scale of 1:10,000 is the smallest scale that is practicable. 1:1,000 is ideal. This is the scale used for Goad Plans.
6. Devise a land use/function recording scheme along the lines of the one shown in Figure 115. A quick ***reconnaissance visit*** before beginning will help you to adjust it to meet the needs of your town. 'Open land' may be too broad a category. Subdivisions could be 'farmland', 'public park', 'allotment', 'cemetery', 'vacant land', 'demolition site', etc.
7. If you have decided to investigate the location of the town centre in terms of pedestrian flow, work out how many recording sheets you will need. Decide whether you should conduct a count on both sides of a road open to traffic.
8. If you intend to include an extra aspect of interest, such as the number of storeys in each building, or the building material, consider how you will record this during your fieldwork. An extra symbol, such as a number, or the use of a second colour, could be recorded on your base-map, particularly if you are using one as big as scale 1:1,000.
9. Discover what ***secondary data*** are available and where and when you can go to use them.

You will need the following equipment:

- Basic fieldkit.
- Two copies of a large-scale map: one for recording details of buildings in the field; and the other for use in your data analysis and final report. A map of scale 1:1,000 is ideal. A Goad Plan could be used for the shopping centre. You may have to update it.
- Land use recording scheme.
- Tables for recording pedestrian flow (see point 7 above).

Fieldwork method

1. Walk up each street in your fieldwork area and record carefully on your base-map the use (function) of each building at ground level and each open space. A survey of the use made of buildings above ground level is interesting. However, piecing together the jigsaw of which firms use which parts of a building can take a lot of time. Valuation records kept at the Valuation Office of your local council can help. They tell you what the different parts of the buildings are used for.

   The appearance of business premises such as shops and offices often reflects the trading standards of the owner, and the desire to attract customers. Similarly, the appearance of a house – its state of upkeep and tidiness – reflects the standards of the people who live there. The appearance is worth recording as it can tell quite a lot. Look out for **zones of discard** and **zones of assimilation**.
2. Conduct pedestrian surveys to locate the centre if you have decided to do this. The way of doing this is explained on page 58–9.
3. If you use your camera, remember to make a note of the number and name of the street where you took each photograph. This will help you to identify them easily afterwards.

An area with a lot of vacant property and general untidiness suggests that the area is undergoing change. It may have been abandoned by its original users, and the term 'zone of discard' is often given to such an area. The opposite to this term is 'zone of assimilation' which means that an area is being taken over or engulfed by a different type of function.

Sources of secondary data

Suggestions of the data sources available are given in the Sources of Information on the Website. When using the population Census it would be wise to work out on a map the position of the ward boundaries. The Census returns for Scotland have used postcode districts since 1991. You may also need to identify the boundaries of parishes for data from the parish registers.

Analysing and interpreting your data

1. Map to show the location of functions

Using a colour key, transfer the function you have recorded for each building onto a neat copy of your map. Shade each building according to a class of function similar to that shown in the following key:

Green = shops
Blue = offices
Red = public buildings
Orange = entertainment
Brown = industry, including warehouses
Yellow = residential
Grey = open space and vacant land

Remember to show the key beside your map.

This colouring scheme has the advantage that when viewed from a distance, the green and blue buildings, being of similar shade, clearly reveal a zone of shopping and professional services. The use of colours in this way could be part of the evaluation of your work.

Figure 115 Land use recording scheme. (See also the scheme for recording amenities in the Towns Extra Investigation on the Website)

Shop function:	SFS	food shop, including supermarkets
	SCS	clothing shop
	SHS	hardware and electrical goods
	SFurS	furniture
	SDS	department store
	SNS	newsagent
	SPO	post office (even if it is part of a shop)
Entertainment function:	EC	café/public house/fish and chip shop including take-way foods
	ER	restaurant open in the evening
	EF	cinema
	ET	theatre
	EH	concert hall
	EB	bingo hall
Service function:	SeO	offices
	SeS	surgery, clinic
	SeH	hospital
	Ses	station (bus or railway)
Public building:	PTH	town hall, post office
	PM	museum
	PG	art gallery
	PS	school
	PL	library
	PP	police station
	PC	council offices
Industrial function:	IW	warehouse
	IF	factory including motor vehicle repair shops
Residential function:	R	house
	RH	residential hotel, bed and breakfast, caravan site
Open space:	L	open land
	D	demolition: this shows land undergoing change, possibly a change of function

Here are some additional features you may want to include in a more detailed investigation. Work out how to record them on your base-map.

Greenery	G	= garden
	0	= tree
Roads and traffic	⟶	one-way traffic system
	═	parking restriction (yellow lines)
	[P]	parking area
	[♿]	disabled parking spaces
	|||||||	pedestrian crossing
	(bus stop symbol)	bus stops
Building materials (There is more detail about building materials in the 'Towns' chapter on pages 60–62)	(brick symbol)	a building mainly of brick
	(stone symbol)	a building mainly of stone
	(timber symbol)	a building mainly of timber
	[?]	a building of materials of which you are uncertain: cement-covered, pebble-dashed, colour-washed, painted
Building height		Add the number of storeys as an extra digit in brackets in your code, e.g. R2 = flats, therefore R2(4) = flats with four storeys
Building age (adapt this to include more detail about architectural styles as described on page 60 in Section 2)	MOD =	since World War II
	INT =	Inter-war Period (1918–1940)
	VIC =	Victorian to Edwardian
	GEO =	Georgian/Regency
	OLD =	older than Georgian
Lichens		for a pollution survey (see page 40 in Section 2)

You know that some functions are of high order. This means that they are expensive and not used by most people on a daily basis. Expensive jewellers and clothing shops, and expensive restaurants are examples of this. These could be emphasised on your map by drawing a thick red line around the edge of the building. Do they seem to cluster in one particular part of your transect? Describe their location, giving reasons why you think they occur here. Page 68–9 suggests how to measure clustering.

There are at least two ways of approaching the interpretation of your data:

a. Are you able to pick out particular land-use zones on your transects? Draw thick black lines to show the boundaries between zones. Measure the distance of each zone from the town centre, either by using a map wheel or the pin and string method described on page 70. Give reasons why you consider the different zones to be distinctive from one another. Can you suggest why they exist?

b. From your knowledge of the area you may have an ***expectation*** that land-use changes at regular intervals. Draw concentric circles around the town centre like those in Figure 116 and describe the land use within each. Count the number of buildings of different functional classes and illustrate them as bar charts. Figures 79 and 117 show you how to do this. Are you able to pick out particular functional zones and give reasons for them?

2. Bar charts to illustrate the functions in each zone

Bar charts reinforce the conclusions you have drawn from your map. The zones you have distinguished may contain different numbers of buildings. To compare them, first calculate each class of function as a percentage of the total in that zone:

$$\frac{\text{Number of buildings in class}}{\text{Total number of buildings in all classes}} \times \frac{100}{1} = \text{percentage}$$

Draw bar charts, as shown in Figure 117, for each zone. Use the same colours as on your map. Place them close to your map to make it convenient for the reader to compare the two. Describe what your bar charts show to reinforce your descriptions of the zones on your map.

Figure 116 Ground-level land use along the four main roads into Clitheroe, Lancashire.

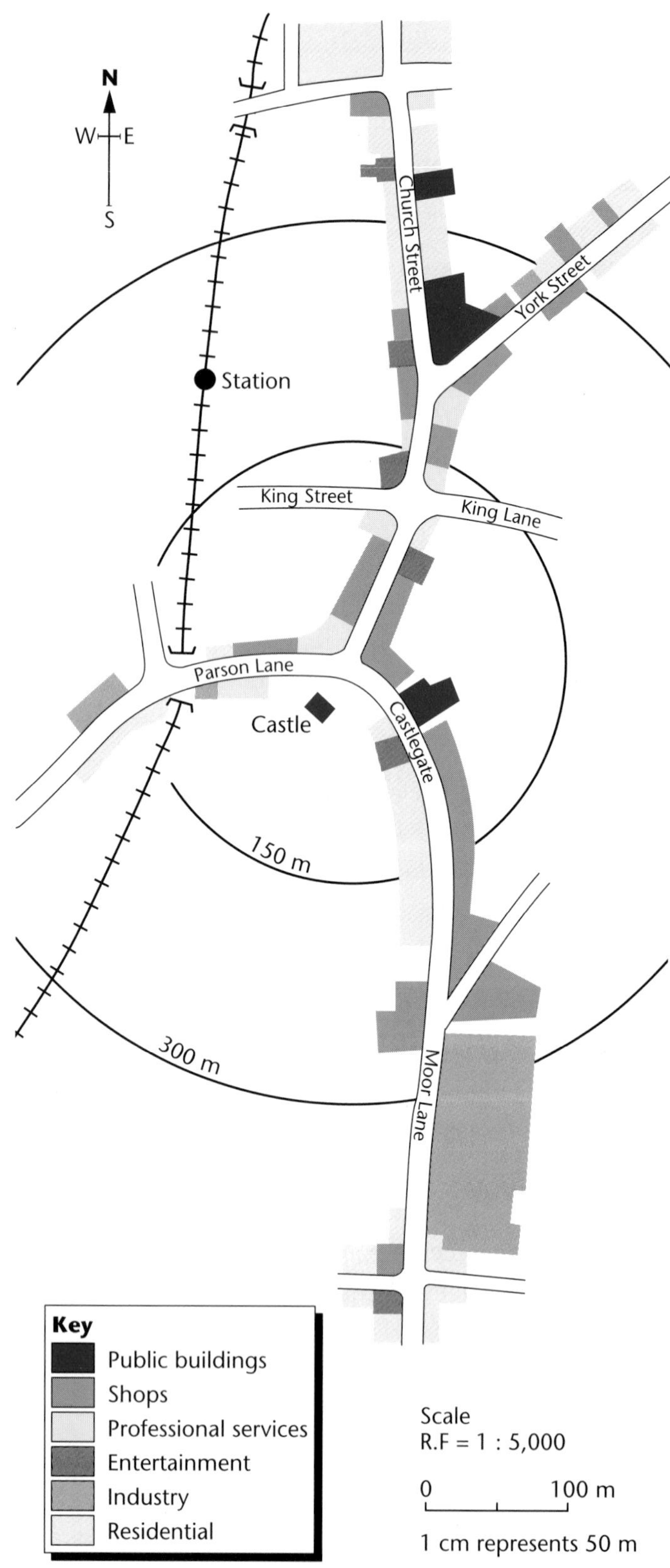

Figure 117 Bar charts to compare land use by percentage in concentric zones from the centre of Clitheroe.

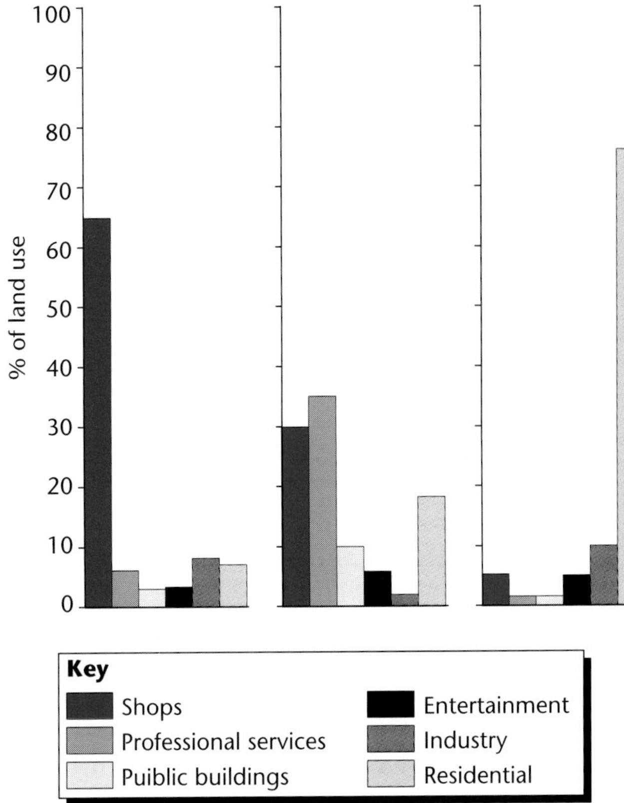

3. How the town centre was identified

Choose the photographs you have taken which are most representative of the different zones. Annotate each photograph and refer to it in your final report. In this way, photographs will be an esssential part of your project, and not appear to be included merely for decorative purposes.

a. The peak pedestrian flow point is best illustrated by drawing flow-line diagrams (see page 81). If your map has wide streets you could draw them on the map beside the locations where you made your counts. Alternatively, you could draw them separately, fold them and attach them at the locations of the counts. The arrowhead should point in the direction in which the pedestrians were moving.

There are different ways of drawing flow-line diagrams. Two are shown in Figure 90 on page 81. Add up the largest number of pedestrians counted in any one place, and devise a scale based on this.

Explain why you have chosen the town centre in relation to the movement of pedestrians.

Figure 118 Rateable value of properties on Bank Square, Wilmslow, Cheshire (obtained from the Valuation Office). The valuation was carried out in 1973.

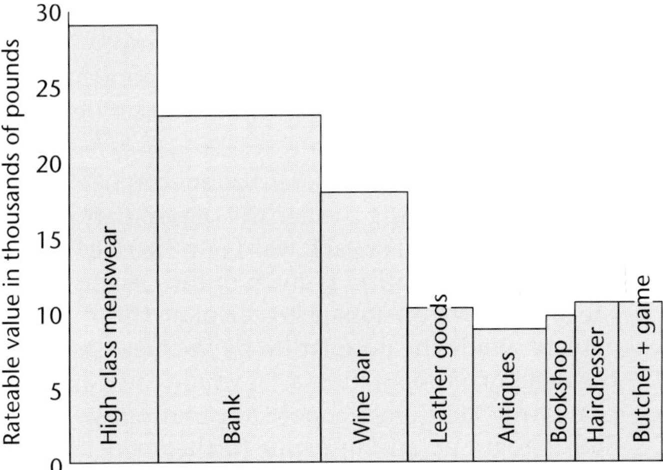

b. The peak land value point can be found by obtaining from the Valuation Office the non-domestic rate for each business. The records are all kept in numerical order along every street. If you really are short of time then take a systematic random ***sample***, such as every second or every fifth building. Keep to the values of ground-level premises only. You should see a pattern emerging as you copy these.

Include a list of the premises and their values as an appendix to your final report. The values may be illustrated as bar charts, one for each street investigated.

Extra interest comes from comparing the land value with:

(i) the length of street frontage
(ii) the area of the premises occupied
(iii) the class of function

These may be analysed by using a correlation technique such as the one illustrated in Figure 118, or a scattergraph or a statistical method such as Spearman's Rank Correlation Coefficient (see pages 87–88).

Figure 118 shows that some of the highest rated premises are very long and narrow. Would the area of the premises be a more accurate measurement that the street frontage? A Goad Plan of scale 1:1,000 would allow you to measure the area.

4. Secondary sources

a. If you compare your map with a Goad Plan of an earlier date you will be able to see whether the shopping area, as defined by the publisher, has extended outwards or contracted, or simply stayed the same. Write in your final report that you have made this comparison and describe the results.

b. More evidence of the different zones can be found by calculating the density of population from the Census. For each ward or postcode district the population is given in the Census and the area shown on a map. To calculate the density divide the population by the area. Does the density of population alter where the transect passes into a different zone? Do variations in the density of population provide further evidence of zones which you have picked out? Example: an area of terraced houses is likely to have a higher density of population than an area of houses with large gardens.

c. The Census returns and parish registers may show population increases or decreases in the previous 10, 20, 30 or more years. You may be able to discover where people have moved from or to.

Drawing conclusions

- When you summarise your interpretation of all of your evidence you will be in a position to make comparisons between your town and the zones identified by Burgess, Hoyt, Mann and others. To what extent does your town match one of these theories? In what ways, and for what reasons, do you feel it differs?
- Return to your main investigation: does your town have distinctive functional zones?

Evaluating your work

- Did you choose the best lines for your transects? If you had put them in different places would the functional zones be easier to recognise?
- If you used a systematic random sample, was the sample interval appropriate? Hint: If the sample interval was too big you could have missed out important buildings. If the sample interval was too small you may have had difficulty in completing your fieldwork in the time available.
- Explain why you calculated the percentage of different functions in each zone rather than simply using raw data.
- Should the buildings have been counted irrespective of their size? A town hall or a secondary schools cover a much bigger area than a small shop or a house. Would it have been more accurate to have measured their area on the map, or at least the length of their street frontage?
- If a car park belongs to the people who occupy the building, is the car park a function in its own right or part of the function of the building?

Interesting extra ideas

1. Your town has been given a large grant of money. Which zones would you spend the money on and in what ways? Examples: improved street lighting; cleaning buildings; demolishing and replacing buildings; more greenery, extra litter bins; better designed 'street furniture' (lamp-posts, benches). These costs can be obtained from your local authority.
2. Discover what each zone was like in the past. Use old editions of the Ordnance Survey map, pictures from the Local History section of the public library and other secondary sources as described on page 109.

Rivers

Rivers are of immense importance. They change the shape of the landscape and all sorts of landform features owe their origin to rivers. They have affected human history: ancient civilisations were located on the flood plains of rivers in areas such as India, China and Egypt. Most towns and cities were originally founded on the banks of rivers to be close to fresh water and to good transport links. We use rivers for water, transport, energy, defence and for leisure activities. Painters and poets often use rivers in their works of art.

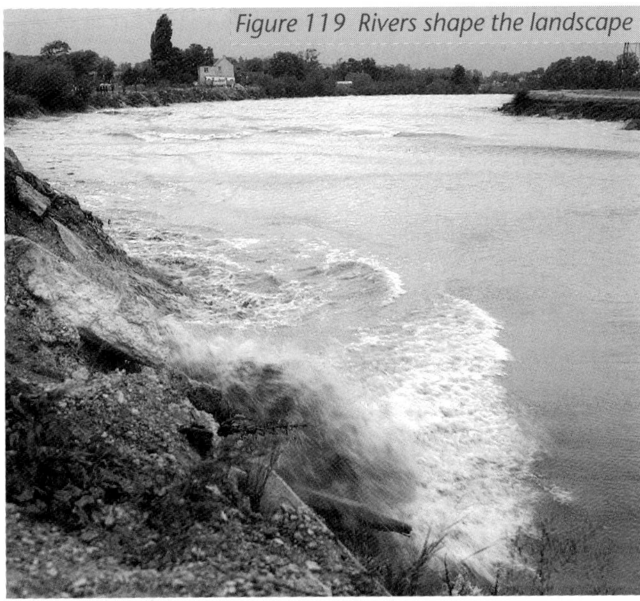
Figure 119 Rivers shape the landscape

All rivers have certain things in common:

- Rivers alter the landscape by eroding in their fast-flowing stretches and depositing material where they flow slowly.
- Rivers are the conveyor belts of the landscape. They transport material from the valley sides. This was loosened from the solid rock by ***weathering*** and moved down into the river under gravity.
- Rivers are to the landscape what the drainage system is to a built-up area. They return surplus water which fell as ***precipitation*** – rain, hail, sleet, snow, etc. – back to the sea or ocean.
- Rivers provide water for households, industry, livestock and irrigation.
- Rivers are enjoyed for leisure and pleasure. We enjoy looking at running water and more particularly listening to it: fountains are simply imitations of waterfalls.

A river flows through the channel it has made for itself. The channel is at the lowest point of the valley.

Rivers and river landforms provide a lot of scope for good and interesting projects. From the list of project suggestions, pick out the aspect(s) which interest you most, or use the list to help you with ideas on which to base your project.

This chapter has been planned to help you with particular aspects:

- Catchment areas and water supply – Trial Run
- River flow – Short Project
- The river's load – Investigation

The Extra Investigation on the Website will help you with channel shape and efficiency.

Valley-sides can be investigated by using the slope-measuring techniques explained in Section 2 on pages 24–7. As evidence of downslope movement under gravity, look out for:

- terracettes (little steps formed naturally on grassy slopes)
- trees with bends in their trunks
- walls with thicker soil on the upslope side than on the downslope side.

Before you make the final choice for the objectives of your project, read through 'Before You Begin'. Help for projects on the use of rivers and valleys for leisure can be found in the Leisure chapter.

Project suggestions

1. How does the speed of flow vary?
   - **a** Does the speed of flow increase downstream?
   - **b** Is it related to the gradient of the long profile/downstream gradient?
   - **c** Does the speed of flow vary across a ***meander***?
   - **d** Is the speed of flow related to the shape of the channel?
   - **e** Does the speed of flow vary according to:
     - **(i)** the size of the river
     - **(ii)** the ***order of the stream***?
   - **f** Does the speed of flow alter when a river flows through a town?

Where to find help:

How to measure the speed of flow, 52–4

How to measure slope angle, 24–27

How to measure channel shape – Rivers Extra Investigation, Website

2. How does the river ***discharge*** vary? How much water passes through the river's channel each second? River discharge is the volume of water passing along the channel at a particular time.
   - **a** Does discharge increase downstream?
   - **b** Is discharge affected by variations in the weather? Carry out investigations after a spell of rainfall and after a dry period.
   - **c** Do water companies affect the discharge? Investigate the discharge
     - **(i)** upstream from/above reservoirs and sites where water is removed (abstracted), and
     - **(ii)** downstream from such sites.

   Compare the two.

   Where to find help:

   How to measure discharge – Rivers Extra Investigation, Website

   How to investigate the weather, 28–5

   The Trial Run will help you to choose sites for this project.

3. What is the channel shape and how efficiently does it transport water?

   The most efficient shape of channel has a width:depth ratio of 2:1, as shown in Figure 120.

   This had been discovered by Roman times and was used by civil engineers in the Roman Empire. Carry out investigations into the channel at two or more sites downstream. As an extra part of the project, relate the channel shape to the speed of flow and/or the discharge.

Figure 120 The most efficient shape of channel.

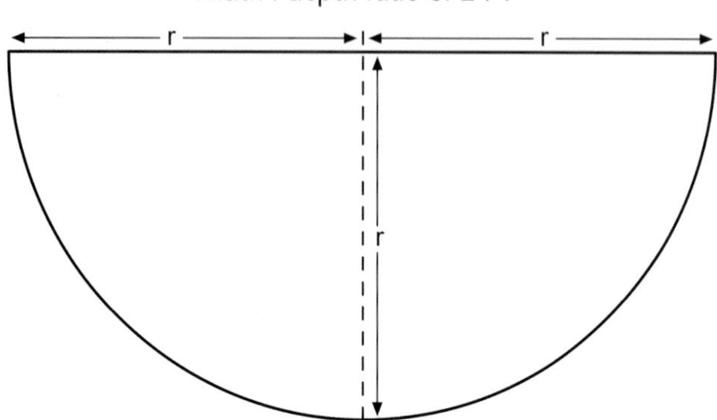

   Where to find help:

   How to measure the width-depth ratio of the channel – Rivers Extra Investigation, Website

   How to measure the speed of flow, 52–4

4. Is the angle/gradient of the valley-side slopes related to one or more of the following?
   - **a** the size of the river (which can be taken as its width and depth, or as the cross-sectional area of the river, or as the discharge)
   - **b** the speed of flow of the river
   - **c** the efficiency of the channel

   Where to find help:

   How to measure slope angle, 24–27

   How to measure the cross-section of the channel – Rivers Extra Investigation Website

   How to measure the speed of flow 52–4

5. What size and shape are the materials on the river bed?
   - **a** Do the shape and size of river bed material alter downstream?
   - **b** Do rivers which flow over different types of rock have material of different shapes and sizes on their river bed?

   This would make an interesting link with Geology.

   Where to find help:

   Measuring the shape and size of particles, 55–6, 172

   Rivers Investigation, 134–139

   Secondary sources on Geology, Appendix 2, page 202

6. Is your river a good source of water supply? Carry out investigations along the lines of the Trial Run, but take your own measurements. Complete your project by investigating:
   - **a** the purity of the atmosphere (see Air Pollution, pages 37–46)
   - **b** the purity of the river water (see Water Quality, pages 47–52)

   This would make a good link with Science.

   Where to find help:

   Your local water company

   Your local authority responsible for water quality

7. How do people use a river and its valley for leisure?

   (See Leisure, pages 177–194.)

   Where to find help:

   What facilities are available?, Leisure Short Project, 185–187

   Leisure Extra Investigation on the Website

8. Have the river's channel and its course been altered:
   a where it flows through a town?
   b over time?
   This would be an interesting link with History.
   Where to find help:
   Secondary sources – old edition of OS maps (see page 109 and Website)

'River' and 'stream' mean the same thing. They are interchangeable terms but try to keep to one or the other in your final report. When the channel is full of water the stream is said to be in its bankful stage. If the water level rises above its bankful stage it is in flood.

Before you begin

According to the number of tributaries that a stream receives, it may be classed into a ***hierarchy*** known as ***stream order***. This system was devised by the American geographer, A. N. Strahler in 1952. It can help you to choose your rivers for fieldwork because a river of one order has the same characteristics as a river of the same order anywhere in the world. If your river is of a very high order your fieldwork results will be similar to those of famous rivers that we all know about.

Find out more about 'the system of stream order'. You could try working it out from Figure 121. Describe it in the introduction to your final report and give the order of the streams that you investigate.

Figure 121 The order of streams (or rivers) within a drainage basin.

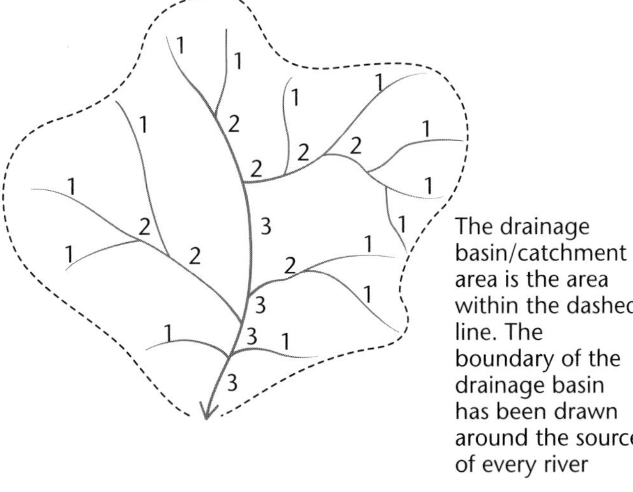

The drainage basin/catchment area is the area within the dashed line. The boundary of the drainage basin has been drawn around the source of every river

To discover what the order of your fieldwork river is, use a small-scale map such as the Ordnance Survey map of scale 1:50,000 or even 1:250,000 which shows all of the rivers that eventually drain into one major river. Trace the river system and mark the edges of the drainage basin with a dashed line as in Figure 121. Next, number each river according to its order.

You could practise on the rivers in the drainage basin of the River Goyt shown in Figure 123.

Fieldwork area

When choosing a river (or rivers) make sure that there is public access to it (or them) or obtain written permission from the landowner (see pages 18–20 for help in writing a letter). The river should be shallow enough for you to be able to walk across in Wellington boots and narrow enough to be able to span with a washing line or tape measure. Figure 122 is a picture of such a stream.

Investigations at two or more locations within the same drainage basin will enable you to make comparisons between features and this will make your project more interesting. Your locations could be on different rivers of the same order or on a river which changes its stream order downstream.

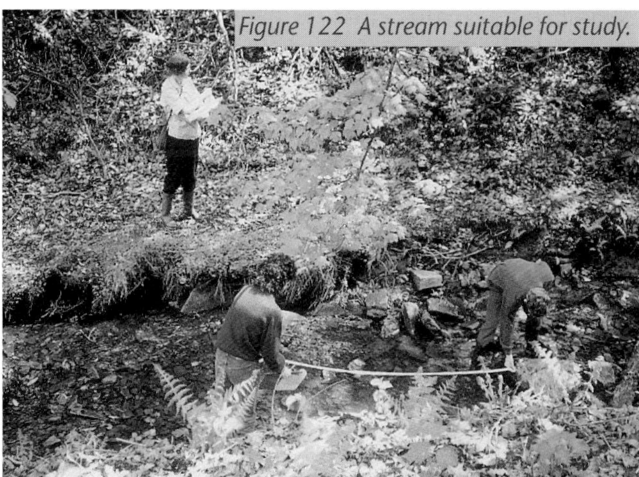

Figure 122 A stream suitable for study.

CAUTION: Safety is more important than anything else. Do not investigate a river that is even as deep as your Wellington boots. If you slip and bang your head on a rock you could drown yourself in water only 10 cm deep.

Do not work in a lonely place. There should never be less than three of you working together.

Rivers Trial Run: How efficient are the River Goyt and its catchment area in supplying water to Stockport?

This Trial Run is based entirely on secondary data.

> **FIELDWORK TECHNIQUES**
>
> **You will use the following techniques:**
> - **Sketching maps**
> - **Recognising a gradient**
> - **Measuring area**

Figure 123 shows part of an Ordnance Survey map that includes the ***catchment area*** of the River Goyt in Derbyshire. This river helps to supply water to the nearby town of Stockport which has a population of 350,000 (1991).

Before you begin

Find Stockport in your atlas and either sketch or trace the map to show where it is located. (Stockport is also shown on the map in the Towns Trial Run on page 110.) Include the location of the River Goyt on your map. A map of the fieldwork area makes a good title page for a geography project.

Next, describe in your own words where Stockport and the River Goyt are located. Finally, look carefully at Figure 123 and describe reasons why the area would be good as a water catchment area. Give reasons why you consider its different aspects could be important for supplying water:

Relief:

- How high is the land?
- Does it slope steeply? Look at page 69 for a quick way of recognising gradients.
- What shape are the valleys?
- You could illustrate the relief by drawing a cross-section as described on pages 70–71. Part of this has been done for you. Does the relief of the area indicate that sensible places were chosen for the reservoirs?

Land use:

- How much of the area is forested and where is the forest located?
- Use your knowledge of the water cycle to explain how forestry helps to maintain a reliable flow of water to the reservoirs.
- Which type of farming is likely to take place in the area? Give evidence from the map.
- Why is it unlikely that this type of farming will cause a pollution problem?
- Part of the catchment area lies within the Peak District National Park. Could this fact involve any problems for water supply?

Fieldwork method

The information used in this Trial Run was given by the Environment Agency. Their officers had collected rainfall daily in a standard rain gauge as described on page 30. They had measured the speed of flow of the River Goyt at the Grid References given in the Equipment box by using a flow-meter. The measuring site has a specially constructed channel with a known cross-sectional area so they are able to calculate the discharge by multiplying the area by the speed of flow.

> ### You will need the following equipment:
> - A base-map, i.e. an OS map of scale 1:50,000 (see Figure 123).
> - The data on rainfall, **stream velocity** and **stream discharge** supplied by the Environment Agency from their own monitoring stations. These were a rain gauge sited immediately to the north of Fernilee Dam at Grid Reference 012777; and river measurements taken at two points: Grid Reference 013778 (close to the rain gauge at Fernilee Reservoir) and just above the River Goyt's entry into Errwood Reservoir at Grid Reference 013747.

> **Discharge is the amount of water flowing past a chosen point on a river. It is usually measured in cubic metres per second – 'cumecs'. It can be expressed as the cross-sectional area of water multiplied by the speed of flow of the river.**

Figure 123 Part of the Ordnance Survey map showing the catchment area of the River Goyt. (The transect refers to figure 76 on page 71.)

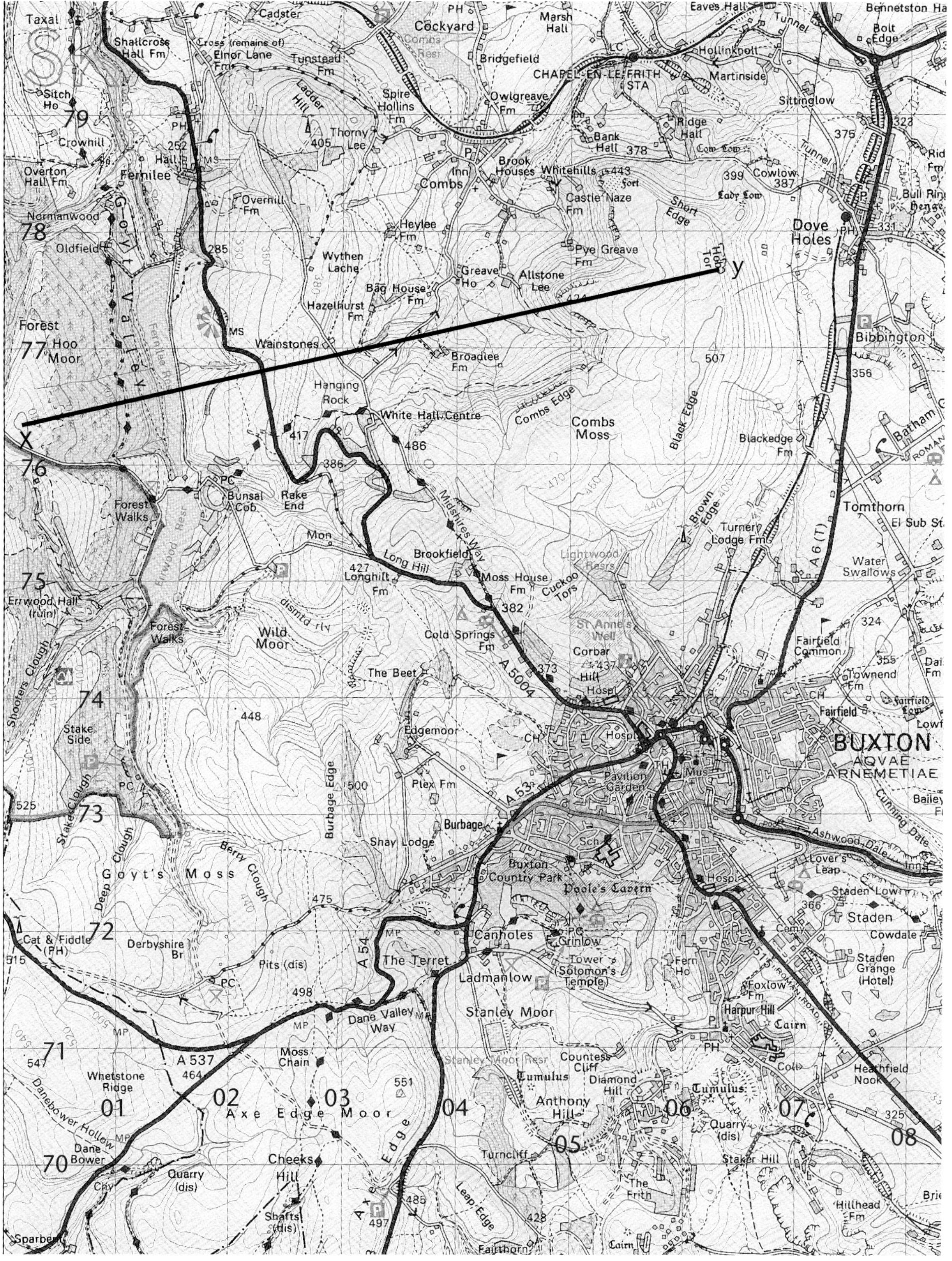

Analysing and interpreting your data

The water companies in Britain use the term 'catchment area'. This means the same thing as 'drainage basin'. Use whichever term you prefer.

1. Measuring the area of the water catchment

Calculate the area of the water catchment by measuring the map (Figure 123) following these steps. The method is also explained on page 70 of Section 2.

a. Cover your tracing paper with a grid of squares whose sides are 1 cm long; each square will have an area of 1 cm^2.

b. Work out the area that each square centimetre represents when the scale of the map is 1:50,000. You will easily calculate that 1 cm on the map and the tracing paper represents 500 m on the ground.

c. Place the squared tracing paper over the north-west corner of the map. On it, draw a line joining the source of every stream that flows into the River Goyt. All of the land within this line is the catchment area of the River Goyt.

d. Count the number of squares that lie within the Goyt catchment area. Include squares that lie halfway or more than halfway within the catchment area. Ignore the others.

e. What does your number of square centimetres represent in square kilometres? Your answer is the area of the Goyt water catchment.

A quick way of measuring the area of an Ordnance Survey map is to count the number of grid squares. The answer will be in square kilometres. Try out both methods and decide which method is the more accurate for calculation of the area. Write your views in the evaluation ***section*** of your final report.

A scale of 1:50,000 means that everything in reality is 50,000 times bigger than it is on the map.

Figure 124 Daily rainfall totals recorded (in mm) by the Environment Agency.

Date	June	July
1	2.8	6.2
2	0.3	8.2
3	1.7	5.2
4	–	6.6
5	–	–
6	–	–
7	14.7	0.6
8	–	–
9	0.9	1.6
10	1.3	–
11	8.0	4.3
12	–	–
13	–	–
14	–	–
15	–	–
16	–	–
17	–	–
18	–	–*
19	–	
20	–	
21	–	
22	–	
23	–	
24	–	
25	2.3	
26	0.8	
27	2.9	
28	9.7	
29	1.2	
30	5.0	

*The discharge was measured on the 18 July 1996.

2. Calculating the amount of rainfall that fell on the Goyt catchment area in June and July 1996

We have to assume that all parts of the Goyt catchment area received exactly the same amount of rainfall. Referring to Figure 124, add up the total received between 1 June and 17 July 1996 and multiply it by the area of the water catchment.

3. Comparing the rainfall received by the catchment with the discharge from the River Goyt

You would expect the discharge of the River Goyt to reflect the amount of water received within its catchment area. First, convert the rainfall received by the catchment area into cubic metres so that you will be able to compare it directly with the discharge measurements. Do it step by step. You will have large numbers so take care to be accurate.

a. Convert the rainfall into metres by dividing the amount in Figure 124 by 1,000.
b. Convert the area into square metres by multiplying the square kilometres by 1,000,000.
c. Multiply the rainfall in metres by the area in square metres to obtain the water received in cubic metres.
d. Divide your answer by the number of days in June and up to and including the 17 July to find the average or mean amount of rainfall received by the catchment area per day.

Remember that 1,000 mm = 1 m, and 1 km^2 = 1 million m^2. If you prefer to work in litres, remember that there are 1,000 litres in 1 m^3.

Irrigation water companies often sell their water in acre-feet. Can you work out what this means?

The 18 July 1996 was the date on which the Environment Agency carried out investigations into the discharge and velocity of the River Goyt. The Grid References of the two sites, known as 'gauging stations', at which they took measurements are given in the Equipment box.

The purpose of the Trial Run was to assess the efficiency of the River Goyt in delivering water from the rain falling on its catchment area. Now compare your mean daily rainfall received with the discharge figures. This means comparing the input with the output.

The discharge and velocity were recorded by the second. Work out how many seconds there are in 24 hours and multiply the discharge by this to find the discharge per day.

Draw bar charts (see pages 72–3) to illustrate and compare the following:

- the rainfall received by the whole of the water catchment per day = INPUT
- the total discharge for 18 July of the River Goyt above Errwood Reservoir = OUTPUT
- the total discharge for 18 July of the River Goyt below Fernilee Reservoir = OUTPUT

Shade the input and output in different colours.

Write a paragraph to compare your figures and bar charts of the rainfall received (input) with the discharge at the two sites (output). Suggest reasons why they may not be the same: reservoirs, geology, soil type, evaporation, land use, etc. Where could you find information on these if you had time to investigate them? Look through the Sources of Information in Appendix 2 and on the Website.

Figure 125 Discharge and mean velocity of the River Goyt at the two gauging stations.

18 July 1996	River Goyt above Errwood Reservoir	River Goyt below Fernilee Reservoir
Discharge	0.0420 cumecs	0.1171 cumecs
Mean velocity	0.1228 m/s	0.2279 m/s

A cumec is the volume of discharge in cubic metres per second

4. How this contributes to Stockport's water supply

Stockport's population is 350,000. In 1995/96 the average consumption of water per head of population was 1,153 litres per person per day (*Whitaker's Almanack*, 1998). Give your views on the efficiency of the River Goyt in meeting the needs of Stockport. Remember that it is only one of several rivers that supply Stockport.

Drawing conclusions

Summarise your results and describe the extent to which you consider the Goyt catchment area to be efficient in supplying water to Stockport.

Evaluating your work

The title of this Trial Run was 'How efficient are the River Goyt and its catchment area in supplying water to Stockport?'. In the light of the facts below do you think the 47 days' rainfall and 1 day's discharge in 1996 were typical enough for you to be able to answer the question with confidence?

1. The total rainfall received by the area in 1996 was only 57% of the average received each year between 1979 and 1990.
2. The total hours of sunshine for June and July 1996 were well above average.
3. The maximum temperature was well above the mean maximum temperature in June and July.
4. A drought was declared during the summer of 1996.

Interesting extra ideas

Water companies depend on long-term records to assess the reliability of their water supply and to calculate how much to charge their customers. Find out the annual rainfall figures recorded at the Manchester Weather Station. (These are available free of charge from the Meteorological Office whose address is given in the Sources of Information on the Website). You could then calculate the amount of water received annually by the Goyt catchment area.

The cost of water charged by North West Water plc in 1997/98 to domestic customers (householders) with a water meter was 64.4 pence per cubic metre. How much would the income from this be?

Find out what the outlay of a water company is likely to be to provide and maintain water pipes, to monitor water for purity, to provide sewerage facilities and so on.

This Trial Run based on secondary sources could lead to fieldwork around your home or school. Experiment with infiltration rates on different surfaces – grass, bare soil, dry soil and damp soil.

Use the techniques described on page 162. Use a watering can fitted with a rose to estimate the effectiveness of a large-leafed shrub, such as a rhododendron, in intercepting rainfall. Put a big plastic bowl underneath and measure the amount that it catches within the first minute.

Rivers Short Project: Where does the river flow most quickly?

This fieldwork is most easily done if 3 people work together.

Fieldwork area

A stretch of river 10 or 20 metres in length.

To make sure that you can reach the river look at an Ordnance Survey map of scale 1:25,000. This map shows footpaths and details such as field boundaries. These are helpful for finding out where you are. If the river is on private land you will have to get permission before starting. For help look at pages 18–20.

Your safety is more important than a fieldwork project. Do not wade into water deeper than the tops of your Wellington boots. Visit the river before beginning to make sure that it is a safe place to work.

Before you begin

1. Draw a sketch map of your fieldwork area. Use the Ordnance Survey map to help you. Include the river, the contours on either side and the road or path you will take to reach the river. A ***sketch map*** makes an attractive title page.
2. Find out as much as you can about the way in which rivers flow. You will then know what to ***expect*** in your fieldwork. Write a paragraph in your own words for the introduction to your final report. Draw a diagram and label it.

You will need the following equipment:

Choose your floats from oranges, dog biscuits, small cucumbers or quarters of orange peel. None of these will harm the environment. All your floats must be the same kind and you will need 9 of each. You will need to take at least 3 sets of recordings, one at the left bank-side, one in the middle and one at the right bank-side. Put a dab of brightly coloured paint on your floats to identify which is which (left, right or middle).

- 2 Washing lines – 1 to act as the starting line and the other as the finishing line.
- 4 Tent pegs to secure the washing lines on the banks.
- Stopwatch, digital watch or a watch with a second hand.
- 30 metre tape measure to measure the distance downstream between the starting line and the finishing line.
- Recording Sheet. Copy the one on page 132 and take a spare one.

Recording sheet

Location	Grid Reference	Date
Time taken by Left bank float (Colour of float...........)		
Time taken by Midstream float (Colour of float..........)		
Time taken by Right bank float (Colour of float ....)		

Fieldwork method

The team will be made up as follows:

- Starter – This person will be in the water at the starting line. He/she will be responsible for putting the floats into the water one at a time and letting the timer know when this is being done.
- Timer – This person will stand on the bank and will be responsible for timing each float from when it is put into the water to when it is taken out. He/she will let the finisher know when a float is coming down the river.
- Finisher – This person will stand in the water at the finishing line and try to pick the float out of the water. He/she will let the timer know when the float reaches the finishing line

For accuracy, repeat each measurement 3 times or more and later calculate the average.

In your final report describe how you took measurements. Say what you did. A diagram with labels will help. You can draw matchstick people.

Analysing and interpreting your data

1. Calculate the average time taken by each float. This means adding up all of the times recorded and dividing the total by three (or the number of times you repeated the measurements).
2. Divide the distance between the starting line and finishing line (distance covered) by the average time taken by each float. The calculation is:

$$\frac{\text{distance}}{\text{average time in seconds}}$$

   The answer will be the speed of flow in seconds.
3. Draw the speed of flow of each float as a bar chart. See pages 72–3. Show the speed of the left bank-side at the left, the midstream speed in the middle, and the right bank-side speed at the right. Which is the fastest speed of flow?
4. Describe what your bar charts show.

Drawing conclusions

Where does the river flow most quickly? Does this conclusion confirm what you expected to find before you began? If not, can you suggest reasons? Hints: Was the river so shallow that your floats got stuck? Was it a very windy day?

Evaluating your work

1. Suggest any improvements you would make to your fieldwork method if you could begin again. Would you try: a heavier float such as oranges, or a lighter float such as orange peel?
2. Would a flow-line diagram (see pages 81–2) have shown the speed of flow better than a bar chart?

Interesting extra ideas

- Repeat the investigation using a different type of float or a flowmeter and compare your results.
- Repeat the investigation along another stretch of river which is different from the one you chose – a meander or a straight stretch – and compare your results.
- Find out from your public library whether the river's course has been altered at any time in the past.
- Would it throw more light on your results if you knew the depth of the river? Go back and measure the depth at the same sites.
- Would your results be different after a spell of heavy rainfall or after dry weather? Try it out.

Rivers Investigation: How does the river's load vary in size and shape?

FIELDWORK TECHNIQUES

You will use the following techniques:

- **Measuring particle size with a pebble measure**
- **Making and using a guide to the roundness of particles**
- **Testing for water quality**
- **Sedimentation and filtration of the suspension load**

This investigation relies mainly upon measurements of the deposits of loose materials on the river bed which have been transported by the river. It is difficult and can be very dangerous to try to measure a ***load*** when it is actually moving, particularly if it contains large pebbles. A river has to have a large volume and be flowing very quickly to move big pebbles. Don't attempt to measure it. You can produce a project of great interest and of real practical value from an investigation of the load that has been deposited. For convenience in this investigation, loose deposits are called 'river-bed material'.

This investigation may form the basis of many projects. Here are suggestions together with an outline of the conclusion you could expect to achieve. Each ***expectation*** is a ***hypothesis*** (see Section 1, page 6).

1. Investigate different sites on the same river:
   - **a** Upstream near to the source and at one or more sites further downstream. Your expectations might include:
     - **(i)** that the size of river-bed material would decrease downstream;
     - **(ii)** that river-bed material would become more rounded in shape downstream.

     You could relate your results to the speed of flow, and/or the river's ***discharge*** at each site.
   - **b** At a sequence of riffles and pools. Your expectations might include:
     - **(i)** that the river-bed material is bigger in size at the riffle than at the pool;
     - **(ii)** that the river-bed material is more angular at the riffle than at the pool.

     You could relate your results to the speed of flow of the river, to the amount of turbulent flow/frothy water/white water present at each site.

CAUTION: Do not wade into pools deeper than your Wellington boots.

2. Investigate the size and shape of river-bed material across a ***meander*** and compare the results with those across a straight stretch of river.

   Your expectations might include: that at the meander the biggest and most angular material is on the slip-off slope. On a straight stretch of river the biggest and most angular materials are close to both banksides.

   You could relate your results to the speed of flow of the river at each site.
3. Investigate sites on streams of similar size but flowing across different rock types. Preferably choose one soluble rock (i.e. one that dissolves) such as chalk or limestone, and one that is hard and insoluble (does not dissolve), e.g. sandstone. Use geological maps to help you to choose your rivers and then ask your teacher to make sure that you have chosen wisely.

   Your expectations could include: that the concentration of chemical compounds dissolved in the river (i.e. solution load) is greater in the river flowing over soluble rock than in the river which flows over insoluble rock.

   What differences in the river-bed material would you expect to find as a result of these differences in the water?

   This project would be a good link with Geology and Science. You should find the section on Water Quality in Section 2 (pages 47–52) of help.
4. Projects based on investigations into ***inter-relationships***:
   - **a** Where river-bed material is small and rounded, is the channel a more efficient shape than where the river-bed material is large and angular?
   - **b** Is the water quality related to the river-bed material and suspension load?
   - **c** Does the solution load decrease after heavy rainfall? Ways of investigating this are explained in detail under Water Quality on pages 47–52.
   - **d** Does a spell of heavy rainfall change the size and shape of river-bed material?

   For **c** and **d** you would obviously have to carry out your investigations more than once: in dry weather and after a rainy spell or after snow has melted.

What is the river's load?

Anything that is transported by the moving water alone is termed the river's load. The quantity of the load and the way in which it is transported are related to the river's energy. Think carefully about why this is so. You can find out more about it from a book on physical geography. Explain it in your own words in the introduction to your final report.

The river's load is made up of solid materials and dissolved materials. Some of them are eroded by the river from the bed and banks of its channel, and others are weathered material which has moved down the valley-sides under gravity and landed in the river.

The dissolved material transported by the river is called the **solution load**. You will find information on this in Water Quality on pages 47–52.

Any part of the load that is deposited by a river is termed **alluvium**.

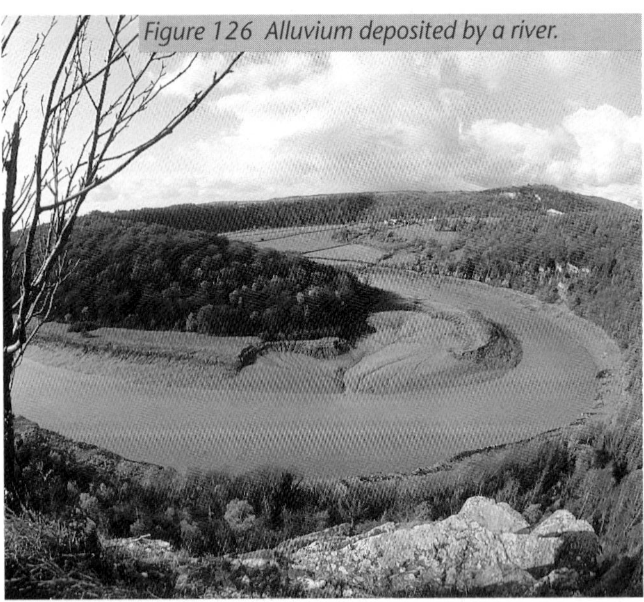
Figure 126 Alluvium deposited by a river.

How does a river transport its load of solid materials?

Solid materials are carried by the river as **bedload** and **suspension load**. You can guess that the bedload is moved along close to the bed of the channel whilst the suspension load is carried in the water without touching either the bed or banks of the channel. In other words, the suspension load is free-flowing.

It is almost impossible to see the bedload actually moving but research has shown that it is transported in two ways: **bottom traction** is the term used when the load is trundled along the bed, but smaller pebbles may hop along or be flirted forward by other moving pebbles. This process is like tiddly-winks and is termed **saltation**.

The smaller particles that a river carries may at some time form part of the suspension load, whilst at other times the same particles become part of the bedload. Can you work out why they change place? It is worth explaining it in the introduction to your final report. You can demonstrate the way this happens by placing a handful of dry soil of different particle sizes onto a flat surface. Blow onto it gently at first and then with greater force and then more gently. Watch out for when particles of different sizes become suspended in the air, and when they fall back down as you increase and then decrease the energy of your breath.

A river needs more energy to pick up a particle and get it into suspension than to keep it there. You can compare this with birds getting into flight. They have to flap their wings quickly and hard to take off, and then use far less energy to fly along.

To help the reader to understand your project right from the start, draw a diagram similar to the one in Figure 127. ***Annotate*** it to explain the different parts of the load, and the ways in which the river transports them.

Figure 127 How a river transports its load.

Copy and then annotate this diagram, explaining it in your own words

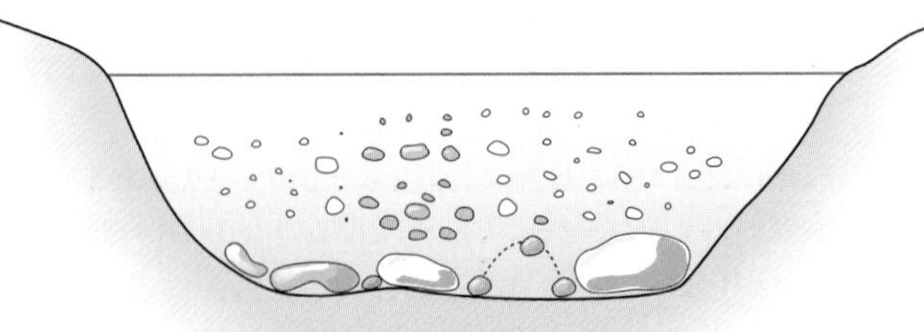

Fieldwork area

If you practise the procedures during a ***reconnaissance visit***, you will become quick and it should be possible to investigate three or four sites within one day.

To choose your investigation sites, begin by looking at the Ordnance Survey map of scale 1:50,000 or 1:25,000. Look at the ***catchment area*** and the height of the highest and lowest points of possible rivers. You will need access, so look for roads and

footpaths; these are shown on both scales of map. Field boundaries and individual buildings are also shown on the 1:25,000 map, and these can be helpful in locating the best sites.

The map of scale 1:10,000 will indicate the width of the channel, as will a quick reconnaissance visit. If the river is wider than 2 m, you will have to use a method of sampling for collecting materials in the load. The different methods are explained on pages 16–18. Look through these and decide which method to use before beginning your fieldwork. To use random numbers may not be a good idea. If you have time, take more measurements than you had expected; this will be an advantage. The bigger the size of the ***sample***, the more representative it will be of the whole picture.

It is useful to be familiar with the official sizes of ***particles***. These are given on page 56 together with suggestions of ways of measuring them.

Before beginning, do a reconnaissance visit, making a quick visit to each of your proposed sites. At each site, do the following:

- Make sure that it is safe to work there.
- If it is privately owned, obtain permission to carry out your fieldwork. See pages 18–20 for help on how to ask for permission.
- A scoop such as a dust pan is useful for picking up the smaller particles. Try it out and see if you can pick up the same volume of river-bed material each time you take a scoopful.
- Decide on a method for choosing which river-bed materials to measure:
  - **(i)** the biggest and the smallest particles at each sample point or from the bed if the river is less than 2 m wide.
  - **(ii)** make a small quadrat (see page 14) and collect all of the loose particles within it. Your quadrat could have both sides either 10 cm or 20 cm in length. Your reconnaissance visit will show you the best size for your investigation sites.
- Consider whether your project will involve taking extra sets of measurements such as those for the shape of the channel, the speed of flow of the river, or the ***discharge*** of the river. You may also want to record the ways in which the river and the surrounding land are used, so work out how to do this.
- Trace a map of scale 1:50,000 or 1:25,000 to show your investigation sites and include this in the introduction to your final report.

You will need the following equipment:

- Cord or washing line to stretch across the river to act as the base-line for your investigations.
- Tent pegs to secure the base-line.
- Metre rule.
- Scoop. A dustpan may be useful.
- A scale of roundness. This will help you to pick out particular shapes in the materials you investigate. Five main shapes are recognised and you can make a set from pencil erasers as in Figure 128. Some patience will be needed though! Label each eraser with indelible (waterproof) ink. Your reconnaissance visit will have shown whether you need all five shapes or just 'angular', 'sub-rounded' and 'well-rounded'.

Figure 128 A scale of roundness made from pencil erasers.

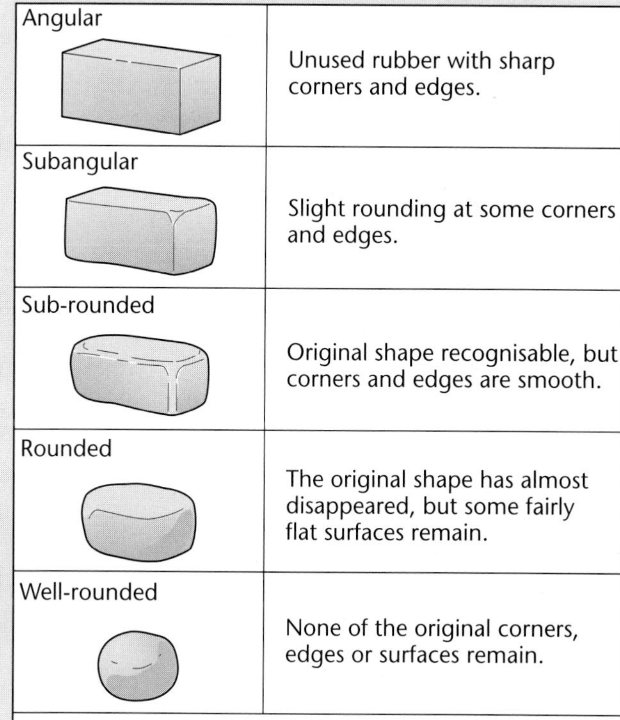

Angular	Unused rubber with sharp corners and edges.
Subangular	Slight rounding at some corners and edges.
Sub-rounded	Original shape recognisable, but corners and edges are smooth.
Rounded	The original shape has almost disappeared, but some fairly flat surfaces remain.
Well-rounded	None of the original corners, edges or surfaces remain.

You may have seen charts of 'Power's scale of roundness'. Cailleux devised a formula for calculating roundness.

- Quadrat for choosing river-bed material, if you have decided to use one.
- Equipment for measuring particles: a pebble measure (see page 56 and 172) or calipers or a ruler. Sieving can be done at school or at home.
- Weighing equipment. If you weigh the materials during your fieldwork, a spring-balance and a mesh bag are ideal. Fishing tackle shops always sell spring-balances. At home or at school,

kitchen scales are accurate enough for large particles, but you will have to use a chemical balance if you decide to weigh the finer particles.

- Polythene containers to carry samples home or back to school. Label each carefully with the name of the site and the number of the sample. Waterproof labels are a help.
- Recording sheet for measurements (see Figure 129), one for each site and some spares.

Equipment for material in suspension:

- Collecting jar of polythene or metal. It should have a wide neck but be as streamlined in shape as possible to avoid disturbing the flow of the river. If you feel that your container is not ideal then say so and explain why in the ***evaluation*** of the method in your final report.
- Watertight containers, each labelled, to take home or back to school.

Equipment for extra sets of measurements:

- For measuring the speed of flow, see pages 52–4.
- For measuring the river's discharge or the shape of the river's channel, see the Rivers Extra Investigation on the Website.
- For measuring the solution load, see page 51.
- For measuring the quality of the water, see pages 47–51.

Fieldwork method

At each site carry out the same procedures:

1. Stretch your cord or washing line across the river's channel at right angles to the direction in which the river is flowing. Secure it on each bank with a tent-peg, heavy stone or tie it around a tree trunk. This will be the base-line for your measurements.
2. Write a description of the river and make a field sketch or take a photograph.

   Work systematically across the base-line from one side to the other to take your measurements. Remember that the left bankside is to your left when facing downstream. Record the name of the site, and at which bankside you started to take measurements. According to the sample interval that you have chosen, work out with the metre rule the point at which you will take measurements as follows:

   - River bed material. Use your hand to feel whether there are any big pebbles on the river bed. Remember that the pebbles must be loose. Lay down the quadrat if you have decided to use it, making sure that it is not swept away by the moving water. Collect a scoopful of loose material and put it into a container.
   - Suspension load. Measure the depth of the water. At 4/10ths of the depth, as measured from the bed upwards, hold your collecting jar horizontally and facing upstream. Why this is the best depth at which to collect your sample is suggested on

Figure 129 Sheet for recording river bed material.

Site name: ____________________ Date: ____________________

Grid reference: ____________________

Method of sampling (if used)	Samples taken working from right/left bankside (cross out which-ever does not apply)	Weight (g)	Long axis (mm)	Short axis (mm)	Shape (use roundness guide)	Colour and other features

page 52 in Section 2. Keep the sample, carefully labelled in a water-tight container, to take for investigation at home or at school.

For the biggest particle in each sample of a river-bed material:

(i) weigh it,

(ii) measure the longest and shortest axes (see page 55),

(iii) use your roundness guide to describe its shape, and

(iv) describe its colour and appearance. You may be able to link this to the geology of the area. Replace the particle in the river.

4. Take any extra measurements such as the speed of flow, water quality, width and depths which you need for your particular project.

Don't be disappointed if you can't 'catch' much suspension load. It is difficult unless the river is transporting a lot in this way, and you know that this partly depends upon its energy.

Completing measurements at home or at school

River-bed materials

For each sample:

1. Open the container and let the samples dry out. This will be quicker if you put them into a slow oven for a few hours, but first transfer them into a metal container and label it carefully.
2. Weigh the whole sample, remembering to include the samples that you weighed at your fieldwork site.
3. Following the methods explained on pages 55–56, divide the particles into different sizes, and make a table of results to record each.

If water quality is part of your project, carry out chemical tests before sieving your samples.

Samples of suspension load

Either:

a transfer each sample, with labels, into a straight-sided clear glass jar and leave for a few days so that the load will settle, then use a ruler to measure the depth of particles of different sizes

or:

b pass each sample through a coffee sieve, and then through a filter-paper shaped like an up-turned cone. Next, dry the particles and sieve them, following the methods on pages 55. Weigh each of the different particle sizes of the sample and make a table of results to record each.

Clay-sized particles which cannot be seen without the use of a microscope can remain in suspension for six weeks or more. If you add barium sulphate to the water this will make the clay particles flocculate (stick together) and they will settle much more quickly. CAUTION: Barium sulphate is poisonous.

For the river-bed material and the suspension load, analyse the particles further. Sometimes if the particles are very small it is difficult to carry out further measurements. You may not be able to do anything more. If so, explain this in your final report.

Take three of the bigger particles and for each:

(i) weigh it,

(ii) measure the long axis and the short axis,

(iii) compare it with your roundness guide,

(iv) make a note of the colour and appearance.

These are the same procedures as those you carried out during your fieldwork.

Include these observations in your table of results.

Analysing and interpreting your data

1. Draw a ***sketch map*** or make a tracing of a small-scale map, such as the 1:50,000 or smaller. Place this in the middle of a double page (A3 size) in your final report. Mark each of your investigation sites and draw an arrow out from each, so that you can include a summary of your results around the map. Draw the threads together and write one or two paragraphs about the size and shape of the load at each site.
2. Copy your tables of results to include in your final report.
3. Calculate the percentage by weight of particles of different sizes in each of the samples you have collected from both the river-bed material and the suspension load, if you have investigated both. The method is explained on page 86. Illustrate the percentages for each investigation as a pie chart (see pages 79–80). Put the pie charts around your map. Describe what each of them shows. Suggest reasons for any patterns that appear. Was there a higher percentage of large particles upstream, on the slip-off-slope of the meander or at the riffles?
4. Depending upon the size of your dried particles, put a small sample of each into a clear polythene bag and place these around your map and beside the pie charts.

5. Look at the results of the size and shape of the particles you have measured both in the river-bed material and suspension load. Do they appear to be related to any of the following:
   - The location on the river's course: upstream; below a reservoir or dam; where a channel has been straightened or the banks reinforced; in deep water; in fast-flowing water?
   - The position in the channel at a particular site: in the middle, or close to one side?
   - A rainy spell or a period of melting snow? After these, large angular particles may have been deposited. For this it would be helpful to have figures from the Meteorological Office (see Sources of Information on the Website) or from your local weather station.
   - The types of rock in the river's ***catchment area***? Hard rock such as sandstone often produces large, angular particles, whereas shale forms small, disc-shaped and rounded particles. Investigations into the solution load will obviously be affected by the geology. Your public library will have geological maps, and descriptions of the geology such as the Memoirs of the British Geological Survey and the Proceedings of the Geologists' Association.

Drawing conclusions

For each site that you have investigated:

1. Describe the size and shape of particles in the bedload and in the suspension load if you have measured it.
2. Explain the proportions of different sizes and shapes in the load at each site.
3. Was it enough to measure only the long axis and short axis of pebbles? Is this a real index of shape? A coin has two axes only but a river pebble has three. You could find out about Cailleux's Index of Roundness and Powers' Scale of Roundness.
4. Look again at the exact aims of your project and the ***expectations*** which you had before beginning. Are you able to link your findings of particle size and shape to any of the features at the site?
   - How far downstream was the site? Was it in the upper course section or further down?
   - Was the site close to alterations made to the channel such as a dam, a weir, artificial embankments?
   - Close to the banks in contrast to the middle of a straight stretch of river?
   - On a riffle or in a pool?
   - On the inner side of a meander?

   Do your investigations confirm or support your expectations?

   Is the solution load related to:
   - the geology of the catchment area and the rocks over which the river flows?
   - the use made of the river for water supply, industry or farming in the region?

Evaluating your work

- Does the size of your sample (the number of collections you have made) seem to be big enough to support your expectations? If not how many more samples would you take if you could begin again?
- Collecting samples of the suspension load has probably been the most difficult part of your fieldwork. Suggest improvements to the equipment and the methods of collection.
- You may have linked your results to those supplied by a professional body such as a water company or the Environment Agency. Their results will have been collected by using sophisticated equipment. Do you feel that your results should be linked with theirs?

Interesting extra ideas

Go back to your investigation sites after a period of different weather – heavy rainfall, dry conditions, melting snow. If the river's volume has increased, and its speed of flow, how will it have affected:

- the size and shape of the bedload?
- the size and shape of the suspension load?
- the amount (concentration) of solution load?

Return to the area to measure the angle of slope or gradient of the valley sides. Does the angle make it likely that much of the river's load at each of your sites has been supplied from the valley sides? Look for evidence of downslope movement under gravity such as bends in tree trunks growing on the valley side, terracettes (little steps) in a grassy valley-side and slumping (caving in) of the banks.

Is there evidence at your sites of erosion by the river? Look for potholes in the river bed. Measure their length, width and depth. Look for lateral erosion into the banks. Are they smooth? Do they overhang the river's edge?

Use the water from your samples of the suspension load to test as the solution load. See page 51 for help on how to do this. Is the solution load related to:

- the distance downstream?
- the geology?
- the land use in the area? around the river?
- the way people use the river?

Transport

The amount of traffic on the roads has become an almost daily item in newspapers. This is not surprising considering that the total length of roads in Great Britain alone (392,712 km in 1996) would stretch around the equator (40,075 km) nearly ten times! The distance that all our vehicles travel in a year would go round the equator more than 11,000 times! Here are the distances travelled on our roads by different types of vehicle:

Estimated distance travelled (in millions of kilometres) by different vehicles on the roads of Great Britain in 1998 (according to the Annual Abstract of Statistics, DETR):

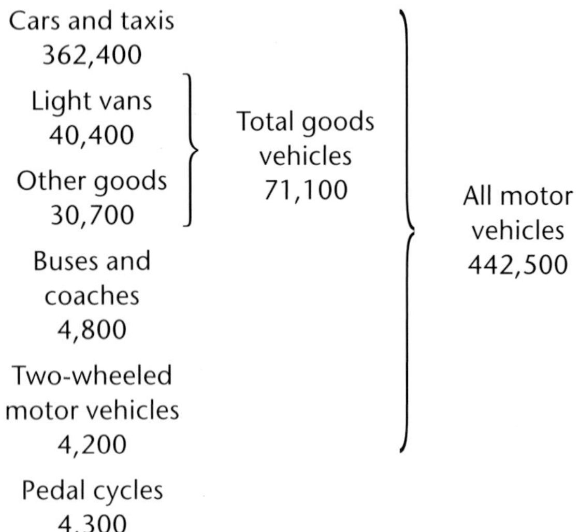

Transport routes of all kinds – road, rail, airway and waterway – are channels in a network for carrying people and goods from one place to another. Roads and road transport make the basis for a very good project. This could later be extended by comparing it with another form of transport in your fieldwork area such as the local railway service or a light rail transit (tram) system.

For most of us, our door-to-door link is by road. We are all familiar with the roads around our homes. These are only part of a much wider network in which our home is connected by road to almost every other house in the country. This simple but amazing fact demonstrates two basic points about the organisation of road networks and the places which they link:

1. the road network is extremely well-connected, or, to use the technical terminology, it has a high degree of connectivity;

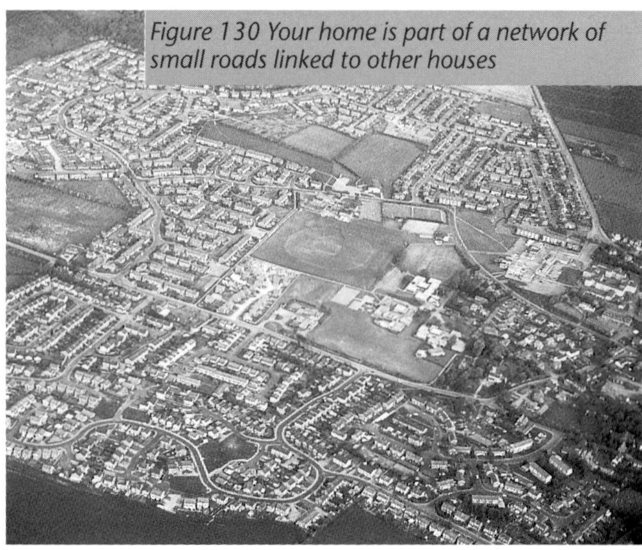

Figure 130 Your home is part of a network of small roads linked to other houses

2. the network makes our homes accessible to all other homes in the network.

Try making a list of all the roads used by members of your family or friends during the last two days. This will help you to see how complex the road network really is. It will probably indicate which are the most direct and quickest routes for getting from A to B.

This chapter has been designed to show ways of investigating the different aspects involved in a project on transport. These are as follows:

- The route itself. This must be wide enough, smooth enough, well lit and pleasant to use.
- How the routes of your fieldwork area fit into the network, either local or regional.
- The flows along the routes. People and goods must be able to move easily and without difficulty.
- The impact on the environment of the route and the traffic it carries. The route should not spoil the view, cause noise, danger or pollution.

You will realise that these are all related to one another.

The Trial Run in this chapter is designed to give you practice in assessing the efficiency of a network and investigating the flow along it. This will help when you plan your own project.

The Short Project investigates the flow of traffic on a particular route.

The Investigation describes ways of investigating the impact of the routes and the traffic on the local environment.

There is also an Extra Investigation on the Website that explains:

a how to assess the efficiency of a network in terms of (i) its connectivity and (ii) the accessibility of places within the network;

b how to investigate the flow of traffic along it.

CAUTION: Safety is more important than anything else. Do not take risks, and do not be the cause of any problems to traffic or other people.

Motorways are unlike other roads. They can be dangerous places and are best avoided in fieldwork. Only use them as part of route analysis from a map such as the Ordnance Survey map of scale 1:250,000 (Routemaster Series).

Project suggestions

1. What are the similarities and differences between a road through town and either a ring road around the town centre or a bypass around the whole town in terms of:
   a the physical appearance of the road (the number of lanes, the widths of pavements and so on)?
   b their part in the town's network of roads?
   c traffic flow?

   Where to find help:
   On street parking, 57
   How to draw a topological map, 65–6
   How to investigate traffic flow, 147–9

2. How do the direction and volume of traffic along a road leading into the centre of a town or other important destination vary according to the time of day, the day of the week or both?

   Where to find help:
   Transport Short Project, pages 147–9

3. In a residential area compare a major road of class 'A' or 'T' with one or more minor roads. Investigate the appearance of each of your chosen roads, the traffic flow along it, and the measures taken to ensure the safety of pedestrians.

   Where to find help:
   Transport Short Project, pages 147–9
   Towns Extra Investigation, Website

4. Choose roads of similar size in two or more different types of area, such as:
   a commuter village
   a rural village
   a suburban residential area
   an area of terraced housing
   the town centre
   close to a leisure centre

   In what ways are they similar/different? Investigate the number of homes, traffic restrictions, on-street parking, traffic flow, lighting.

   Where to find help:
   Land use recording, 118–9
   On-street parking, 57
   Interesting Extra Ideas, 122

5. How important in your fieldwork area is the local bus service or local train service? How efficient is the route network for the buses or trains? How frequent is the service? Could the service be improved and, if so, in what ways?

   Where to find help:
   Topological Maps, 65–6
   Accessibility in a network – Transport Extra Investigation, Website
   Secondary sources – public transport timetable

6. Are there patterns in the numbers of goods or passenger vehicles on the roads of your fieldwork area? Use the list below for guidance:

Goods transport	Passenger transport
heavy lorries (HGV classification)	buses
container lorries	coaches
lorries with trailers	cars
light vans	motorcycles
specialised types, such as removal vans, cement mixers	pedal cycles
refrigerated lorries	pedestrians
livestock removal vans	
tankers	

   For passenger transport, discover the capacity of buses and coaches. The capacity is how many people they can carry. By law the capacity of a bus has to be displayed beside the door. Estimate how many people are actually carried.

   Can you pick out patterns in the numbers of vehicles of different type at particular times of day, or on particular days of the week?

Where to find help:

The Freight Transport Association and the Department of Transport, Appendix 2 and Website

How to conduct a traffic survey, 147–9

7. How effective are either or both of bus lanes and cycle lanes in improving traffic flow? Does on-street car-parking cause problems? What are the alternatives?

   To assess the effectiveness of these measures which are designed for convenience, choose two roads of similar size and in the same sort of area. One should have bus lanes or cycle lanes or on-street parking whilst the other has not. The one without can act as a 'control' for your project.

   Where to find help:

   How to conduct a parking survey, 57

   How to conduct a traffic survey, 58–9 and 147–9

8. How does a major road affect the quality of the area? Investigate the following:

   traffic flow

   noise level

   the effects on the atmosphere

   ease or difficulty for people crossing the road

   restrictions for parking

   Where to find help:

   Investigation, Transport 150–156

   How to investigate air pollution, 39–40

Recommendations for parking provisions can be found in a publication of 1997. This was produced jointly by the DETR, the Association of Town Centre Managers, Sainsbury's and Marks & Spencer. It recommends parking spaces to be 5 m × 2.5 m. Those for disabled people and for parent and child with pushchair should have extra space at the side.

When the first motorways were built in Britain they had only two lanes whereas by the 1990s many had four lanes. We are now contemplating converting them into six-lane motorways.

Details of the size and weight of the following types of vehicles can be found in publications of the Department of the Environment, Transport and the Regions. The numbers registered each year are also given:

cars and taxis

light vans

other goods vehicles

two-wheeled motor vehicles

buses and coaches

pedal cycles

Transport Trial Run: How efficient is the network of routes that connects the rooms at school/home?

FIELDWORK TECHNIQUES

You will use the following techniques:

- Drawing topological maps
- Pacing out distance
- Counting moving pedestrians

Before you begin

Inside every building there is a route network. This enables people to move from one room to another, and every room has to be accessible within the network. When designing schools or homes, architects have to plan for people to move as directly and easily as possible from one room to another. Some rooms, such as an assembly hall or a living room, are designed to allow access to more people at any one time than say a geography classroom or a bedroom.

Figure 131 A museum walking plan

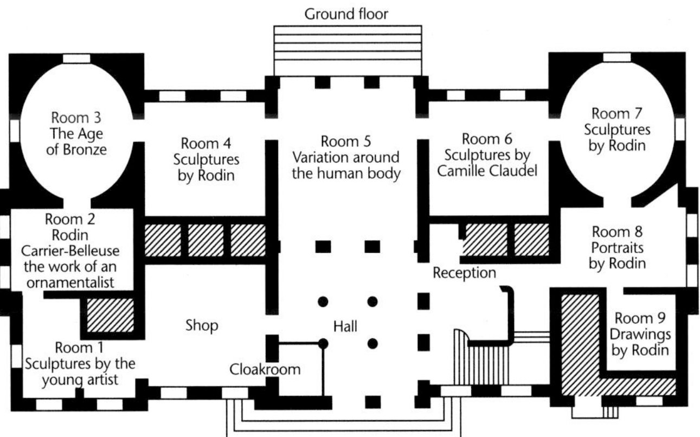

You will realise that planning an efficient network is not as easy as it seems. Three things have to be considered:

1. People must be able to move from room to room as directly as possible.
2. Rooms that are used by many people have to be more accessible than others.
3. People must be able to move easily and without congestion.

In your own words, describe the route network of one floor/storey in school or at home. Use the three points above to give your views on the efficiency of your network. Write this in the introduction to your final report.

You will need the following equipment:

- An architect's plan or blueprint may be available, but if not, you will be able to make your own sketch map quite easily. (Scale and compass direction are not important because you will convert it into a topological plan.)
- Equipment to measure the width of corridors would be a help, but you can pace out the width (see page 14), or step it out after first measuring the length of your feet.
- Pedestrian survey sheet (see Figure 58 on page 58), one copy for every time you count at each location and some spare copies.
- Noise-meter (look at page 151 for ways of measuring noise).

Fieldwork method

Remember that your Trial Run must be done for only one floor/storey at a time.

1. Convert your architect's plan into a ***topological map***, or make your own. This will show the rooms and the routes between them. Every doorway from the corridor, hall or landing, and those for entering the building from outside becomes a node. Include on your map all communicating doors between adjacent rooms. Access to stairs or a lift is also a node. The parts of the corridor between doorways are edges. Figure 132 shows the plan of the ground floor of a house with the doors and stairs marked as nodes (N1, N2, etc.) and the routes between them as edges (E1, E2, etc.).

   'Node' and 'edge' are terms used on topological maps, but you could use 'D' or 'R' or any other initials to indicate the doors and the route between them.

   A topological map simplifies a plan and makes it easier to see: (i) the links between nodes and (ii) the accessibility of the nodes within the network.

Figure 132 A scale plan of the ground floor of a house converted into a topological map.

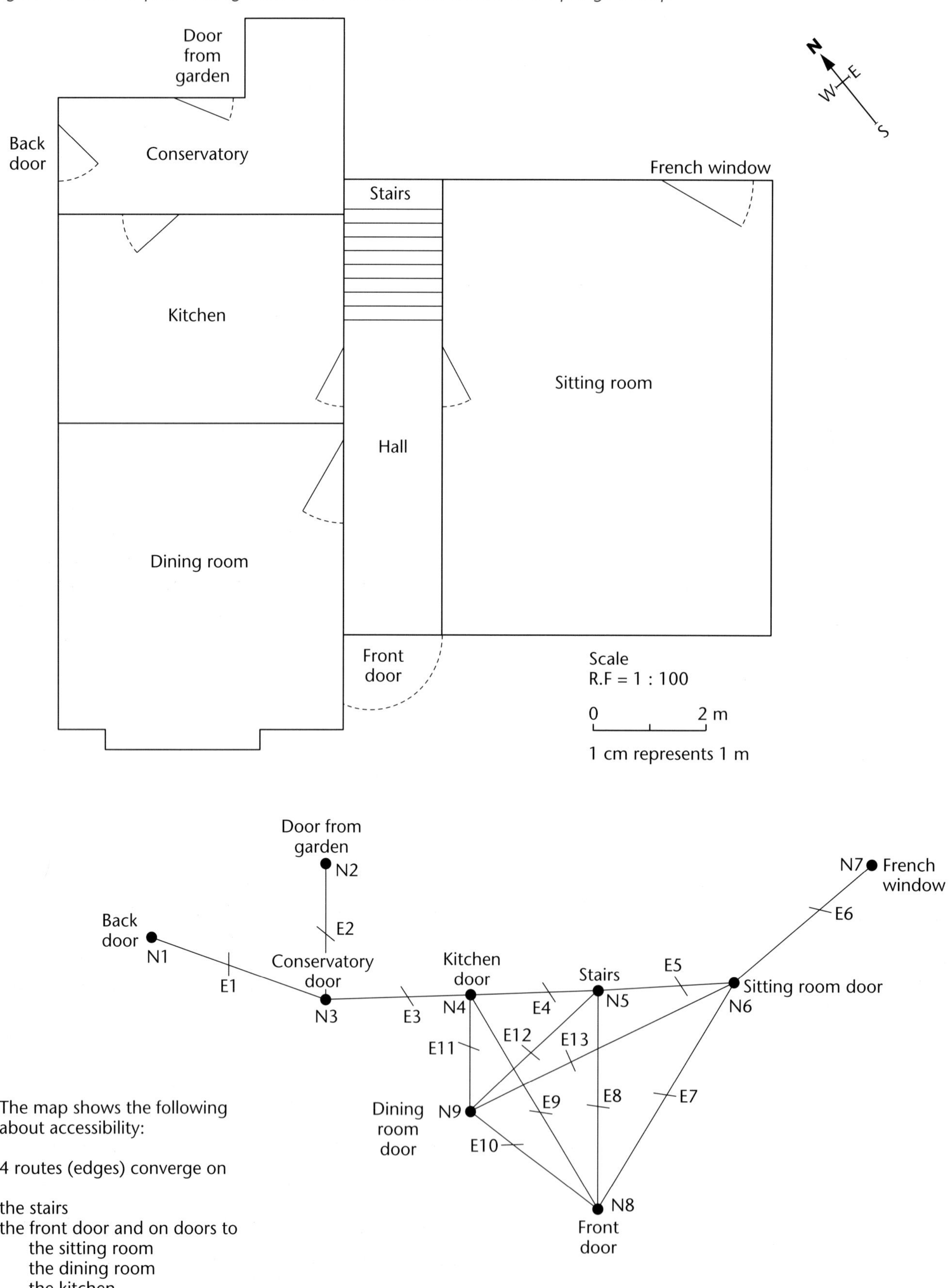

The map shows the following about accessibility:

4 routes (edges) converge on

the stairs
the front door and on doors to
- the sitting room
- the dining room
- the kitchen

These are the most accessible points within the network because all the rest have fewer routes converging on them.

A direct link when the route between two doors does not pass any others in between is, in this chapter, called an 'edge'.

2. In school: conduct a survey of pedestrian flow along each of the corridors on your map. Work with a friend so that one of you can count the people passing in one direction whilst the other counts the people passing in the opposite direction. Count for 5 minutes at a time. Write down the number of people passing on your pedestrian survey sheet (see Figure 58 on page 58).

   To enable you to cover all of the corridors on your map, take a survey at a different location at the same time on different days. Break would be a good time.

   At home: do this during a weekend or holiday when most of the family is at home. For half-hour periods ask each person for a detailed description of his or her movements during that half hour. Write it down in detail. Repeat this on four or five occasions and keep a careful record of your results.

3. At different points along the network (one where many people pass and another where few people pass) carry out the following:
   - a Assess the level of noise and write it in your field notebook.
   - b Look at the floor covering and the state of decoration of the walls. Are there signs of wear and tear? Record these as 'little', 'moderate' or 'large' levels of wear.
   - c Record furniture, newspapers and other forms of clutter. Estimate how much of the corridor is covered by these.

4. Measure the width of corridors near to rooms which cater for large numbers of people at places where you have found congestion or very low flow. Choose a quiet time to do this.

Figure 133 A matrix to identify the best connected/most accessible nodes.

	N_1	N_2	N_3	N_4	N_5	N_6	N_7	N_8	N_9	Direct links between nodes
N_1			1							1
N_2			1							1
N_3	1	1		1						3
N_4			1		1			1	1	4
N_5				1		1		1	1	4
N_6					1		1	1	1	4
N_7						1				1
N_8					1	1			1	3
N_9				1	1	1		1		4

Analysing and interpreting your data

1. Analyse the efficiency of your network step by step as follows (topological analysis):
   - a Count the number of nodes (doorways) and then the number of edges (direct links between pairs of doorways). If every doorway were linked to every other one directly, the network would be completely linked and could therefore be regarded as being 100% efficient.
   - b Divide the number of edges by the number of nodes. If the result is a figure less than 1 then the network would need more links to make it efficient. The higher the result is above 1 then the more efficient the network is.

     For Figure 132 the calculation is:

     $$\frac{e}{n} = \frac{13}{9} = 1.4$$

     The network is reasonably efficient in allowing movement from one place to another. This should confirm ***objectively*** what you have already described in the introduction to your project.
   - c Either count the number of edges which converge on each node – on Figure 132 these have been written beneath the map – or draw a ***matrix*** like the one shown in Figure 133 and use this to calculate an index of accessibility for the best connected node.

The alpha index and the beta index are methods of calculating the degree of connectivity of networks. The method of calculating each of these indices is explained in the Transport Extra Investigation on the Website.

2. Draw a flow-line map to represent the movement of people in school or at home. The method for drawing flow-lines is described in Section 2 on page 81. Does your map show places of maximum flow? Do these places coincide with the nodes which have the largest number of direct links? Make a list of the flows at different

places. Put these into ***rank order***, and then illustrate them as a bar chart. See pages 72–3.

Describe what your map and bar chart show. In school, does your flow-line map indicate that rooms such as the assembly hall and the tuck shop are located at accessible positions in the network?

Look at your measurements of the widths of corridors. Are they appropriate for the numbers of people who pass along them at any one time? Would you recommend widening the 'route' at certain points if that were possible?

At home you may be in a position to advise on moving some pieces of furniture from a congested point to a less congested one.

3. Use different densities of shading (see page 65) on your map to indicate the following:
   - a levels of noise
   - b levels of wear and tear
4. Divide the widths of corridors into categories (see page 15). Choose different colours to indicate particular widths and shade your map in the appropriate colour.
5. Draw scattergraphs (see pages 76–78) to reveal whether or not there are relationships between the following:
   - a the numbers of pedestrians and noise level
   - b the numbers of pedestrians and your index of wear and tear ('little', 'moderate', 'large')
   - c the numbers of pedestrians and the width of the corridors

   You will have to convert noise and wear and tear into value numbers such as 1–5 and 1–3.

Drawing conclusions

1. Your aim was to investigate the efficiency of the network of routes.
   - a. Does your analysis of the network indicate that there are enough direct routes between the different rooms?
   - b. Summarise your description of what your flow-line map shows. Point out places of peak flow and low flow. Are there bottle-necks of congestion? If so, suggest ways of solving them. Does the width seem to you to be adequate for the numbers at peak flow? Do the most accessible nodes (doorways) appear to be related to the point of peak pedestrian flow?
2. Give your views on whether the noise level and wear and tear on flooring and decorations are unavoidable. If not, are they really related to the amount of flow along the routes?

Evaluating your work

1. In the introduction to your final report you have written a description of the efficiency of the network in your own words. Since then you have done a topological analysis of the efficiency. Is the end-result the same?
2. Do 'little', 'moderate' and 'large' (and the value numbers into which you have converted them) accurately describe the wear and tear? Would it have been better to take measurements and then group them into categories (see page 15)? Give your views.

Interesting extra ideas

Improving the system of routes in the network:

Describe ways in which you consider that the system of routes could be improved. Here are some suggestions:

- Introduce a one-way system of pedestrian movement.
- Erect flexi-cord barriers such as those in use for queues in some post offices and banks to direct the flow.
- Put down carpet in noisy places and shield the walls with clear plastic sheeting.
- Widen the corridors.
- Add extra doors.

The last two would be very expensive. This is a ***cost–benefit analysis***. The benefits have to be balanced against the financial costs involved in making the improvements. You could describe your recommendations in the form of a report for the school governors or for your parents.

Transport Short Project: How many and what types of vehicles travel along a road in opposite directions?

Work in pairs. One of you can watch for each type of vehicle (the observer) while the other records it (the recorder). Take it in turns.

Fieldwork area: how to choose your fieldwork sites

Choose a main road, one classified by the government as 'A', 'B' or 'T' leading towards a town. This should be a straight stretch of road not near a pedestrian crossing, a crossroad or a major turning place such as a retail park.

Safety is very important. Stand well back on the pavement.

Before you begin

1. Use an Ordnance Survey map of scale 1:50,000 or 1:25,000 to help you to draw a ***sketch map*** of 'your' road. On it, mark:
   - (a) the place where you will stand for your traffic count;
   - (b) the government's classification number, both the letters 'A', 'B' or 'T' and the number;
   - (c) arrows with labels to show where the centre of the nearest town is, and where the road has come from;
   - (d) shade and name the built-up area;
   - (e) crossroads, bridges, viaducts and other features.

   A sketch map drawn and coloured carefully makes an attractive title page for a project.
2. Explain in your own words the reasons why you have chosen:
   - (a) this road for your project and
   - (b) the place at which you will carry out your traffic count.
3. Write down any patterns you expect to find in:
   - (a) the total number of vehicles travelling in opposite directions;
   - (b) the different types of vehicles travelling in opposite directions.

   You could call these patterns your ***'expectations'***

You will need the following equipment:

Traffic survey recording sheet – see page 59

One for each count you plan to take plus a spare copy

A watch for timing the count

'Count' and 'survey' mean the same thing: use the one you like best.

Fieldwork method

Before beginning, decide with your partner how long to count the traffic, possibly for 10 minutes in each direction.

Each time count the traffic on one side of the road only.

1. When you have agreed the time and length for the count, write in your field notebook both the starting and the finishing time.
2. The observer will call out the type of vehicle as it approaches. The recorder will mark each vehicle as a tally stroke in the correct box on the traffic survey recording sheet. An example is shown on page 59.
3. Repeat the procedure on the opposite side of the road.

Analysing and interpreting your data

1. (a) Add up the total number of strokes on your tally chart of vehicles travelling in one direction. Repeat this for the other direction.
   (b) Draw a bar chart for each direction - see page 72 to 74 illustrate your results. Write a sentence to describe the total numbers travelling in opposite directions.
   (c) Write a sentence to describe what it shows.
2. (a) To analyse the different types of vehicles travelling in opposite directions, use your tally chart to add up the numbers in each type.
   (b) Make a table of these ***ranking*** them from the biggest to the smallest.
   (c) Write a paragraph to describe what your table shows.
3. Draw a flow line diagram to show the number and types of vehicle travelling in opposite directions. This is easily done on graph paper. Choose a scale such as 1 millimetre or the width of 1 small square to represent 1 vehicle. Write the scale beside your diagram.
   Place these back to back below one another as in Figure 134.

Figure 134 Data analysis for a typical traffic survey

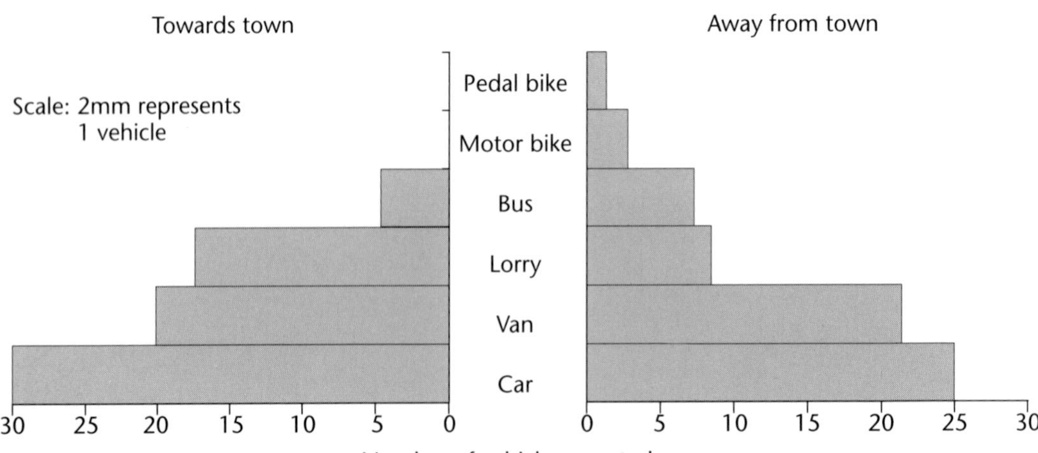

Work out a colour key. Use a different colour to represent each of the different types of vehicle such as blue for cars, red for lorries. Remember to add the key beside the diagram.

4. Can you suggest reasons for the patterns in your results?

Drawing conclusions

Write a paragraph to describe:

1. the total number of vehicles travelling in each direction
2. the numbers in each type travelling in each direction

Before you began you had expectations of what your project would reveal. Do your results confirm them?

Evaluating your work

1. Should you have counted for a longer period of time?
2. (a) Should lorries be divided into more than one category based on their size?
   (b) Should large passenger vehicles such as Range Rovers be classed with cars or with vans/minibuses?
3. In what way does the ranking of figures help to reveal patterns? You can read about this on page 84.

Interesting extra ideas

Here are the total number of vehicles on the roads in Great Britain in 1998. Look at the proportions of the different types of vehicles. Were yours similar to these?

Private cars and light good vehicles	24,267,758
Motor cycles, scooters, mopeds	655,137
Coaches and buses	79,663
Large goods vehicles	417,646
Electric vehicles	11,651
Others	1,897,227
TOTAL	27,329,082

Source: DVLA.

Your investigation was a ***sample***. Was it typical of that time of day? Repeat it at the same time on other days. How different would the traffic be at rush hour or the weekend?

Transport Investigation: What impact do roads and traffic have on an area?

FIELDWORK TECHNIQUES

You will use the following techniques:

- **Field sketching and/or use of a camera**
- **Making a scale for measuring noise**
- **Assessing pollution**
- **Devising a questionnaire and conducting interviews**
- **Devising a system of value numbers to increase objectivity**

Three ways in which transport routes affect the landscape are:

- visual appearance: how do the route and its traffic affect the visual/scenic attractiveness of the area?
- noise: what is the impact of traffic noise upon the area?
- pollution: motor vehicles give off gases and create dust; do these cause problems?

Fieldwork area

Concentrate on a small number of roads. Interesting comparisons can be made between two roads of the same type in different areas – one built-up and the other rural/countryside – or between two roads of different type within the same area.

To help you to choose, look first at the Ordnance Survey map of scale 1:50,000 (Landranger Series) or 1:25,000 (Pathfinder Series or Explorer Series). Maps of these scales show the Department of the Environment, Transport and the Regions (DETR) class of roads (A, B, T, etc.) and the type of area through which they pass.

To assess the impact made by the road you will have to rely on ***samples*** located along ***transects*** of up to 1 km on both sides of the road. Use the map to find the best places for your transects. Two transects on either side would ensure that your results are more reliable than if you rely on one transect only.

There were over 21,172,000 cars in Britain in 1995 and the forecasts predict that there will be 32 millions by 2025. The British are the biggest car users in the EU!

Every year since 1990 motorway congestion (when traffic regularly slows to 30 mph or less) has risen in all parts of the country, and, with fewer major roads being built or widened, the traffic on minor roads is likely to increase.

Figure 135 Cars are starting to congest even our small roads

Find out more about attempts to address the impact of roads from the following:

Strategic Traffic Action in Rural Areas (STAR), begun in 1993

The Road Traffic Reduction Act of 1997

Sustrans National Cycle Network

Addresses are given in the Sources of Information on the Website.

Between 1994 and 1996 the average number of car journeys per year per person in Britain was 631, and the average length of journey by car was 8.5 miles.

Before you begin

Here are some suggestions on how to assess the impact of the roads. Try them out and adapt them if you need to before beginning your investigation. Describe what you did in your final report.

1. The visual impact

a Take a photograph or make a field sketch at each site. Do your best to take all of your photographs in the same weather conditions. If the weather is very changeable explain this in the ***evaluation*** section of your final report.

b Devise a questionnaire along the lines of the one on page 152 and then interview people (see pages 20–22 of Section 2) to gain their opinion on the effects of the road.

2. Traffic noise

There is more noise around us all the time than we realise. Some people have more acute hearing than others because we are all good at ignoring the noises we do not want to hear. Here are some ways of assessing noise. Try them out and choose the one you think best.

a Record the traffic noise with a sound meter. Describe the recordings by looking at a scale along the lines of the one given below.

b Use a portable tape recorder to make a recording of the traffic noise at each site. As you try this out you will probably realise the importance of being able to pick out the traffic noise from other sounds. At home or back at school, assess the noise level by comparing it with a scale such as the one given below.

c Prepare a tape with the recordings of different noise levels to make your own noise scale. Take this with you when you do your fieldwork and compare the level of traffic noise with your recordings. You may have done something like this in Science lessons, but, in your final report describe how you made your own noise scale and why. Use the one below for guidance.

It is interesting to record the noise made by different types of vehicle, but this is more difficult to do. Look at the maximum noise levels allowed in Australia and Switzerland in the box below.

A scale of noise:

Noise	Approximate decibel level	Description
Rustling leaves	10	Very faint
The ticking of a watch at 1 m from the ear	30	Faint
Normal conversation	60	Moderate
Emergency vehicle or a sports car travelling quickly	90	Loud
Pneumatic drill	95	Very loud
Rock band using amplifiers	110	Extremely loud
Jet aeroplane taking off at an airport	140	Deafening

The threshold of pain to the human ear is usually taken to be 120 dB.

Maximum noise levels allowed in vehicle tests in Australia are as follows:

Motor cars:	**90 dB (A)**
Motor cycles:	**94 dB (A)**
Diesel lorries and buses:	**99 dB (A)**

Tests are carried out when a vehicle is stationary, either in the street or in a test centre.

(Source: Organisation for Economic Cooperation and Development (1991) *The State of the Environment.*)

The maximum basic noise levels from main roads allowed by law in Switzerland are as follows:

by day	**79 dB (A)**
by night	**60 dB (A)**

3. Emissions

Emissions of gases, solid particles and light at night have to be measured with specialised equipment. Your school may have instruments for measuring levels of carbon monoxide in the atmosphere.

a. At each site record whether you can smell exhaust fumes strongly, slightly or not at all. Ask others whether they too can smell exhaust fumes and also whether on a sunny day they can see an exhaust haze. Adapt the questionnaire in Figure 136.

b. Cover square ceramic kitchen tiles 10 cm × 10 cm in size with transparent sticky-backed plastic with the sticky side up. Leave these outside for two or three days and then examine them under a microscope. Carbon and other solid particles will stick to them and they provide good evidence of ***pollution***. However, all of the solid particles may not be from the traffic. You will have to find sites where you can leave your tiles safely.

c. Look for lichens as these are indicators of pollution. Different species of lichen have particular tolerance levels: *Lecanora* (on tree bark) and *Xanthoria* (on stone) are the most tolerant of a polluted atmosphere, whereas *Evernia* and *Usnea* are the least tolerant. The size of the lichen is less important than the species, but you can watch them increase in size over the months and years. This has been happening in a lot of large cities in recent years in spite of the gloom of some news reports. Identify the lichens you find by comparing them with the chart on page 40.

Your results can be compared with those of a national survey of Britain carried out by schools in 1974. These results form a database which is kept and updated by the Department of the Environment at their laboratory in Abingdon. The address is given in the Sources of Information on the Website. By comparing your results with those of 1974, you will

Figure 136 Questionnaire to be used when investigating the impacts of a road or railway.

SCHOOL NAME:

Location of interview: .... Date: ....

Grid reference of location: ....

As part of a geography fieldwork project into the effects of the road (name it) upon this area, I should be very grateful if you would answer a few short questions.

1. Which of the following do you think best describes the appearance of the road within the area from here?

(If it is completely hidden from view then don't ask this question!)

(a) It can be clearly seen and it spoils the view/is ugly ☐

(b) It can be clearly seen but I don't mind ☐

(c) It is unsightly and I wish it was not there ☐

(d) It is unsightly but it is far enough away for me not to be bothered by it ☐

(e) It is hardly noticeable ☐

If the answer is (a), could you suggest any ways in which it could be improved such as screening it with spring-flowering trees or evergreen trees?

....

....

....

2. Do the street lights or the lights of the vehicles spoil the area at night? Yes/No/Don't know

3. About the appearance of the road itself:

Do you feel that any of the following are unsightly? Please answer 'Yes' or 'No'.

(a) street lights: design of the lamp standards, material they are made from and how they are coloured Yes/No

(b) overhead wires, if any, as needed for trams and light rail transit systems Yes/No

(c) road signs and markings on the road Yes/No

(d) kerbstones Yes/No

(e) bridges, if any Yes/No

(f) noise barriers or safety barriers if present Yes/No

Could you suggest any ways in which the appearance of the road could be improved so that it would spoil the area less?

....

....

....

4. How much do you notice the background noise of the traffic from the road?

By day ....

By night, if the interviewee lives here ....

Try to avoid recording answers such as 'It depends . . .'.

5. At this distance from the road/railway are you troubled by:

(a) exhaust fumes? ....

(b) dust? ....

Remember to thank the person whom you have interviewed.

be able to discover whether the level of atmospheric pollution has increased or decreased. The 1974 data must be referred to as ***secondary data*** and the source given in your final report.

It is important to try out these methods two or three times before beginning your fieldwork so that you can iron out any difficulties. Include a description of these in your final report; they are part of your project.

In some areas lichens grow on only two days a year and in other areas may remain dormant for years.

You will need the following equipment:

- Ordnance Survey map of scale 1:10,000 (Landplan Series). On this scale of map the widths of roads and pavements are drawn to scale and can easily be measured.
- Field sketching equipment. See page 12.
- A camera, if you intend to take photographs of the route from different distances.
- Copies of your questionnaire. You will need about three for each transect, but the exact number will depend on the type of area in which you are working. Take a few spare copies.
- Noise-assessment equipment.
- Sticky tiles to leave out for measuring solid particles in the atmosphere.
- Specialised equipment for measuring air pollution if you have it.
- Take along a copy of the chart for identifying lichens (see page 40). If Usnea and Evernia are present in your fieldwork area, it is unlikely that traffic pollution is a problem.
- Fieldwork recording sheet (see Figure 137), one copy for each investigation site and a few spare copies.

Fieldwork method

1. Draw your lines of ***transect*** on your base-map at right angles to your chosen roads and on both sides of each to a distance of up to 1 km.
2. Choose your investigation sites as a ***systematic sample*** (see page 16). Decide on the interval for investigation of sites along the transects away from the road: every 100 or 250 m. Maps of scale 1:10,000 or 1:25,000 show every building, field boundary, right of way and road junction.

   Choose the exact sites for your investigations as close to your chosen points on the transects as possible. For those which are clearly on private land, write to the person in charge for permission to visit (see pages 18–20). Similarly, if you intend to leave sticky tiles in place for two or three days, ask permission to do so. People are usually very willing to help when they know that it is important to you.
3. Carry out a traffic survey on your chosen roads during peak flow and low flow. Choose carefully the days for your survey so that you will have evidence of the maximum impact of traffic flow upon the area. The method for carrying out a traffic survey is given on pages 58–59 of Section 2.
4. At each investigation site carry out the following procedures and record the results on your fieldwork recording sheet.
   - (i) First, record the weather conditions at the time of your fieldwork. Wind can carry both sound and emissions from traffic, so make a note of the direction from which the wind is blowing and its speed. Hints on how to do this are given on pages 34–35 of Section 2.
   - (ii) Complete a questionnaire yourself, giving your first impressions.
   - (iii) Interview up to a total of five people per transect. If possible, choose people from different age groups.
   - (iv) Take a photograph or make a field sketch (see pages 11–14 of Section 2). Make a note of the photograph number or the site from which you made the sketch.
   - (v) Assess the level of traffic noise. Do your best to make sure that the noise you measure is that of the traffic on your chosen road. Record it.
   - (vi) Put the sticky tiles in as open a place as possible where they are most likely to catch the solid particles yet be safe. They must not be in anybody's way.
   - (vii) Look for the presence of lichens, and identify them by comparing them with the chart. Record the types that you find. Carry out any specialised methods of monitoring gases present in the air.

Anticyclones and ridges of high pressure, which bring spells of settled weather with clear skies and sunshine, increase air pollution and the effects of exhaust fumes, particularly in valleys.

Fieldwork recording sheet

Name of investigation site: ....

Date: ....

Grid reference of the site: ....

Time: ....

Weather conditions

Wind direction (from which it is blowing): ....

Wind speed: ....

Other weather conditions:

....

....

Look at the barometer in school or at home, or find the atmospheric pressure from a weather map in a newspaper or on television.

Atmospheric pressure: .... millibars

Visual appearance and **level of traffic noise** of the road used. Both of these are recorded on the questionnaire sheets. **Clip them on to this recording sheet.**

Air Pollution Results

Lichen species present: ....

Solid particles on sticky tiles. After 2 or 3 days, collect them and use a microscope to discover what has stuck to the sticky side.

Estimate the percentage covered by particles and record this here: .... % covered.

Make a note of the length of time the tile was left out in the open: ....

Sources of secondary data

- The Highways Department of your local authority may have carried out investigations into traffic flow and noise levels along roads of a similar type to your roads. The results of such surveys are available to the public, so make a polite enquiry explaining why you would like the data (see pages 18–20). Before using it, look very carefully at the map to compare the Highway Department's results with your own. Look at the ***relief*** in particular. Estimate how closely the official area compares with your own
- The Highways Department will also tell you whether there are any plans to improve the appearance of the road in ways such as installing noise barriers or screening with trees within the near future.
- The Environmental Health Department of your local authority will give you the results of air quality testing at their monitoring stations. Make sure you find out exactly where the monitoring station is located. Write, explaining exactly what information you want – carbon monoxide, sulphur dioxide, oxides of nitrogen and solid particle collections – with dates. Explain that you need them for your project. (Pages 18–20 of Section 2 suggest how to write a letter to ask for information.) Compare the area in which the official monitoring station is located with your fieldwork area.
- The laboratory of the Department of the Environment, Transport and the Regions is situated in Abingdon. Information is available for different parts of the country. The address is given in the Sources of Information on the Website, as are addresses of other organisations from whom you could obtain help.
- The Countryside Commission (see the Sources of Information on the Website) has a range of publications, some of which are free.

Analysing and interpreting your data

The results of the interviews may be combined with your interpretation of the following:

- sketches and/or photographs
- investigations into traffic noise
- investigations into the emissions of gases/fumes, solid particles

As the number of replies that you have received may vary according to the question, you may decide to show the reply to each as a percentage. This will make them easy to compare. However, try it out first to decide whether it distorts the results of what may already be a small size of sample. Give your views in your final report.

1. Description of the area

Write a description of your area and explain why you chose to investigate the impact of those particular roads. How did you select your transects and the sample sites along them?

2. Map to show the roads, transects and sites investigated

Make a tracing or take a photocopy of your base-map of scale 1:10,000. Tracing is preferable because it will enable you to show only the details that are important to your project. Annotate it to give details such as the number of traffic lanes.

Add your lines of transect and the sites at which you carried out your investigations. Mark on your map the locations where you carried out your traffic surveys. The results of these should be illustrated as flow lines (see page 81).

3. Analysing the results of the interviews

When analysing the responses to your questionnaire, take the questions one at a time.

Question 1

Add up the total number of replies given for descriptions (a)–(e) in Question 1. Illustrate your results as bar charts (see pages 72–93). Write a paragraph to interpret what the bar charts show. Do you personally agree with the views of the people whom you interviewed? If not, suggest why not: perhaps they lived in the area and you were a visitor.

For all of the people who answered (a) to Question 1, make a list of all of their suggestions on ways of making the road less unsightly. Could you put the suggestions into groups?

Do you think your sample size of interviewees was big enough (see page 15)? Do you feel that your suggestions of screening the road with different types of trees may have influenced people's answers? Do you think it is a good idea to give suggestions when interviewing people?

Question 2

Draw a pie chart (see pages 79–80) to illustrate the number of people who felt that the street lighting spoilt the area, those who did not and those who didn't know. Describe what your results show. ***Evaluate*** the question according to the number of people who were unable to answer. Do you feel your results are valid?

Use the suggestions you received on reducing the unsightliness of the road, and people's views on the effects of light at night, as the basis for a short report. This could include recommendations on the impact of the road on the appearance and character of the area.

Question 3

Draw bar charts of the 'Yes' replies and the 'No' replies. Make a list of the suggestions given for improving the appearance of the road. Group these into categories if possible. Describe what your results show, including the recommendations.

Questions 4 and 5

Look through the answers you received and then award number values of 1–3 or 1–5 to them: 'Not much' could be '1' whereas 'It's bad sometimes' you may judge to be '3'. Treat a 'No' answer to Question 5 as '0'. Add up the total values for each answer. The higher the total, the greater the nuisance value. Write the total as a fraction or as a percentage (see page 86) of the total possible nuisance value, in answer to each question.

Illustrate your answers as bar charts or proportional circles or squares (see pages 72–73 and 82). Describe in your own words how you have awarded value numbers, giving two or three examples.

4. Small-scale map illustrated by annotated field sketches or photographs

Draw a ***sketch map*** of your fieldwork area, about the size of scale 1:25,000. You have studied geography for a long time so have confidence in your own ability to draw sketch maps. Place it in the middle of the page and put the sketches or photographs around it, locating each to its place on the map with an arrow rather like desire-lines.

Your investigation was into the impact of the road on the area in terms of appearance, noise and pollution. ***Annotate*** your pictures to emphasise anything in them that relates to these three kinds of impact.

5. Choropleth map of the impact of traffic noise from the road on the surrounding area

Make a list of the noise values recorded during your fieldwork. If you used a scale of your own then award a number value according to the loudness of the noise. The biggest number will indicate the loudest noise. Explain in your final report how you awarded the values. ***Rank*** the values to indicate the range and then divide them into three groups: high, moderate and low traffic noise.

Use another copy of your map of scale 1:10,000 to indicate the level of traffic noise at each of your investigation sites. Draw a line to join the sites at which the noise level was 'high', another to join the sites at which it was 'moderate', and finally a third to show where it was 'low'. These lines will have become ***isopleths*** (see pages 64–5). Shade in different colours the areas between each pair of lines to make a ***choropleth map*** (see page 65). Remember to add a key to your map.

Add bar charts of your traffic flow at peak-flow and low-flow times as suggested in the Transport Extra Investigation on the Website. What was the state of the traffic flow when you assessed the noise level?

Use your map and the results from Question 4 of your questionnaire to describe the impact of traffic noise on your fieldwork area. Include any ***secondary data*** that you have received.

6. The road's impact on pollution

Results in the form of numbers such as measurements of carbon monoxide, and ones converted into value numbers, can be illustrated as bar charts, pie charts, line graphs or proportional circles. Choose the method that you feel illustrates them best. Choosing the right technique to use is a skill itself, and you should explain the reasons for your choice in your final report.

For all other results about pollution write a description of what you have discovered at each site. Include both the results obtained from answers to Question 5 of your questionnaire, and results obtained from secondary sources. Decide whether to include noise and artificial lights at night as forms of pollution. Descriptions written in good English are another valuable skill.

Drawing conclusions

Your aim at the outset was to investigate the impact of the road(s) and their traffic on the surrounding area from the following points of view:

- visual appearance
- traffic noise
- pollution

Summarise your conclusions on each of these in turn.

By this stage of your project you must have expert knowledge about the area. Give your own personal views on the extent to which the feel and character of the area are affected by the roads and traffic.

Evaluating your work

- Was your questionnaire satisfactory? For example: Do you think it is a good idea to give suggestions when interviewing people? Could your suggestions of screening the road with trees have influenced people's answers?
- What improvements to the questionnaire would you make?
- Did you interview enough people? Was the sample number of interviewees big enough?
- Noise and air pollution:
  - Did you investigate a large enough sample of sites?
  - If the weather during your fieldwork was windy or changeable, could it have distorted your results?
  - Was your method of assessing noise accurate enough for your project? How could it be improved?

Interesting extra ideas

1. If the road is a fairly recent development (motorways, bypasses, ring roads, and recently widened main roads in towns) it would be interesting to discover what the character of the area was like before. Go to the Local History section of your public library or contact the secretary of either the Local History Society or the Civic Society.
2. Certain types of noise can be irritating to people and add to levels of stress. Compare your findings with those allowed by law in Switzerland (see page 151).
3. If the predicted growth in motor traffic over the next 10 or 20 years were to materialise, consider what the road's impact would be then. Would you suggest any alterations?
   - New designs for street lights in town centres which would complement, rather than clash with the light from shop windows?
   - Prevent on-street car parking in both rural and urban areas?
   - Build more bicycle lanes and plan for secure bicycle lock-up 'garages'/'cycle and ride'?
   - Encourage through-ticketing between different forms of public transport such as bus, train and tram within local authority areas?
   - Implement park-and-ride in your fieldwork area?
   - Encourage at-home shopping via the Internet?
   - Introduce quieter and less polluting forms of transport such as electrically powered cars?
   - Charge motorists for driving into town centres, or form car clubs for commuters.

The list is seemingly endless. Decide which two ways you consider would most help the situation in your fieldwork area and find out more about them. Describe the advantages and disadvantages of each.

Coasts

Most people like being at the seaside. If the weather is good it is a lovely environment for someone doing a fieldwork project. Great Britain and Northern Ireland alone have 16,895 km of coastline. This includes a great variety of coastal scenery and provides many possibilities for projects.

Make a list of the ways in which coasts are used. It could include everything from seaside resorts to container ports, and from lighthouses to bird sanctuaries. Over the centuries we have possibly done more to alter the coastline to meet our needs than any other natural environment. Throughout history, schemes for the improvement and protection of the coastline have been well documented. These records, together with maps, would make a good coursework project.

Figure 137 Coasts are used in many different ways

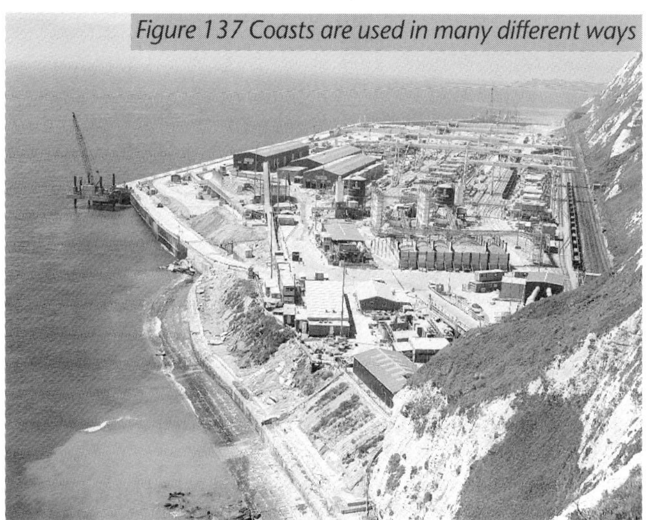

This chapter is divided into three parts, and these are intended to give guidance on different aspects of coasts and ways in which they would make successful projects:

- The Trial Run concentrates on ***inter-relationships*** between sand, slope, vegetation and soil in an area of sand dunes. It is an ***ecosystem*** study. *A project along similar lines would be a good link with Science, and with Biology in particular.*
- The Short Project looks at the differences in the shore above and below the high tide mark.
- The Investigation tells you have to investigate materials on the beach, and could include surveying the profiles of the beach and a cliff-line. Surveying techniques are described on pages 24–27 of Section 2.
- The Extra Investigation on the Website looks at the ways in which we use and try to manage the coast.

Read through the list of Project Suggestions and pick out the one that you think best suits you and your area.

Project suggestions

1. Investigate in detail a ***transect*** of the shore from low tide level up to the land. Record both the physical features and those made by people. This project could be extended to include a survey of the cliffs, sand dunes, sea wall or other coastal defences beyond the backshore. For a detailed guide on how to do this follow the Investigation.

   Where to find help:

   Coasts Investigation, 170–176

   Coasts Short Project, 166–169

   Laying a line of transect, 14

   Coastal defences – Coasts Extra Investigation, Website

2. Are pebbles of a particular size and shape related to their position on the profile of a storm beach/storm ridge (see Figure 138)?

   Expectations of the inter-relationships between pebble size and shape and the profile could be worded as hypotheses:

Figure 138 Profile through a storm ridge.

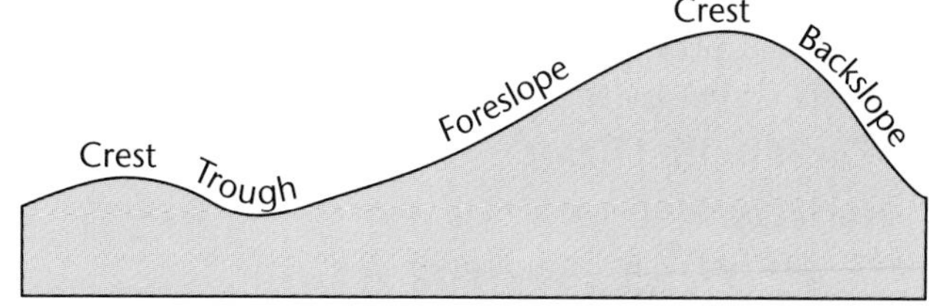

   a 'That large flat pebbles accumulate on the crest and on the backslope, where some may be angular as a result of being thrown by the waves.'

   b 'That large rounded pebbles occur on the foreslope.'

   c 'That pebbles of all shapes and sizes are found in the trough.'

   Where to find help:

   How to measure pebbles, 55–6 and 172–3

   How to survey a slope, 24–27

3. What are the colours, shapes and sizes of beach materials along transects in a bay? Where have they come from?

   Where to find help:

   Where the beach materials may have come from, 175

   How to identify rocks, 41–2

   Secondary sources – Geological maps and guides, Appendix 2 and Website

4. Are there more pebbles on the beach near to the sea than on the back of the beach near to the land? Instead of taking a transect from low tide level to the land, lay lines of transect parallel to the sea: close to the sea, close to the land, and any in between if you have time. Use small quadrats whose sides are 25 cm in length. Work along your transect and choose an appropriate size of systematic ***sample*** interval such as 5 m or 10 m. At each sample point, count the number of pebbles in the quadrat, and investigate them further along the lines explained in the Investigation.

   Where to find help:

   How to measure pebbles, 55–6, 172–3

5. **a** How does ***longshore drift*** move pebbles along a straight stretch of coastline or along a spit or bar?

   b Discover the relationship between the direction from which the waves approach the shore and the direction and speed of the wind. This would involve returning to the area in different weather conditions to observe the waves and measure the wind (see pages 34–5 and 54).

   A project along similar lines could be carried out in a bay. You would relate the movement of pebbles to the refraction (bending of approach) of the waves by the depth of water in the bay.

   Where to find help:

   Measuring the movement of material by longshore drift, 54–55

6. **a** How do ***groynes*** affect a beach?

   b What effects do they have further along the coastline?

   Use both fieldwork (see the Coasts Extra Investigation on the Website) and ***secondary data*** for this investigation.

   Where to find help:

   Coasts Extra Investigation, Website

   Planning and Engineering Department of your local authority, 18–20

7. For a project on a cliffed coastline, carry out all or some of the following investigations:

   a Measure the height of the cliffs.

   b Make a field sketch of the cliff face to identify and ***annotate*** features such as:

   joints

   bedding planes

   an estimate of the width of beds in sedimentary rock

   the wave-cut notch

   caves, arches and other features

   c Investigate the foot of the cliff. Look for the wave-cut notch. If the sea reaches it then erosion of the cliffs will be continuing. On the other hand, if the beach comes right up to it, erosion will probably have ended on this part of the cliffs.

   Look for evidence of a splash zone. Orange-coloured seaweed on the cliff face is the main clue. What is the height of the splash zone? Feel the surface of the cliff face at the splash zone. Is it rougher or smoother than it is above the splash zone?

   Are there angular fragments of rock at the cliff foot? What processes will have led to their accumulation here?

   d Measure the slope of the wave-cut platform towards the sea.

   e Are the cliffs protected by a sea wall or by gabions and other revetments? How effective do they seem to be?

   Where to find help:

   How to measure the heights of cliffs, 173–4

   How to make a field sketch, 11–13

BE CAREFUL! Cliffs can be particularly dangerous. Never attempt to climb the cliff face and beware of the possibility of falling rocks. Make sure that you are not likely to be cut off when the tide comes in.

Before you begin

It is important to be sure of exactly what the various terms relating to coastlines mean.

- The coast is simply where the sea meets the land.
- The coastline is the coast as shown on a map or aerial photograph. Both of these enable you to pick out the bays, headlands, straight stretches and so on.
- The shore is the land bordering the sea. This can be divided into two parts, as shown in Figure 139. Work out what the foreshore and the backshore

Figure 139 *The two parts of the shore.*

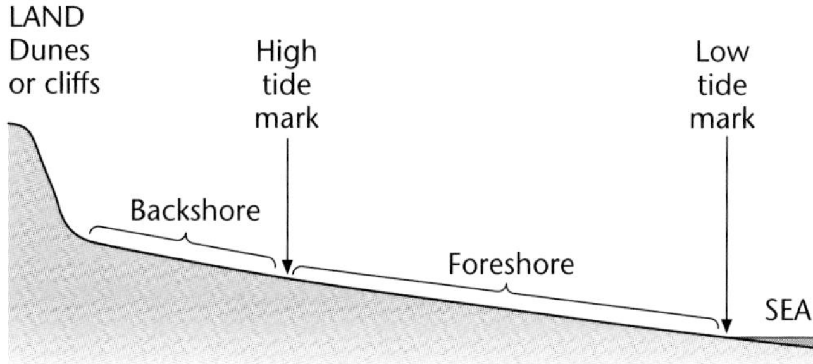

are and then describe them for the Introduction to your final report.

- The beach is made up of any loose rock fragments of various sizes which have accumulated on top of solid rock. We tend to talk about pebble beaches, shingle beaches and sandy beaches according to the main size of beach materials. See page 56 of Section 2 for the exact sizes of particles.

On the foreshore there may be a variety of landforms and it is important to be able to recognise them when you see them. The main ones are listed below. Look them up in a geography textbook or in a geographical dictionary. It may help to write them in your field notebook as a glossary of terms. See page 203 to see how a glossary is organised.

berm	cave
storm beach/storm ridge	blow-hole
wave-cut platform	arch
wave-cut notch	stack

Landforms at the coast are affected not only by the waves, and the height of the tide, but also by the wind. It transports fine particles. When the wind speed falls the particles are deposited and become part of the beach materials. They may even build up into sand dunes. Rock surfaces affected by wind erosion can become fluted by its abrasive action.

Waves are generated by the wind. The length of open sea over which the wind blows is termed the 'fetch'. The longer the fetch, the more powerful the waves. Some geographers refer to areas and times of powerful waves as high energy environments.

When storm waves reach the coast of north-west Scotland they break with a force equal to 2 tonnes/cm^2.

Stormy weather in winter contributes to high energy conditions, while anticyclones with gentle winds produce lower energy conditions. If you visit the same beach after different conditions or in different seasons you may well see alterations to the landforms. **Constructive waves** and **destructive waves** are explained on page 54 of Section 2.

CAUTION: Beaches and coasts have many hidden dangers. Always check the times of the tides, as given in a local tide table. Three people working together must be the minimum: if someone is in danger one person must run for help immediately and the third remain. Always inform a responsible person – a parent or teacher – exactly where you are going and exactly what time you will leave the beach. Stick rigidly to the place and time.

Fieldwork area

Concentrate on a small area such as a bay, or one or more transects along a straight stretch of coast. Most fieldwork investigations on coasts have to rely on ***transects*** (see page 14).

Your own safety cannot be stressed too greatly: it is far more important than any geography project.

Before deciding on a fieldwork area you must make sure of two things:

1. Access to and from the beach must be safe and easy. The Ordnance Survey maps of scale 1:25,000 and bigger will help you to find shores which appear to be accessible. Go along and check though. Remember that if you have to cross private land you must write a letter to request permission (see page 18–20).
2. The time and height of the tides will allow you to work in safety. You will find tidal tables for the British Isles in *Brown's Nautical Almanac*, and for the British Isles, northern France, Belgium, the Netherlands and Germany in *The Macmillan Nautical Almanac*. The tides at most ports are also published in *Whitaker's Almanack*. The heights of high tide and low tide are given for every day of the year ahead. All of these almanacs are produced annually and are kept in the Reference section of public libraries. Plan your work carefully to fit in with the tides.

Coastguards are the 'police force of the coast' and their role is to safeguard life at sea. They are employed under the Admiralty. They are one of the emergency services for which the telephone number is 999.

Coasts Trial Run: Slope, vegetation and soil in an area of sand dunes. Are they linked?

FIELDWORK TECHNIQUES

The following techniques were used:

- Laying a line of transect
- Choosing sample sites for investigating plants, animals and soils
- Using a quadrat to measure the percentage of vegetation cover
- Measuring the infiltration rate

Before you begin

The location of Garlieston Bay

Garlieston Bay lies on the south coast of Galloway in south-western Scotland. The nearest town is Wigtown. Begin your project by copying from an atlas a ***sketch map*** of south-western Scotland to locate the general study area. Next, make a tracing of Garlieston Bay from Figure 140 to show the study area in detail.

Figure 140 Map to show the location of Garlieston Bay and the line of transect followed.

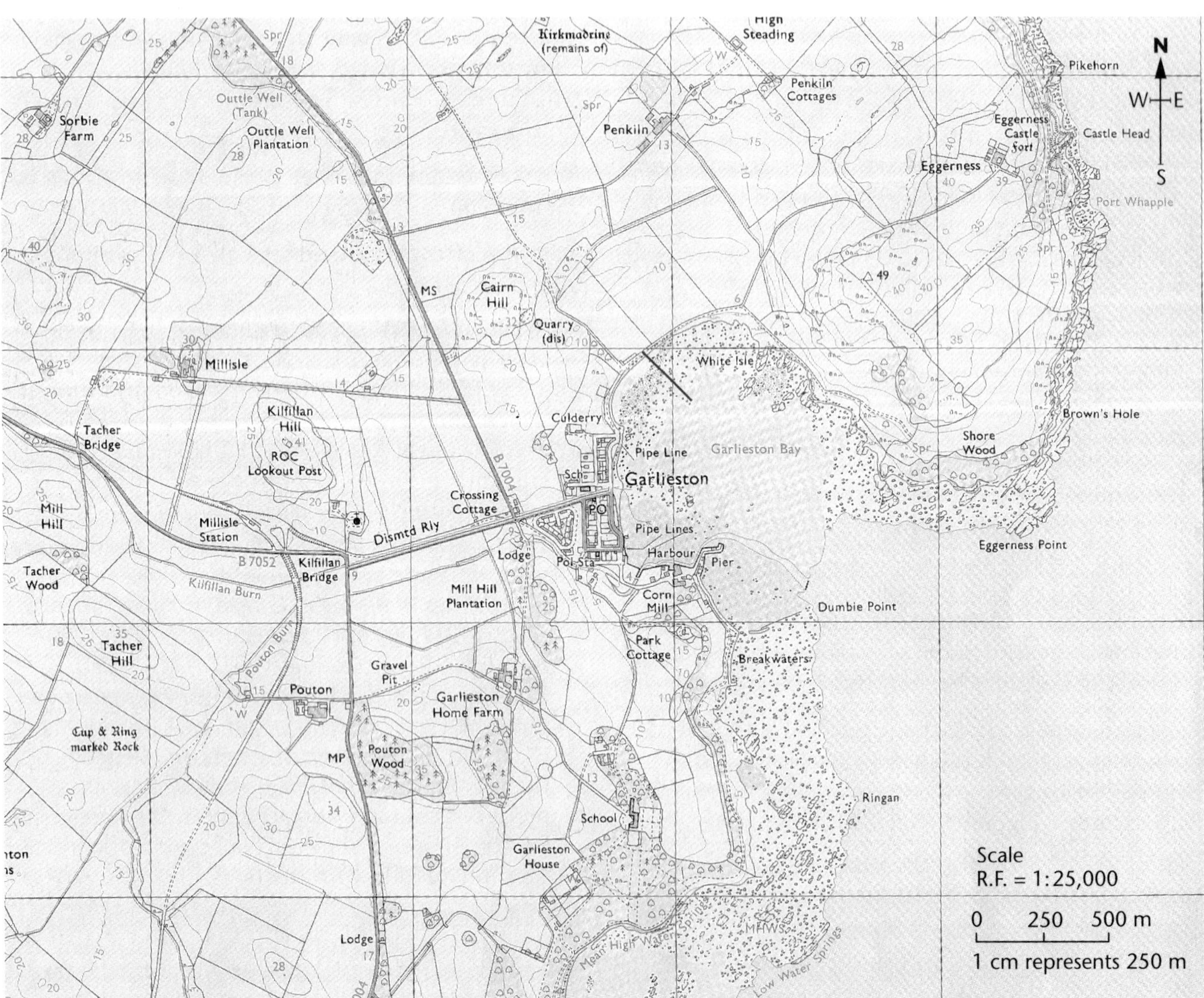

Figure 141 Coastal sand dunes with marram grass.

What are sand dunes?

This is how the Countryside Commission describes sand dunes:

> 'Sand dunes are beautiful and natural landscape features found in many areas along Britain's coastline. They are fragile habitats and host a rich variety of plant and animal life.
>
> Dunes first begin to form when windblown sand is trapped by strand line plants. As the plants grow, the sand accumulates and forms an 'embryo' dune. Eventually the build up of sand becomes too much for the plants. Sand is blown beyond the existing dune and starts to form a new dune behind.
>
> As the dune grows, sand is blown over the dune and onto its leeward side. All or part of the dune may move. Over time a series of parallel dunes may form (a dune series). The whole process can take thousands of years.'

Use a geography textbook to discover:

1. the kinds of coastal area where sand dunes are found
2. how a sand dune system develops

Explain these in your own words, drawing diagrams to help.

The sand dune ecosystem

The ***ecosystem*** develops in stages:

> Sand is the parent material.
>
> It is colonised by plants and becomes the home of animals which find shelter in them.
>
> The remains of plants and animals help to turn the sand into soil. It then becomes a habitat which is able to support more varied and sophisticated forms of plant and animal life.

The climate is also important in the development of an ecosystem. As the plant and animal life becomes more varied and the soil richer, the ***microclimate*** also changes. This project could be combined with weather recordings to investigate changes in the microclimate across a dune transect.

Find out more about the way in which ecosystems work and then write a few paragraphs to explain how a sand dune ecosystem develops. Try to suggest why the Countryside Commission describes the habitat of the sand dunes as 'fragile'. If this is not clear now, leave it until you have completed the Trial Run.

Tide marks on Ordnance Survey maps:

On the 1:50,000 scale: High water mark is a solid black line. Low water mark is the seaward edge of the blue shading.

On the 1:25,000 scale: High water mark is a thick black line labelled 'Mean High Water Springs'. Low water mark is a thinner black line labelled 'Mean Low Water Neaps'.

MHWS and MLWN are the average of the predicted heights of Spring and Neap tides respectively over a period of 18.6 years.

Aims

1. Does the height of the dune ridges decrease with distance from the sea?
2. Does the vegetation cover increase with distance from the sea?
3. Does soil become better developed with distance from the sea?
4. Are the dunes, vegetation and soil inter-related?

Decide whether 'distance from the sea' means the distance from the low water mark (low tide level) or from the high water mark (high tide level). Measure this on Figure 140 and write a sentence to explain your choice.

The usefulness of marram grass in trapping sand and stabilising dunes was recognised by Queen Elizabeth I. She made it a criminal offence to uproot it.

The following equipment was used:

- Washing line and compass to mark the line of transect.
- Pantometer to survey the angle of slope (see page 25).
- Quadrat, with sides 1 m in length, to assess the plant cover. Each side was drilled with holes at intervals of 10 cm. String was threaded between the holes to subdivide the quadrat into 100 smaller squares (see pages 14–15).
- To measure the infiltration rate:

  an infiltration can was made from a baked beans can with both ends removed and covered with sticking plaster for safety

  stopwatch or digital watch

  wooden mallet

  500-ml polythene container for carrying water from the sea.
- To measure the acidity of the soil:

  trowel

  small-range pH papers

  small carton of distilled water.
- Plant guidebook to identify plant species.

Fieldwork method

The fieldwork was carried out by four people and took one day in July 1997. The weather was warm and sunny and there had been no rain for two weeks beforehand.

The dunes at Garlieston Bay are 250 m wide but only the first 125 m were investigated. The fieldwork involved the following procedures:

1. First the line of transect was chosen at right angles to the sea. The compass was used to check this. The washing line was laid on the ground and weighted at both ends by a heavy stone brought from near the town.
2. The pantometer was used to measure the angle of slope in metre intervals all the way along the transect. Two people did this.
3. a The sites at which the vegetation and soil were to be investigated were chosen after the whole length of the ***transect*** had been viewed in a ***reconnaissance visit***. The sites chosen were the summit of each dune ridge and the slack (low ground) between the dune ridges. This was considered to form an accurate stratified sample (see page 18) of the highest and lowest ground.

   b At each investigation site the following procedures were followed:

   (i) The quadrat was used to assess and record the percentage of bare sand.

   (ii) The number of different plant species within the quadrat was counted. As many as possible were identified using a guidebook to plants.

   (iii) A trowelful of topsoil was wet with distilled water and a pH paper used to test the soil sample for acidity.

   (iv) The infiltration can was hammered to a quarter of its depth into the ground and quickly filled with 500 ml of water. The time taken for the water to infiltrate (disappear) into the soil was recorded in seconds. The water containers had to be topped up from the sea. It was important to use distilled water to test for acidity. Sea water would have affected the result.

   (v) Animals near to the investigation site were recorded.

Plants and animals were not harmed in any way.

Remember that it is a criminal offence to remove plants growing wild.

Results

To make this Trial Run of manageable size, some of the slope angle recordings have been left out and the results of only four vegetation and soil investigations are given.

Note that each number means 'degrees uphill' unless there is a minus sign before it, in which case it is the number of degrees downhill. The arrows indicate the site on the transect where vegetation, animal and soil recordings were made.

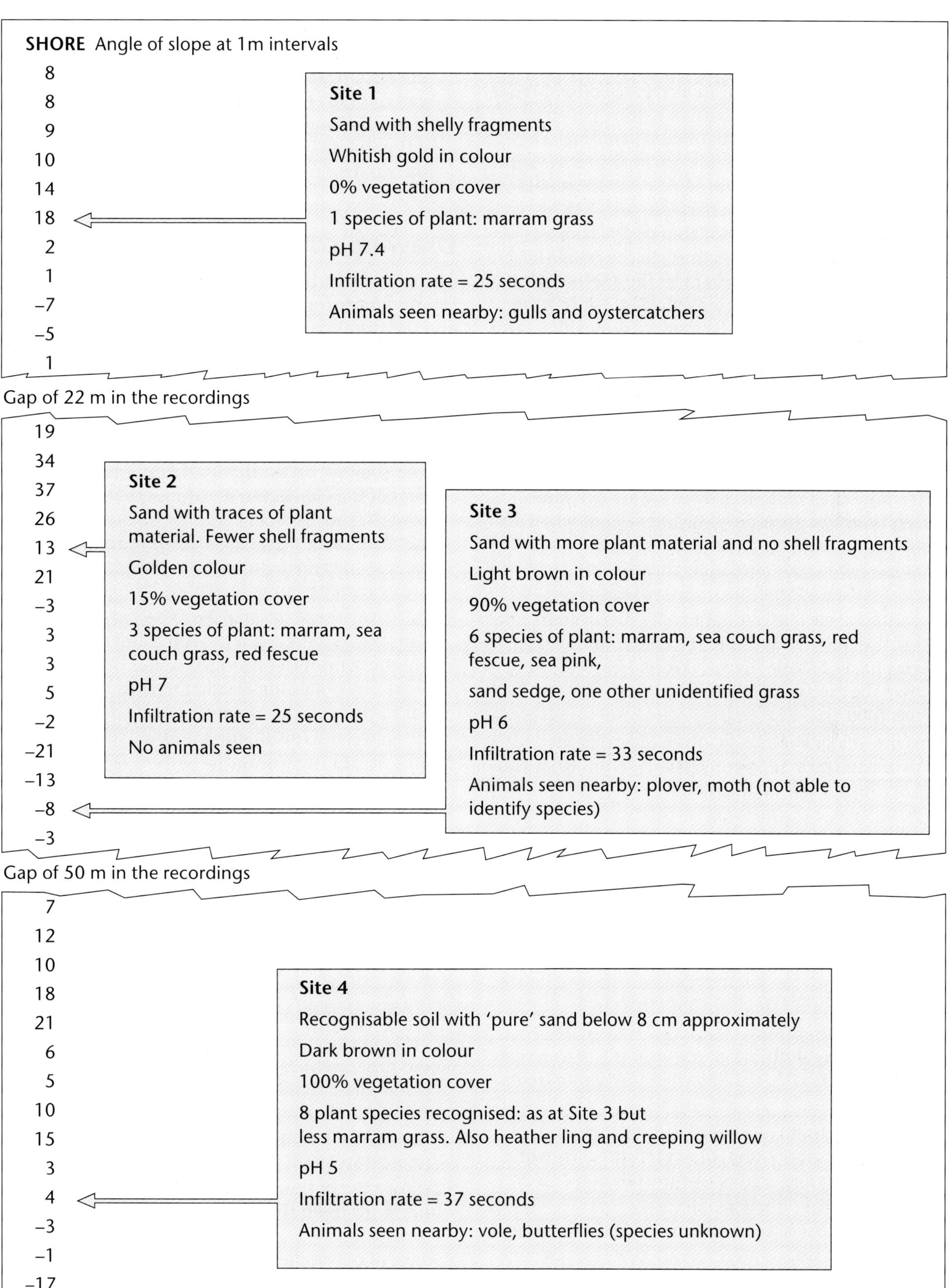
SHORE Angle of slope at 1m intervals
8
8
9
10
14
18
2
1
−7
−5
1
Site 1
Sand with shelly fragments
Whitish gold in colour
0% vegetation cover
1 species of plant: marram grass
pH 7.4
Infiltration rate = 25 seconds
Animals seen nearby: gulls and oystercatchers
Gap of 22 m in the recordings
19
34
37
26
13
21
−3
3
3
5
−2
−21
−13
−8
−3
Site 2
Sand with traces of plant material. Fewer shell fragments
Golden colour
15% vegetation cover
3 species of plant: marram, sea couch grass, red fescue
pH 7
Infiltration rate = 25 seconds
No animals seen
Site 3
Sand with more plant material and no shell fragments
Light brown in colour
90% vegetation cover
6 species of plant: marram, sea couch grass, red fescue, sea pink,
sand sedge, one other unidentified grass
pH 6
Infiltration rate = 33 seconds
Animals seen nearby: plover, moth (not able to identify species)
Gap of 50 m in the recordings
7
12
10
18
21
6
5
10
15
3
4
−3
−1
−17
Site 4
Recognisable soil with 'pure' sand below 8 cm approximately
Dark brown in colour
100% vegetation cover
8 plant species recognised: as at Site 3 but less marram grass. Also heather ling and creeping willow
pH 5
Infiltration rate = 37 seconds
Animals seen nearby: vole, butterflies (species unknown)

Analysing and interpreting your data

1. Draw a cross-section/profile of the transect through the sand dunes. Choose an interval, such as 1 cm on graph paper or the lines on writing paper, to represent 1 m (the length of each pantometer reading). When you reach a gap in recordings show this either as a zigzag line (⋁⋁⋁) as you would indicate a gap on a **bar chart** (see page 73), or as a dashed line. Write the horizontal scale above or below your profile. Work through the results in turn, using a protractor to draw the angles of slope. When your profile is complete add the following labels: 'embryo dunes', 'summit of dune ridge', and 'slack' (depression/low land) between each pair of dune ridges. Also mark the position of the four investigation sites.

   If your profile is big enough you could put the pie chart (see point 2 below) and other information above the investigation sites on your profile and indicate the exact place by using arrows. ***Inter-relationships*** are more easily picked out when all the information is presented together.
2. Draw a **pie chart** (see pages 79–80) to illustrate the percentage of vegetation cover and bare ground at each investigation site. Use colours on the pie charts to indicate the colour of the bare ground and shade the vegetation in green. Print over the green shading the number of species recorded.

   Write one or two paragraphs to describe the pattern shown by your pie charts. From what you have read about plant colonisation in an ecosystem, can you suggest whether (a) time or (b) distance from the sea is likely to be the more important influence on the amount of plant cover?
3. The infiltration rate at each site may be shown as an arrow around your pie chart. The length of the arrow will represent the time taken for the water to infiltrate into the ground. Devise a scale to do this, bearing in mind there are 360° in a circle.

   Draw a **scattergraph** (see page 77) to enable you to compare the infiltration rate with the percentage vegetation cover. Describe what the scattergraph shows.
4. Draw **bar charts** (see page 72–3) to show the number of species present at each site. Write one or two sentences to describe the relationship between the following:
   - **a** the number of species recorded and the distance from the sea,
   - **b** the number of species recorded and the percentage vegetation cover.
5. Draw a **scattergraph** (see page 78) to examine the relationship between the acidity of the soil and the percentage of plant cover. Describe what your scattergraph shows. Consider which of the other factors measured could have affected the acidity of the soil. Give your views on which you feel is likely to be the most important influence on soil acidity.

Drawing conclusions

The aim of this Trial Run was to investigate the inter-relationships between sand, slope, vegetation and soils along a dune transect at Garlieston Bay.

Begin to draw the three together in the following way:

1. Refer to what you have written about the formation of sand dunes in the Introduction to your final report on this Trial Run. Identify the parts of the Garlieston Bay dunes that are likely to be the most stable. Is this (a) because they are sheltered from winds blowing from the sea or (b) because they are being held in place by plants? Use evidence from your profile.

   The strongest winds may be expected to come from the sea. Suggest why. You could find out whether or not the strongest winds do come from the sea by obtaining weather records for Galloway from the Meteorological Office (see in the Sources of Information on the Website).
2. Give reasons why both the percentage vegetation cover and the variety of plants increase inland.
3. Sand is the parent material of this ecosystem. It is one of the most indestructible and chemically inert natural substances on the earth. Write one or more sentences to show how the vegetation has helped to develop the soil on the transect in each of the following ways:
   - **(i)** changes in colour
   - **(ii)** alterations to the acidity
   - **(iii)** alterations to the ***infiltration rate***
4. Find out the characteristics of the plant species and others which might be found in an area of sand dunes. Which plants do you think might be the next to begin growing at site 4? Find out more about colonisation and plant succession in an ecosystem.
5. Make a list of the animal species recorded. Find out more about the habitat in which each of them flourishes. What do they tell us about the stage of development reached by the sand dune ecosystem?

Evaluating your work

- Slope angles were measured at 1 m intervals along the first 125 m of the transect. If you had planned this field investigation would you have measured the angle at 2 m intervals across the whole width of the sand dune system? Give detailed reasons. What extra features might this have revealed about the dune ecosystem?
- At how many sample sites would you have investigated the vegetation and soils along the transect? Which method of sampling would you have used and why?
- The entrance to Garlieston Bay is to the south-east. Examine your map and consider how this affects the fetch (the distance of open water over which the wind blows, in turn, generating waves). Briefly explain whether you feel it would be necessary for this project to discover more about the wind direction and speed. How would you go about it if this really was your project? (Hints: fieldwork, secondary sources.)
- If you had been carrying out the fieldwork for this investigation would you have collected samples of soil and taken them home or to school for further analysis? What further tests would you have applied? (Hints: organic matter, tests for the presence of sodium chloride.)

Interesting extra ideas

You have been asked to write a report on turning the dunes into a useful area. Consider two of the following possible uses:

1. Creating a nature reserve. How would you encourage birds, insects and mammals to come to the area? How would you develop the habitats for them?
2. Planting coniferous trees. A very big and successful example of such a scheme is in the Landes region, south of Bordeaux in France, and there are many smaller-scale schemes in Britain. How would the trees affect the area? How do you think the people of Garlieston would feel? Consider the different views you might receive. Would farmers welcome protection from sand blowing onto their land?
3. Developing the area for tourism. Describe the facilities that would be needed. In what ways might Garlieston Bay be affected? What views would the people of Garlieston and the surrounding area be likely to hold?

Coasts Short Project: What differences are there in the shore above the high tide mark and below it?

Another title which means the same thing is 'How is the backshore near the high tide mark different from the foreshore?' Figure 139 on page 159 shows the backshore and foreshore areas.

Fieldwork area

Use the Ordnance Survey map of scale 1:25,000 to find a beach which is wider than 30 metres and which can be reached easily by a road or a footpath. Ask your teacher whether it is a safe place for your fieldwork. The high water mark and the low water mark are shown on OS maps. Their meaning is explained in the box on page 161. Look at the key to the map to see how they are shown.

Before you begin

1. Find out from a geography textbook what these terms mean: 'wave-cut platform', 'beach'. Describe in your own words how each develops. Diagrams with labels will help.
2. Find out as much as you can about the ways in which the area above high tide is likely to be different from the area below high tide level. Draw a diagram such as Figure 139 on page 159 and label it. Include this in your final report. Figure 144 on page 171 will help.
3. Make a quick visit to the shore when the tide is out to see what features you may find. This is called making a ***reconnaissance visit***. You will know from the map whether your shore has a beach or a wave-cut platform, but check on what these features look like.
4. For the introduction to your final report draw a ***sketch map*** of your fieldwork area. Include about 1 kilometre of coastline on both sides of your area. Show as much detail as you can using symbols and colours for such features as cliffs, dunes, wave-cut platform, high tide mark, low tide mark, and roads and paths leading to 'the part of the shore' which you will investigate.
5. The shore is affected by the waves and the geology of the area. Find out as much as you can about:
   - (a) Waves
     - how are they formed?
     - when and why do some waves help to build beaches?
     - how do waves transport beach material?
     - what is ***longshore drift?*** Is there longshore drift in your area?
   - (b) Geology
     - what type of rock is your coast made up of?
     - if there is sedimentary rock, in which way do the ***beds*** dip?
     - use a guide book of the area or books on the geology of the area

6. Discover the time of the high tide. You could use tide tables in one of the almanacs listed on page 159 and in Appendix 2 but check with a responsible person. The best time for your fieldwork would be as soon as possible after high tide. The areas below high tide level – the foreshore – will be wet and you will have time available before the tide starts to come back in again. Check exactly how long you will have.

Coasts can be very dangerous areas. You should always work with two other people so that if someone is in danger, one person can run for help immediately while the other person stays put. Always tell a teacher and/or your parents exactly where you are going, when and for how long. Never attempt to climb cliffs.

You will need the following equipment:

- Stopwatch, digital watch or watch with a second hand.
- Washing line and something heavy to weight it at both ends.
- Trowel
- Containers for collecting beach materials, with labels, preferably waterproof ones.
- Metre rules
- Tape measure
- 1 metre square quadrat. How to make one is explained on page 14.
- Make a guide to pebble shape – see page 136.
- Wide clear sticky tape

Fieldwork method

1. Pick out the line of debris left by the last high tide. It will probably still be wet from being deposited by the sea.
2. Three times during your fieldwork, time the numbers of waves which break on the shore in 1 minute.
3. At right angles to the high tide mark lay your washing line an equal length on both sides. Measure it and write the length down in your field notebook. This will be your line of transect.
4. At regular intervals, such as every 3 metres along your ***transect***, put down the quadrat beside it. These will be your ***sample*** points. Write on your map or in your field notebook the distance along the washing line between the sample points. Number the sample points (quadrats) 1, 2, 3 etc., upwards away from the sea.
5. (a) In each quadrat pick out the three biggest pebbles and a trowelful of fine material such as sand. Put them into containers. Label them with the number of the sample quadrat. Measure the pebbles during your fieldwork if you have time. Follow instruction '2' in Analysing Your Data. If not, take them home or back to school.

   (b) Write down anything else that you find in the quadrat such as seaweed, shells, corks, bottles and so on.

6. At the high tide line itself lay two or even three metre rules along it. Write down in order all the materials you find along the metre rules.
7. Make a note of rippled sand, rock pools, beach ridges and other interesting features on either side of your transect.

Analysing and interpreting your data

1. Draw to scale two parallel lines to represent the length of your fieldwork transect. A scale of 1 centimetre represents 1 metre would fit well on a page of your final report. Mark on it the position of each of your sample points (where you put down your quadrat), and the high tide mark. Number your sample points. Look at Figure 9a on page 16 and Figure 144 on page 171 for ideas.
2. For the largest pebbles in each quadrat:
   - (a) Measure the longest axis
   - (b) Measure the shortest axis
   - (c) Describe the shape. See page 55 and Figure 128 on page 136 for help.
   - (d) Write down all of these beside the appropriate quadrat number on the scale diagram of your transect
   - (e)
     - Are the pebbles bigger or smaller or the same size on the foreshore below high tide mark, and on the backshore above high tide mark?
     - Are the pebbles more rounded above the high tide mark?
   - (f) To analyse further the size of your pebbles:
     - (i) Draw scattergraphs, one for the backshore above the high tide mark, and the other for the foreshore below the tide mark. How to draw a scattergraph is given on pages 76–78, but look at Figure 142 and plot the lengths of the pebble axes as shown.
     - (ii) To represent the shape of the pebbles either make up a key as in Figure 142 or use crosses in different colours.

Figure 142 Scattergraph to show the size and shape of pebbles on the foreshore

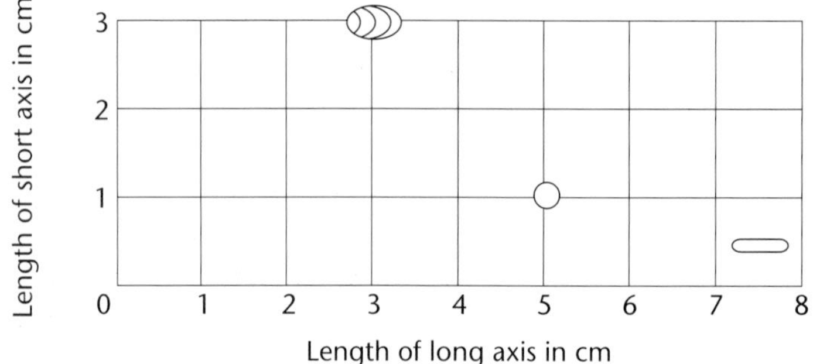

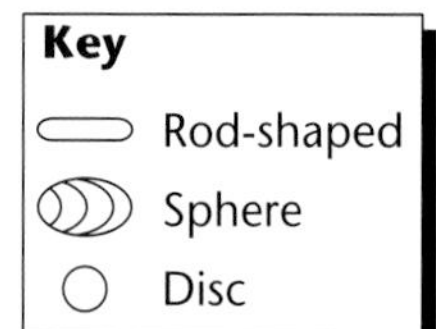

3. (a) Sprinkle a small amount of each sample of fine material - about a teaspoonful - onto the sticky tape. Put each sample beside the place on the scale diagram of your transect. Is there any difference in size or colour between the samples?
   (b) The size of small particles may be measured by putting both a ruler and the particles together and looking at them through a magnifying glass or by sieving. See pages 55 and 56.
4. Describe the materials found on the high tide mark itself.
5. Add together the three results of your timing of the waves. Divide the total by three to find the average per minute.

Drawing conclusions

Write one or two paragraphs to describe your results under these headings:

The shore below high tide mark/the foreshore

The shore above high tide mark/the backshore

1. Describe the following:
   (a) all the features you observed on the shore during your fieldwork
   (b) the size of the pebbles
   (c) the shape of the pebbles
   (d) the colour and size of fine materials
   (e) the appearance of the high tide mark
2. Were the waves beach-building or non-beach building on the day of your fieldwork? See page 54. Are your results confirmed by the shape of the beach or by the fact that there is very little beach at all at your fieldwork site?

Evaluating your work

1. Did you put down enough quadrats to be representative of the whole transect or were some features missed out? Name or describe such features. You can read more about sampling methods on pages 16–18.
2. Should you have collected more than three pebbles from each quadrat? Should they have been picked from a particular part of the quadrat such as the top right hand corner rather than by deliberately choosing the three biggest pebbles?

Interesting extra ideas

- Find out what the fetch of the wind is (see page 165). From which direction must the wind blow to gain the maximum fetch? What was the wind direction on the day of your fieldwork? Would it influence the number of waves (wave ***frequency***) per minute?
- Go back to your fieldwork area with a clinometer or pantometer to measure the angle of slope of the shore above and below high tide level (see pages 25 and 26). Remember that it will not be exactly the same on any two days, but it will be similar.

Coasts Investigation: What are the features on the shore at low tide?

FIELDWORK TECHNIQUES

You will use the following techniques:

- **Making field sketches and/or taking photographs to identify features**
- **Making and/or using a scale for measuring noise**
- **Assessing air pollution**
- **Designing a questionnaire and interviewing**
- **Annotating a map and field sketches/photographs**

This project could be extended to include an investigation of the sand dunes (see the Trial Run) or the cliffs. Suggestions on how to investigate cliffs are given on page 153 of this investigation. A project of extra depth and detail would include surveying the gradient/slope angle of the shore.

Fieldwork area

If you know the area well, you may have a favourite spot, and if this is suitable for your project you will end up by liking it all the more. Choose your fieldwork area by looking first at an Ordnance Survey map of scale 1:10,000. Large-scale maps show a lot of detail and this is a great help.

Aims

There are two parts to the fieldwork for this project:

1. Recording both the physical features and those made by people along a ***transect*** of the shore.
2. Relating the ***distribution*** (whereabouts they are) of features to one or more of the following:
   - (i) the angle of slope of the shore
   - (ii) the rock type and formation of the coast
   - (iii) the prevailing (main) wind direction and the speed and direction of the wind during your fieldwork
   - (iv) the direction, size and type of waves
   - (v) the use made of the shore

Before you begin

Using one of the almanacs recommended on page 159, check the tides to discover the best time to start your fieldwork. Write the time of the tides in your field notebook.

For this project the transect should be at least 50 m long. You may choose to investigate two or more transects on different parts of the coastline. This would enable you to make comparisons or draw contrasts, and then discover the reasons for them.

Make a ***reconnaissance visit*** to the area to carry out the following:

1. Assess the time it takes you to carry out the measurements and decide how much you can do in the time available.
2. Assess the factors affecting the position of features on the shore:
   slope
   geology
   wind
   waves
   people's use of the shore.

Factors affecting the position of features on the shore

Guidance on equipment and ways of investigating each factor are given below.

Slope

The different methods for measuring slope are explained on pages 24–27. Read through them and choose the one you feel would work best for you along your transect. If you are not sure, try out different methods during your reconnaissance visit and explain in your final report how and why you did this.

Geology

Guide books to areas often contain a section on the geology, and these are often very useful (see Appendix 2). Maps of the Solid geology and the Drift geology will be available in your local public library. Unless the map is extremely complicated, trace the coastline for a distance of 10 km on both sides of your fieldwork area(s). Label the rock types as shown on the map. This will help you to discover where the loose materials of local origin come from. For the ***evaluation*** of your work read more about how beach material is transported and where it comes from (see pages 54 and 55).

Use a book such as the *Observer's Guide to Rocks* to help you to become familiar with the colour and other features of the rocks you are likely to find. You could make your own rock guide as suggested on page 42. Your reconnaissance visit will show you the variety of types you may need to identify.

Wind

The types of equipment you could use are described on pages 34 and 35. The nautical almanacs mentioned on page 159 include a section on 'nautical weather'; in other words, weather at the coast.

Waves

Read page 54 and take measurements along the same lines.

People's use of the shore

Your reconnaissance visit will show you the kinds of features you are likely to find, such as ice-cream stalls, sea wall, ***groynes***, noticeboards, etc. Depending on the number of features, that is if there are not too many, you can simply record these features in your field notebook at the appropriate place on your transect. Alternatively, devise a scheme for recording them similar to that in the Coasts Extra Investigation on the Website. If you do this, remember to include a key.

In your field notebook, rule parallel lines to represent the length of your transect(s). When complete, a transect will look something like Figure 144. You will have made a map of the transect if you draw it to scale.

Figure 144 Features along a transect of the shore at low tide.

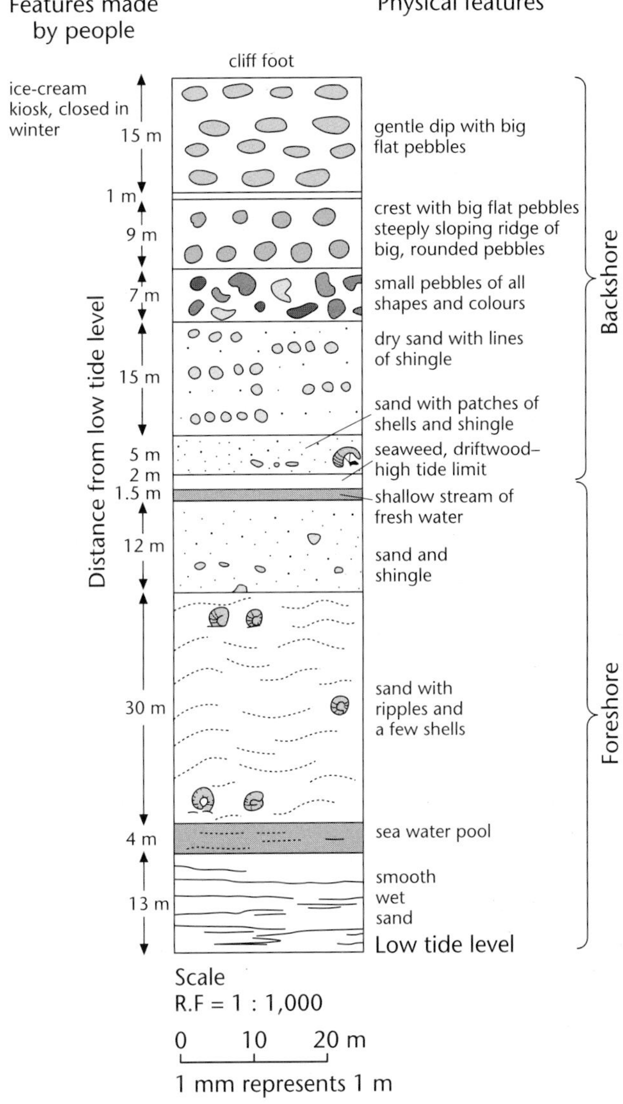

Figure 143 Shoreline with physical and human features

You will need the following equipment:

- Washing line to mark the line of transect.
- Compass to measure the compass direction of your transect. This is important for relating features to the direction of the wind and/or waves.
- Tape measure and/or metre rule.
- Trowel or scoop (see page 136).
- Quadrat for samples (see page 14).
- Plastic buckets or containers for collecting samples; each must be labelled carefully. Waterproof labels are helpful.
- Pebble measure. One type is shown on page 56, and another type that is easy to make is shown in Figure 145.
- Spring balance and mesh bag for weighing beach materials during fieldwork. Alternatively, use kitchen scales at home. Fine material will have to be weighed on a chemical balance at school.
- Sieves to measure the size of particles (see page 55).
- Particle shape guide. This can be made as explained on page 136.
- Equipment for field sketching (see pages 11–13). In a field sketch you could emphasise features that may not be obvious in a photograph.
- Table for recording beach material (see Figure 146).
- Equipment for measuring the angle of slope (see pages 24–27).
- Equipment for identifying rock type (see page 47).
- Equipment for measuring wind (see pages 34–5) and waves (see pages 54 and 167).
- Stopwatch or watch with second hand.

Figure 145 How to make a simple pebble measure.

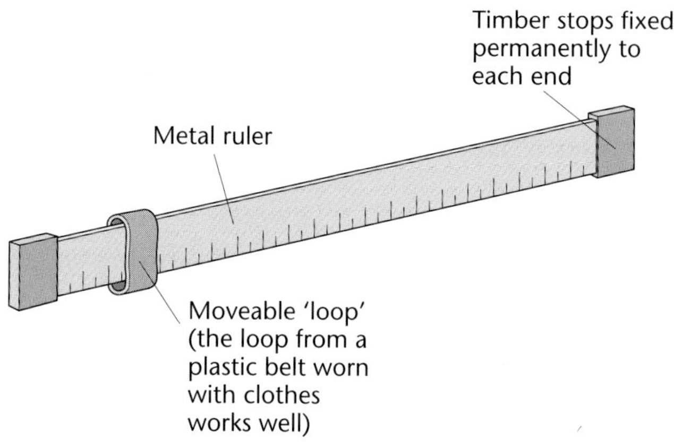

Fieldwork method

1. Investigating shore features

a. Lay the washing line up the beach from the sea and weight it at both ends. This will be your line of transect. Measure the compass direction of the transect and record it in your field notebook.

b. Start at the sea and work inland. In your field notebook record the features in detail: beach ridges; rock pools; shape, size and colour of pebbles; and samples of sand. To locate the position of the feature on the transect use the tape or metre rule to measure the distance from the sea.

c. If possible, measure the size of beach material during your fieldwork. If the weather is bad, collect samples, label them with the place collected, and place them into a container to take home. Whatever the weather, you could collect fine material and stick this onto clear sticky tape to include as illustration in your final report.

If changes in slope on the beach are clearly noticeable, collect sample materials from each different angle of slope. If the beach appears to be uniform in angle of slope, choose an interval, perhaps 1 or 2 m, as a ***systematic sample*** along the transect and collect material accordingly.

Figure 146 Table for recording beach material.

Location of transect: ______ Grid reference: ______
Date: ______ Weather conditions: ______

Distance of investigation site from the sea in metres	Long axis in cm	Long axis in cm	Shape	Description: colour and appearance of rock	Estimated rock type

At each location place the metre rule or quadrat across the line of the transect. The length of the long and short axes and the weight of every pebble within the quadrat should be measured and recorded on your table for recording beach material (Figure 146). If you are short of time, choose the two pebbles lying nearest to the corners of the quadrat and the two nearest to the centre. This will give you a sample of 10 pebbles at each investigation site. Collect a trowelful of sand if present. If the sand is wet you will have to take it home to dry it before sieving. Label it accurately to identify where you collected it. The more samples you collect, measure and weigh, the more representative your results will be of the whole picture.

2. Investigating slope

Take measurements of the slope angle as you work up the transect away from the sea. The tide could turn and cover the seaward end of your transect without your having measured the slope – measure it straight away!

To make sure that you collect an unbiased sample of materials, toss the quadrat over your left shoulder. Take care not to hit anyone and don't be too vigorous and end up by breaking the quadrat frame!

3. Investigating wind

As for the waves, take measurements on three separate occasions during your fieldwork.

4. Investigating waves

Three times during your fieldwork, count for three minutes the number of breakers arriving on the beach. Calculate the average per minute and record this in your field notebook. Use your compass to find the direction from which the waves are approaching.

Extending your study to include an investigation of sand dunes or cliffs

Sand dunes

The Trial Run on pages 160–165 explains how to investigate sand dunes.

Cliffs

Make a field sketch of the cliffs (see pages 12–13) and ***annotate*** it to describe the main features. What type of rock is it? Refer to your rock guide if you have made one. You can check the details of the rock type later by using books and geological maps, but describe the colour during your fieldwork. Are there angular fragments of rock at the cliff foot or does the beach reach the cliff foot? Is the rock well-jointed or not?

If it is a sedimentary rock, are the ***bedding planes*** (the 'cracks' separating beds or layers of rock) clearly visible? Estimate the thickness of the beds. Figure 147 may help you to describe your cliffs. Look for slumping of the cliff face as you might find in cliffs composed of clay.

CAUTION: Beware of falling boulders. Never attempt to climb the cliffs.

You can measure the height of the cliffs using a hypsometer. Hypsometers are expensive to buy but the one shown in Figure 148 can be made fairly easily.

Figure 147 How the shape of the cliff face is affected by the dip of the rock strata.

Cliff with a steep face

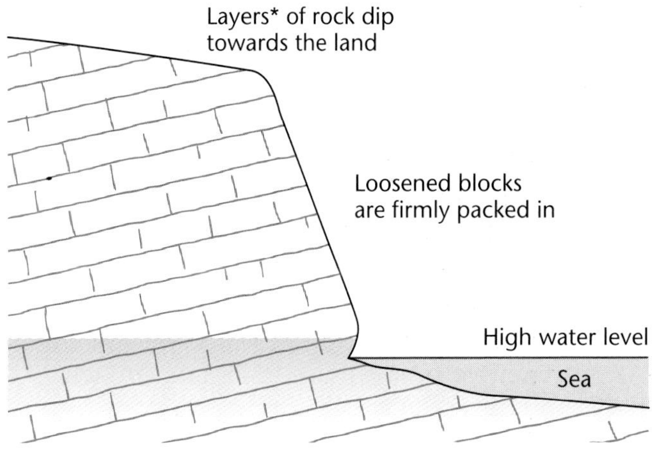

Cliff with a sloping face

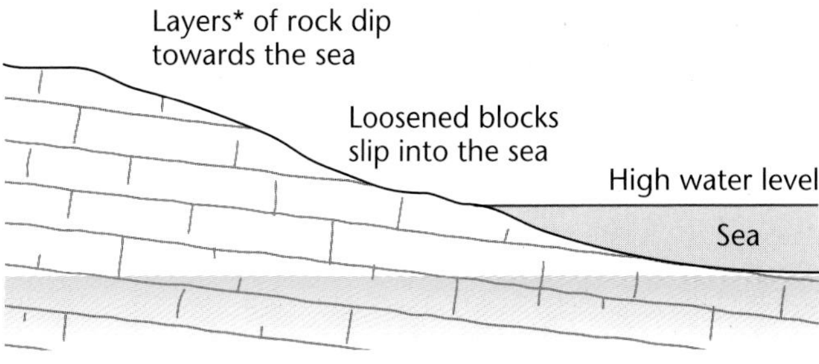

*The layers (or strata) may be beds in sedimentary rocks, or layers of well-jointed rock of other types.

Figure 148 A home-made hypsometer for measuring height.

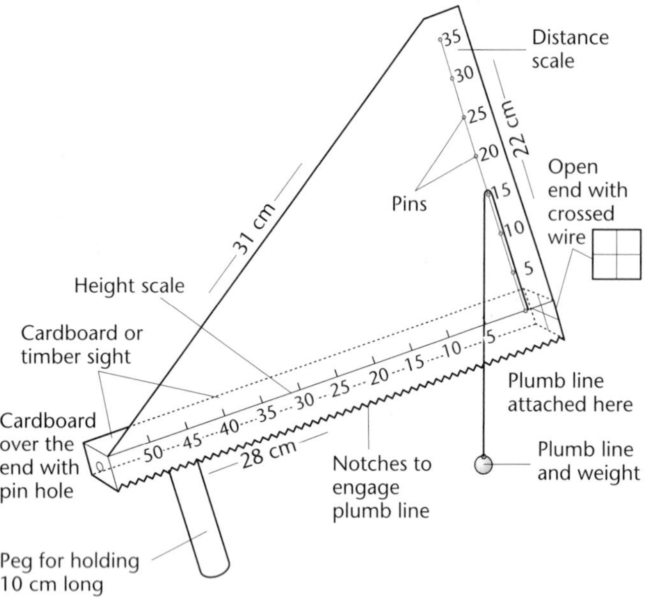

Begin with a right-angled triangle of thin hardboard. Cut the two corners off (not the right-angled one) to form a pentagon with sides 22 cm, 3 cm, 31 cm, 3 cm, 3 cm and 28 cm. Notch the base (the 28 cm side). Mark in paint or indelible ink every five units on the distance and height scales: 2.5 cm represent five units. Insert panel pins at every five units on the distance scale. Add the plumb line (a weighted string) to the intersection of the distance scale with the height scale. Attach a piece of timber 28 cm long to the height scale. Drill a hole through it to use for sighting.

A hypsometer is simple to use. Stand far enough back from the cliff until you can see the top through the pin hole. Measure the horizontal distance between the cliff face and the spot where you are standing. Loop the plumb line over the pin on the distance scale at the distance you have just measured. Sight the top of the cliff again through the pinhole and then get a friend to read the height directly from the position where the plumb line hangs on the height scale.

A hypsometer can also be useful for discovering the height of a sea wall or the thickness of rock strata.

Analysing and interpreting your data

Complete any measurements of beach material at home or at school. Obtain the secondary data that you need. This may include the following:

- geological maps and guides
- weather recordings from the Meteorological Office (see the sources of Information on the Website) or your local weather station
- the tidal range on the day of your fieldwork, and the date of the last high spring tide at your fieldwork site(s) from the nautical almanacs

1. Draw map(s) to show the location of your transect(s). Explain why you chose each particular one.
2. Draw a scale plan of each transect investigated and annotate it to show the results of your investigation. Figure 144 will show you how to go about it. Describe any patterns you see. Where is the rippled sand? Where are the most pebbles? Can you suggest any reasons for these?
3. Calculate the average size of beach materials sampled. Decide whether to concentrate on measurements of the long axis or the short axis (or both) of the pebbles you have collected. Pebbles are usually deposited with their short axis projecting upwards. Look at page 55 and suggest reasons why pebbles on a beach may not always end up in this way.

   For each sample, calculate the average lengths of the long axis and then the short axis and the average weight. Which shape (angular or rounded) best describes the sample?

   Illustrate the size and shape of your samples as bar charts (see pages 72 and 73) or pie charts (see page 79). Place these beside the plan of your beach transect, and then describe any patterns that you see. To divide the beach materials collected at each investigation site into particle sizes, follow the method given on pages 55–56.

Some small particles can be measured by placing a ruler and the particles together under a magnifying glass.

Looking for inter-relationships

Explain each of the following in detail.

Shore profile

If you have measured the angle of slope, draw the profile of the shore from your measurements. The method for this is explained in the Trial Run (page 164). If you use the same scale as that of your plan you will be able to place them side by side. Pick out any ***inter-relationships*** between the shape of the beach or the angle of slope and the features on the beach. Project Suggestion 2 on page 157 may be of help to you. Describe the inter-relationships and suggest reasons for them wherever possible.

Wave-type and the shape of the beach

From your timing of the waves suggest whether they were constructive (beach-building) or destructive (removing material from the beach) (see page 54). Constructive waves should produce beach ridges. Did you find this to be so?

Look at the profile of a storm beach on page 157. Are any of the biggest particles on your transect likely to have been hurled by the sea onto the dry part of the beach? Was a **strand line** obvious? This is a line of material left by the highest of the most recent high tides. It is usually made up of a mixture of seaweed, driftwood, shells and shingle. On Figure 144 the strand line is 60.5 m from the sea. On which date (high water springs) could the strand line on your fieldwork transect have been deposited?

Winds and wave approach

Do your measurements of wind direction match those of the prevailing (most frequent) winds? You may obtain information on winds over months or even years from records kept by the Meteorological Office or your local weather station. Do your wind results match your wave approach results? Describe your findings and suggest reasons for them wherever possible.

Can you link the distribution of materials on the beach to the direction of the waves? Read pages 54–55 to help you with ideas.

Where the beach materials may have come from

For each transect, ***tabulate*** (make a table of) all the different materials that you classified: 'sandstone', 'chalk', 'shale', 'speckled', etc., including the 'don't knows' (call these 'others'). Make a tally chart of the types along the lines of Figure 149.

Draw a ***sketch map*** to show the geology of the area (see Figure 150), and either draw bar charts (see page 72-73) to show the rock types, or draw flow-lines (see page 81) to show where the rock types may have come from. Now describe the results.

Figure 150 Sketch map to show the geology and possible origin of beach materials.

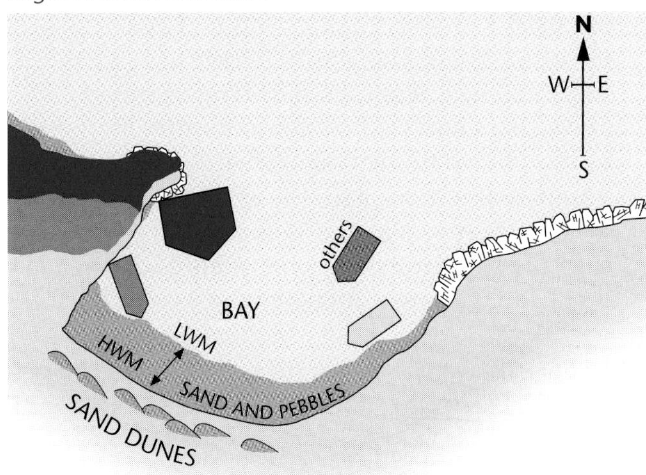

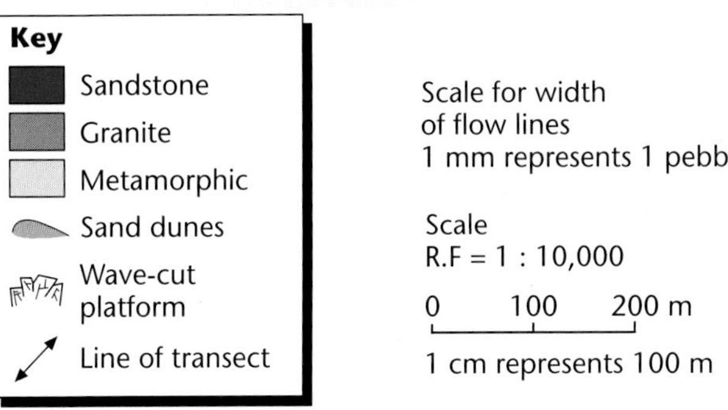

Interesting extra analyses

1. Calculate the axis ratio of pebbles as an index of pebble shape. For each sample choose the pebble which has the shape and size nearest to the average and divide the longest axis by the short axis. If the number obtained is small it suggests that the pebble may be flat like a coin. This could be taken as a rough measure of sphericity. To achieve a more refined result experiment on some of the samples you brought home by using

Figure 149 Tally chart of beach materials investigated along a transect.

Tally chart of the beach materials investigated on

Transect (name)	Grid reference		
Sandstone	卌	卌	卌
Chalk	I		
Speckled	卌	I	
Shale	卌		
Others	卌		

the third axis and plotting the axes on triangular graph paper. If you consider that this method produces a more accurate result you may substitute triangular graphs for the bar charts suggested next. For each rock type collected, draw a bar chart to show the axis ratio. Are your results related to the rock type of the pebbles?

2. Compare the shape with the weight, and relate it to the rock type. Figure 151 is a scattergraph showing the results of pebble analysis on the beach at Penmon in Anglesey.

Figure 151 Scattergraph to show the size, shape and weight of pebbles from samples of Penmon Beach in Anglesey.

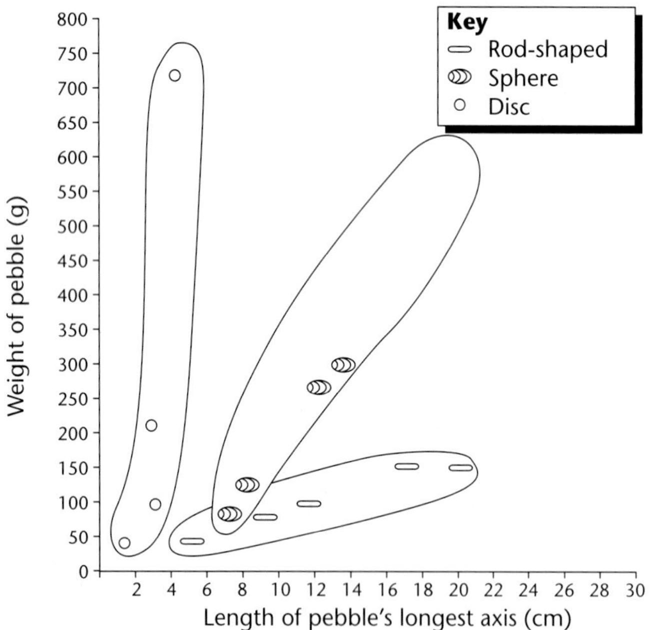

Drawing conclusions

1. For each transect that you have investigated, write a detailed description of the ***distribution*** (the whereabouts) of beach materials found (a) on the foreshore, and (b) on the backshore.
2. If you have investigated more than one transect describe the similarities and the contrasts between them.
3. Suggest reasons why certain parts of beaches have particular features. Relate them to the following:
   - The tide level: at high tide the water is deep and has high energy for transport.
   - The geology within the 10 km on both sides of your fieldwork area.
   - The direction of ***longshore drift***.
   - The use made of the coast.
4. If you have investigated sand dunes:
   - Do they seem to show patterns similar to those in the Trial Run?
   - Are they wider or narrower than those at Garlieston Bay?
   - Does the beach appear to be a good source of fresh sand for the dunes?

   Discover from historical sources when the dunes were first recorded.
5. If you have investigated cliffs:
   - Describe them, including ***annotated*** sketches and photographs.
   - Does the beach reach the cliff foot?
   - Find out more about cliff erosion. Suggest whether or not the cliffs are being eroded by the sea at the present time.

Evaluating your work

- Give your opinion as to whether the results from your transect(s) are likely to have been representative (typical) of a large area of the shore where you worked. Was it difficult to identify a transect that was typical of the area? If it was difficult, how many other transects would you recommend investigating if time were no object?
- Do you consider your method of collecting beach materials to have been accurate? How many pebbles and how much sand or other fine material would you have liked to have collected at each sample site?
- What were the advantages and disadvantages of using (i) a trowel and (ii) a scoop to collect fine materials?
- If you have calculated the axis ratio of pebbles, give your views of whether it is worth the extra effort to analyse pebble shape in this way.

Interesting extra ideas: predicting the future

Sea level is rising throughout the world, but north-west Scotland is also rising, while south-east England is sinking. Find out more about these long-term changes. Use your knowledge of the processes at work at the coast to suggest what may happen to your fieldwork area in the next 100–150 years.

Leisure

'Leisure time' is free time to be used in whatever way you choose. In countries such as those of Western Europe, North America and Australasia, people have more leisure time and more money to spend on it than ever before.

Ask your friends and members of your family for their top two favourite leisure pursuits. List them and then classify them into categories (see page 15). This can be more difficult than it sounds. There are all sorts of different kinds of leisure pursuits: active and passive, indoor and outdoor, organised and unorganised, expensive and inexpensive. You may decide to make **Venn diagrams** (see pages 80–81) of your list so that some activities can be put into more than one category!

Some types of leisure pursuit are difficult to investigate for a geography project. At venues such as cinemas, concert halls, arenas and sports grounds, 'spectators' go in and come out at the same time according to the timing of the activity they go to see. It can be daunting to try to interview people who are queuing, and many events take place in the evening.

This chapter concentrates on parks and public open spaces. There are no age limits for using these and entry is often free of charge. They come in all shapes and sizes from National Parks to village greens.

Public open spaces developed mainly as a meeting place for the local community. Every village and small town has a market place, a market square or a green. Big towns and cities often have public squares surrounded by fine buildings.

Parks have always been spaces devoted to recreation. They originated in Ancient Persia and Ancient Greece, but most public parks in Britain date from 1831 when the first Act providing 'Gardens for the Poor' was passed. Parks and allotments are still governed by these laws. Early parks were often established by benefactors. An inscription on the statue of Sir Herbert Waterlow in the park which he endowed in Highgate in London reads '. . . to provide a garden for the gardenless'. You know from both Geography and History all about the areas of closely packed terraced housing that was built in the industrial towns to keep pace with the need for housing for the factory workers.

Figure 152 A garden square

There was no space or time for private gardening. Important Victorians such as Octavia Hill, John Ruskin and Beatrix Potter brought about the founding of the National Trust in England in 1895, and 50 years later the Dower Commission was set up to investigate the need for National Parks.

The Garden Square was 'invented' in Britain in the eighteenth century to 'bring the countryside into the town'. Nearly all of them were privately owned and for the use of the residents of the houses in the square.

The Dower Report of 1943 summarised two of the main purposes for National Parks in England and Wales as being:

1. the protection of large areas of beautiful and relatively wild country, and
2. the ample provision of access and facilities for public open air enjoyment.

Today, the two most visited National Parks in the world are:

1. Mount Fuji National Park in Japan, and
2. the Peak District National Park in England.

For the Introduction to your project, discover more about the people responsible for the founding of the public park or open space you have chosen and its development through history. Find out from the Local History section of your public library how the facilities were planned and the way in which they have developed. Write two or three paragraphs on this for your final report.

This chapter has been planned to give guidance on how to achieve a successful project based on public open spaces and parks of all types.

The Trial Run compares the numbers and age groups of people using city centre parks with those using country parks. The length of visit and the place of origin of the visit to the parks are also considered. If your project is on urban parks, country parks, parts of a National Park, or if you aim to pick out contrasts between two different types of park, then you may follow this investigation.

The Short Project explores the leisure facilities that are available in local public parks.

The Investigation tells you how to make an ***inventory*** of the recreational facilities available, and the numbers and age groups of the visitors who use them. In this way, the popularity of an area or of particular facilities can be assessed.

The Extra Investigation on the Website tells you how to find out the ways in which an area has been altered for use by the public and how to assess the impact that visitors have on an area.

Project suggestions

1. A project to assess the recreational potential (possibilities) of an area could be based almost entirely on Ordnance Survey maps. It could be a coursework project based entirely on ***secondary data*** or a worthwhile part of a fieldwork project (see Leisure Investigation, page 188–189).

   Where to find help:

   Guidebooks are suggested in Appendix 2 and on the Website

2. Does the ***distribution*** of facilities reflect the physical geography (relief and local climate) of the area? Investigate the location of different facilities such as benches, buildings, viewpoints, boating lakes, flowerbeds and fountains in relation to the following:
   - shelter from or exposure to the wind
   - ***aspect***, i.e. the facility's position in relation to the sun
   - slope angles and the way they affect a view or affect sunshine and shadow
   - slope and good drainage for soil, and their effects on plants
   - slope and the position of water features

   Where to find help:

   How to survey a slope, 24–27

   How to investigate the length of shadow cast, 103

   How to investigate the weather, 28–37

3. Are the facilities available appropriate to the age groups of the people who use them? How could the range of facilities be extended and/or improved? Would this be an advantage?

   Where to find help:

   How to make an inventory of facilities – Leisure Extra Investigation, Website

   How to estimate age groups, 189

4. In the 1980s and 1990s concern was expressed about the way in which many of the public open spaces in our towns and cities had become little more than car parks.
   - Trace the use of one or more urban open spaces through time.
   - Has the comment ever applied to open space(s) in your town?
   - If so, what has been done or is planned to improve the situation?
   - In what ways may open spaces in towns be used for the greatest benefit of the public?

   Where to find help:

   The Parks and Leisure department of your local authority

   The Local History section of your Public Library

Parts of Project Suggestions 5 and 6 could be combined:

5. Roads and paths occupy less than 5% of our recreational areas. As most people stay near them, they form an economical use of leisure space. Choose two roads or paths within the area. Investigate the numbers of people and types of facility available within 100 m or less of the road/path and then those further away. Would you recommend establishing more roads/paths?

   Where to find help:

   How to estimate distance, 189

   How to make an inventory of facilities – Leisure Extra Investigation, Website

   How to record numbers of people, 191

6. The planning and management of a park. Is there a honeypot site to concentrate visitors in a small area? Does this successfully maintain the tranquillity of other areas for visitors who seek peace and quiet? Investigate both the busy area and the quiet area from the following points of view:

- the facilities in each area
- the number of people using each area
- the age groups of people in each area
- the impact of visitors in the ***honeypot*** area

Would you recommend establishing another 'honeypot'? Where would you create it? What facilities would you introduce?

Where to find help:

How to record numbers of people, 191

Write to the manager of the Park, 18–20

7. What is the catchment area of the park or open space?
   - Discover where visitors come from to the park.
   - How do they travel to the park?
   - If your park is advertised, where are advertisements? Are they on billboards, in the local newspapers or on radio or television programmes? Most of this part of your investigation will rely on information supplied by the manager of the park, so it will be mainly secondary data.

Where to find help:

Traffic survey/where cars come from, 57

Public transport maps and timetables

Write to the manager of the Park, 18–20

CAUTION: Always carry out your fieldwork in broad daylight and never in lonely places. Three people should be the minimum number working together. Make sure that you know where to go and how to summon help in an emergency.

Leisure Trial Run: What are the patterns of use in four parks in Greater Manchester?

FIELDWORK TECHNIQUES

The following techniques were used:

- **Drawing a sketch map or tracing a map**
- **Using hypotheses as a framework for the investigation**
- **Designing a questionnaire and interviewing**
- **Observing and recording people, including estimation of age-group**

This Trial Run is based on fieldwork investigations into two city-centre parks and two country parks: one in the suburbs and the other in rural land beyond the conurbation. Although the Trial Run is based on the contrasts in use between the two main types of park, you could follow the same methods for a project on either urban parks or country parks.

A coursework project based entirely on secondary data could be carried out along the lines of this Trial Run. Information on the facilities available and data for visitor numbers could be obtained by writing to the manager of a park which charges a fee for entry or for the use of a car park and/or coach park.

The map in Figure 153 shows the location of the four parks. The two parks of each type were chosen because they were similar. It was hoped that this fact would increase the reliability of the results.

- City-centre parks: Piccadilly Gardens occupy a site that was bombed in 1941, and St John's Gardens were established in 1931 when St John's Church was demolished.
- Country parks: Heaton Park is a former stately home with grounds covering 240 hectares of parkland. It is in the northern suburbs of Manchester. Tatton Park is also a former stately home surrounded by 400 hectares of parkland, situated in open countryside to the south of Manchester.

Before you begin

As part of the Introduction to your report on this Trial Run:

1. Use an atlas to draw a ***sketch map*** or to make a tracing of north-west England to locate the study area. This would make a good title page.
2. Make a tracing of the map in Figure 153 to show the edge of the Manchester conurbation and the location of the four parks studied.
3. To assess the visitor potential of the parks, either
   a use the Census or a source such as *Whitaker's Almanack* to find the population of Manchester and some of the towns surrounding it; this will indicate the 'visitor potential' for the parks

   or

   b calculate the built-up area of the Manchester conurbation and the surrounding towns (follow the method explained in on page 70).
4. Using the information above, write a description of each of the parks. You could discover more by writing to the Tourist Information Officer in Manchester for Heaton Park and the city-centre parks, and in Chester for Tatton Park.

Aims

In this Trial Run the aims have been worded as ***hypotheses***. They were observations from ***reconnaissance visits*** made in their free time by the pupils involved. Each hypothesis is, therefore, based on an ***expectation*** rather than merely on a hunch, as suggested in Section 1 on page 6.

- H1 'That visitors to the city-centre parks are mainly of working age, whilst visitors to country parks are of all ages.'
- H2 'That most visits to the city-centre parks are short term, whilst those to the country parks are made for a longer time.'
- H3 'That visitors' journeys to city-centre parks are shorter in length than journeys to country parks.'

The fieldwork was carried out by two different classes who visited the parks at a weekend and on a weekday between 11 am and 3 pm. The work was carried out in the summer term and the classes were divided into the following groups:

10 people visited Heaton Park

10 people visited Tatton Park

4 people visited Piccadilly Gardens

4 people visited St John's Gardens

The investigations were carried out in pairs.

Figure 153 A map to show the location of the parks and places where the visitors came from.

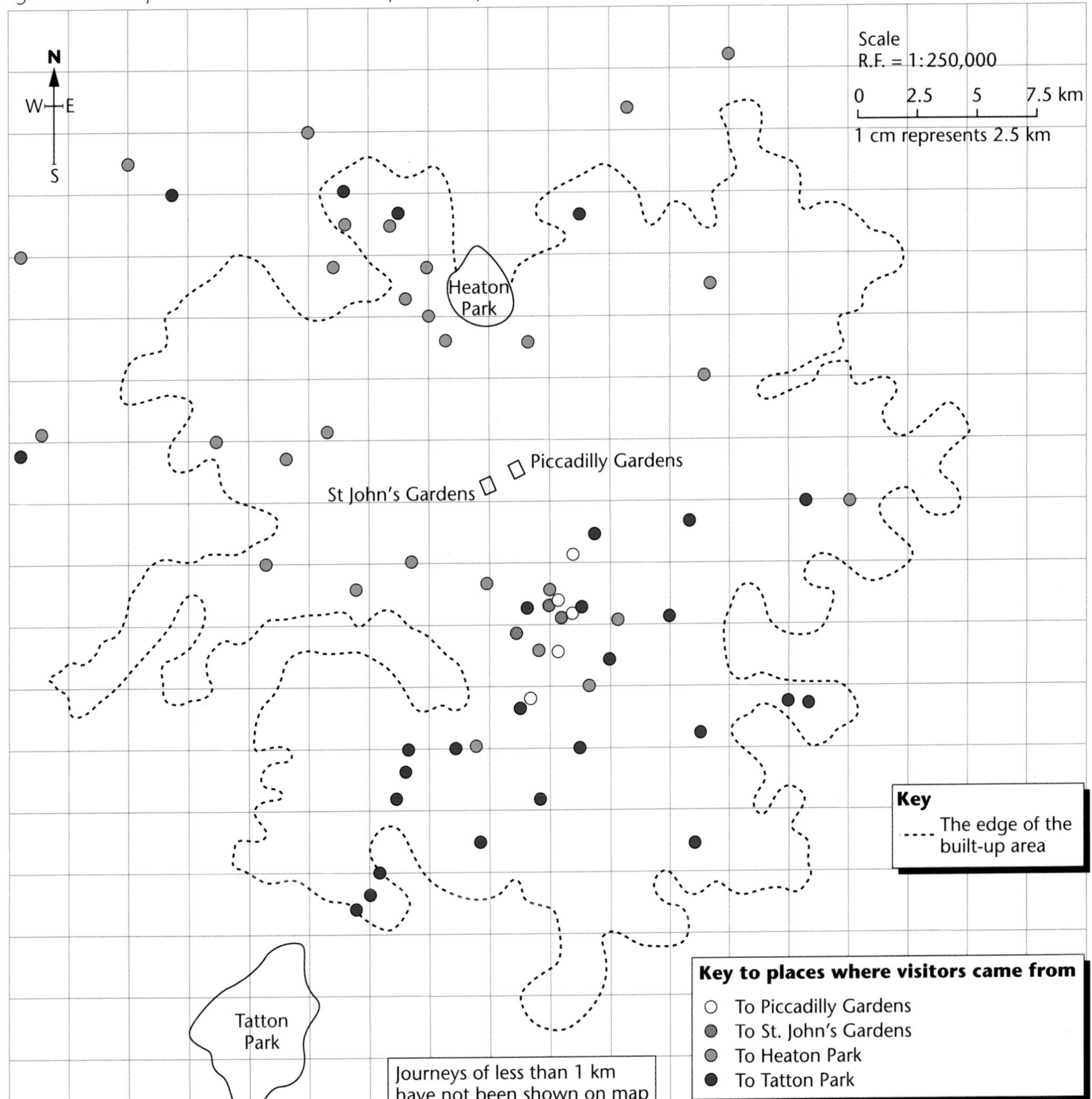

The following equipment was used:

- Base-map of scale 1:10,000 for the area to be surveyed by each pair.
- Questionnaire which included the following questions:

1. a Did your journey to this park begin from home/place of work/other? (*Cross out those which do not apply.*)

b Where is that? Please name the town or village/street or part of the city.

2. How long are you spending here? *Record the duration in minutes for the city-centre parks; record in hours for the country parks. Do not ask how old the person is, but record which of the following age groups he/she belong to:*

Under 16

16–60

Over 60

Fieldwork method

The geographers who worked in the city-centre parks had base-maps which included the whole park. Those in the country parks were allocated two Grid Squares whose sides represented 100 m, i.e. 1 hectare. Although only a sample of 10 hectares was surveyed in each country park, the reconnaissance visits had shown them to be the ones with the most popular facilities: the Hall, Pets Corner and the Boating Lake in Heaton Park, and the Hall, the Japanese Garden and Tattondale (the 1930s working farm) in Tatton Park.

The following methods were used:

1. The numbers of people were observed and recorded and their age groups noted.
2. Interviews were conducted using a systematic random ***sample*** method: every third person in the city-centre parks and every fifth person in the country parks.

In addition, the facilities and the numbers and age groups of people using them were recorded, as explained in the Investigation. The results have not been included here.

Results

1. Numbers of visitors counted and recorded by age group:

	Under 16 years	16–60 years	Over 60 years
St John's Gardens	3	46	3
Piccadilly Gardens	8	45	4
Heaton Park	68	105	12
Tatton Park	52	102	48

2. The length of stay:

Minutes	10 or less	11–20	21–30	31–40	41–50	51–60
St John's Gardens	1	1	7	5	2	1
Piccadilly Gardens	6	7	2	2	1	1

Hours	Less than 1	1–2	2–3	More than 3
Heaton Park	5	27	4	1
Tatton Park	1	21	15	3

3. The place where the journey to the park began. The results for places of origin within the Manchester conurbation are shown as dots on the map in Figure 153. In addition to these, the following were recorded:

St John's Gardens: 14 from places of work and elsewhere less than 1 km from the gardens.

Piccadilly Gardens: 12 from shops and places of work less than 1 km from the gardens.

Heaton Park: 1 person from each of the following places:

Preston
Halifax
Blackburn
Macclesfield
Burnley
Warrington
Liverpool
Chorley

Tatton Park: 1 person from each of the following places:

Carlisle
Chester
Barnsley
Birmingham
Buxton
Leek
Leicester
York
Cheltenham
Market Drayton
St Helens
Blackpool

Analysing and interpreting your data

H1 'That most visitors to the city-centre parks are of working age, whilst visitors to the country parks are of all ages.'

1. Add up the total number of visitors of all ages to each of the four parks in turn, and then follow one of the three different methods for analysis described below. Think carefully about which method you feel will help to emphasise the contrasts in the patterns and so help to prove the hypothesis. It would be a good idea to try out the methods in rough first. In your final report explain that you did this, and why. Also give reasons for choosing the method you prefer.

Method 1

Draw a bar chart (see pages 72–73) for each park to illustrate the number of visitors in each of the different age groups. Choose a different colour or type of shading (see page 65) to represent each age group. Take care when choosing the scale. Look at the difference between the biggest number and the smallest number that you have to show. Would it be sensible to use a zigzag line on the bar chart? This chart could be drawn as a cumulative bar chart (see page 73) or as bars placed side by side.

Method 2

For each park add up the total number of visitors. Calculate the number in each age group as a percentage of the total (see page 86). Finally, show the results for each park as a bar chart or as a pie chart (see pages 79–80).

Method 3

For each park add up the total number of visitors. Draw a proportional circle (see page 82) to represent the total. Divide the circle into pie sectors according to the different age groups.

2. Describe any patterns shown. Are you able to say that the hypothesis has been proved or has it been disproved? Is the age range of people using the parks likely to be simply a reflection of the location of the park and its immediate **hinterland** or might the age range be influenced also by the facilities available?

   As part of the evaluation of the method consider what the picture might have been if the fieldwork had been carried out on different days or at different times of the day.

H2 'That most visits to the city-centre parks are short term, whilst those to country parks are for a longer time.'

For each of the parks:

1. Draw a bar chart to show the number of visitors who were there for each of the time intervals investigated. Remember that people interviewed in the city-centre parks were asked to give their answers in 10 minute intervals whilst those in the country parks were asked to give their answers in 1 hour intervals. The scale must enable worthwhile comparisons to be made between the country parks and the city-centre parks.
2. Describe your results, and consider whether it might be worthwhile:
   a to calculate the average length of stay in each of the parks, or
   b to look at the modal length of stay, or the inter-quartile range (see pages 84–85).
3. Has the hypothesis been proved?

   As part of your ***evaluation***, comment on the time intervals chosen for the questionnaires.

H3 'That visitors' journeys to city-centre parks are shorter in length than the journeys to the country parks.'

Look again at the map in Figure 153. This shows where each journey of more than 1 km began within the Manchester conurbation and in the area immediately surrounding it. On page 182 origins of journeys from further afield are listed and the numbers of people who walked for a distance of less than 1 km are given.

1. Assume that all of the people who came to the city-centre parks from less than 1 km distance had walked 0.5 km. Add up the total distance travelled to each of the city-centre parks. On a copy of the map draw for each a bar, circle or square proportional to the total distance travelled (see page 82). How could you find out how far people have walked? Are they aware of the length of distance in a built-up/urban environment?
2. For the place of origin of visitors from longer distances, draw a desire-line (see page 66–67) from the origin to each of the parks.
3. Finally, on an outline map of Great Britain, draw desire-lines to show the places of origin beyond the map in Figure 153. These are listed on page 182.
4. Describe your results. The map in this Trial Run is drawn to scale so it is possible to work out the average of the straight-line distances travelled to each park. In your report, say whether you consider that this further analysis would be worth doing.

Drawing conclusions

As a final conclusion, summarise the results in turn. Give your views on whether you have enough data to prove or disprove the hypotheses and suggest other information that would have been helpful.

Evaluating your work

- Can the country parks really be compared? One is in the suburbs of Manchester and the other in a rural area. Does your analysis of the results reveal any differences? If so, suggest possible reasons for them.
- Comment on the size of the sample of people interviewed. Was it adequate?
- If you had planned this investigation would you have altered any of the methods? Consider:
  - fieldwork carried out in a different season; on a different day; at a different time
  - recording the length of visit to both types of park in minutes or in hours.

Interesting extra ideas

- Calculate the ***catchment area/sphere of influence*** of each of the parks based on the evidence provided.
- Assume that passenger vehicles travel at the following speeds:

  90 kph on motorways

  55 kph on 'A' class roads

  40 kph on 'B' class and minor roads

  Calculate the average journey time to each of the country parks.
- Obtain from the Valuation Office the value of land in the area close to the park, and work out the monetary value of the area covered by each public park. Next, prepare a report for the Planning Department of your local council outlining the importance of public parks.

Leisure Short Project: What leisure facilities are available in the local public park?

Public parks, gardens and squares are a feature of all towns and cities in Britain so it is likely that there will be one not far from your home or school.

Fieldwork area

Use the Ordnance Survey map of scale 1:25,000 or an A-Z Guide to pick out a small urban park. For this short project the area to investigate should be approximately 250 metres by 250 metres.

Before you begin

1. Make a copy of a large-scale map for recording the leisure facilities in your fieldwork area. An Ordnance Survey map of scale 1:1,000 or 1:2,500 would be an ideal size of **base-map**. To help your fieldwork recording, cover the map with a grid to divide your park into squares with sides representing 25 metres in length. On the 1:1,000 scale the squares in the grid will have sides 2.5 cm long. On the 1:2,500 scale the squares in the grid will have sides 1 cm long. Down the sides of the map number the squares and along the top give them letters. You can see the system in an A-Z Guide and in some atlases. You will then be able to pick out each square easily by its letter and number. Look at Figure 156 on page 190 for help.
2. Make up symbols to represent each of the facilities you expect to find: **F** for flowerbed, **B** for bench, **L** for litter bin and so on. Arrange them in alphabetical order. This will make them easy to find during your fieldwork. Call them your 'Scheme for Recording Facilities in a Leisure Area'.
3. Find out when the park and the area surrounding it were developed. Look for date stones on houses and their architectural style. See pages 60 – 62. You can read about the history of public parks on page 177. Street patterns give clues to the time that an area was developed. Begin by looking at street patterns on Ordnance Survey maps of scale 1:25,000 or 1:50,000. The history section of your local public library may have early editions of the Ordnance Survey map and books which might give information for your project. Remember to give the author and title of books and the name and edition of maps which you use.
4. Make a quick visit to the area. This is termed 'making a ***reconnaissance visit***'. Use the time to:
   - (a) Look for extra facilities to add to your list.
   - (b) Consider whether to make a field sketch and where or whether to take a photograph of the facilities. How to do field sketches and their advantages are explained on pages 11–13
5. Describe in your final report all the preparations you have made.

You will need the following equipment:

- Base-map of scale 1:1,000 or 1:2,500 with a grid for recording facilities – 2 copies: one to use during your fieldwork and the other to keep neatly for your final report.
- Scheme for Recording Facilities in a Leisure Area.
- Tape measure, preferably 30 metres long.
- Field sketching equipment and/or camera

Fieldwork method

Stand in each square in turn on the grid you have drawn on your base-map. To be very accurate use the tape measure. In the correct place on your map write the symbol for each facility according to your 'Scheme for Recording Facilities in a Leisure Area'.

Draw the edges of grassy areas and large flowerbeds as accurately as you can. You could use the tape measure to help you but take care not to trespass onto areas where you are not allowed. You may decide to divide grassy areas into two or more kinds:

rough grass for ball games and picnics, and
fine grass which is carefully trimmed and well cared for

Analysing and interpreting your data

1. Transfer all of the information from your base-map to the new copy.
2. Shade areas of grass, gravel, tar Macadam as complete shading using different colours. Add a key to your map: blue = grass, black = tarmac, etc.
3. Estimate the proportion of the park which is covered by grass, tar Macadam or other types of surface. Write one or two sentences to describe the different surfaces.
4. ***Tabulate*** (make a table) of the smaller leisure facilities you marked on your map. For the second, third, fourth time you have recorded them put a tally stroke beside the facility:
   Rank the figures from the largest number in a facility to the smallest. The number of times a facility occurs is termed its '***frequency***'.
5. Draw a bar chart or pie chart (see pages 72–3) to illustrate the numbers of facilities in your table. Begin with the largest number (highest frequency).
6. Describe what your bar chart or pie chart shows.
7. Are some of the facilities grouped together? Examples could be a sand pit, ice-cream kiosk, litter bins and benches; refreshment stall, picnic tables and litter bins. Describe any groups which you see and suggest reasons why they might cluster in this way.

Drawing conclusions

1. Write a summary to describe what your investigation has shown about:
   (a) the variety of facilities in the park;
   (b) the numbers (frequency of occurrence) in different categories of facility;
   (c) where in the park the facilities are located.
2. (a) Do some of the facilities in the park date from the time when it was first developed? Bands performed from bandstands more than once a week in Victorian and Edwardian times, for instance.
   (b) Describe modern facilities in the park.
3. Does the park cater for all age-groups? If not, how would you make it more attractive to those who are at present 'missed out'?

Evaluating your work

- Some facilities, such as lawns, cover a large area, whereas others, such as a fountain or tree, take up little space. How accurately can they be compared?
- Was the grid you drew over your base-map helpful?

Interesting extra ideas

- Find out what the area around the park is like. The Small Area Statistics of the Census of Population will tell you the types of households which exist in the area around the park. Does the park provide leisure facilities of the type needed by the people in the surrounding area?
- Discover the age-group of people who use the facilities. Go back to the park to investigate who uses what, as in the Leisure Trial Run.

Leisure Investigation: How successful is the park/public open space?

FIELDWORK TECHNIQUES

You will use the following techniques:

- **Covering a base-map with a grid for recording drawn to scale**
- **Recording a base-map of features by key and people by tally stroke**
- **Evaluation of a leisure potential from a map (optional)**
- **Practise in recognising features at particular distances**
- **Measuring local climate**
- **Measuring slope angle**

Mount Fuji and the Peak District are considered amongst the most successful National Parks in the world. Why do they attract more visitors than any others?

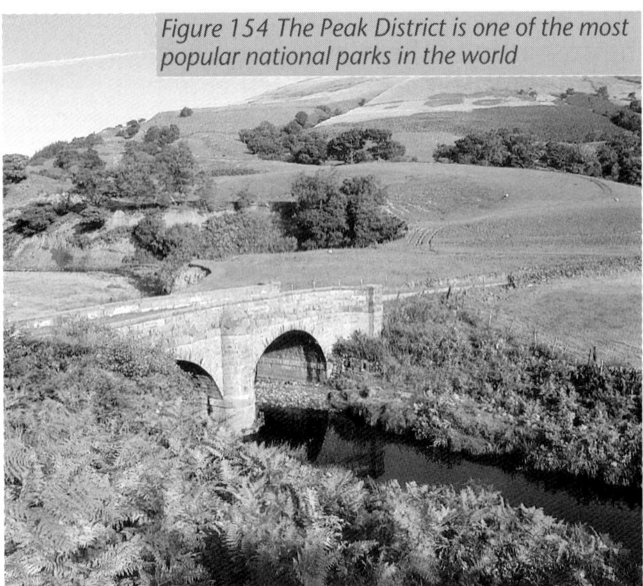

Figure 154 The Peak District is one of the most popular national parks in the world

A project that aims to assess the success of parks and public open spaces falls into two parts:

1. Making an ***inventory*** of the facilities available. This includes an investigation of their ***distribution*** (whereabouts they are) within the area and why.
2. Recording the numbers and age groups of people who use the different facilities.

The popularity of particular facilities tends to vary with the age of the visitors. Some facilities have an obvious 'target age group' – a paddling pool appeals to very young children whilst people of all ages enjoy looking at fountains and flowerbeds.

Fieldwork area

It is useful to know that in a day, two people working together can make a detailed investigation of 1 km^2 or a transect 4 km long by 250 m wide.

An interesting project can be achieved by comparing two different types of leisure area as in the Trial Run. There is a great variety of types of park and public open space: a city square, a children's playground, a public park, an Area of Outstanding Natural Beauty, a Site of Special Scientific Interest, or part of a marked footpath or tourist trail. There are many more.

Your local authority will have a Parks and Leisure Department and may even have a Tourist Information Centre. Details will be available about the different types of leisure area and their facilities. Leaflets on the area may tell you when and how the park or public space was established and how it has developed up to the present time. Some of these details could be written in your own words and included as one or two paragraphs in the Introduction to your final report.

CAUTION: Always work in broad daylight. Never work alone in quiet places. Three people working together should be the minimum number for safety's sake.

Further suggestion: assessing leisure potential from a map

An investigation carried out as explained below makes an excellent basis for a coursework project. It can also be used to extend the depth of a fieldwork project as follows:

- If completed before beginning your fieldwork it produces a clear picture of what could be expected from your fieldwork results. These ***expectations*** can form the basis of hypotheses. Your value numbers for each square would be the values you would expect to confirm by fieldwork.

A hypothesis could be worded 'that fieldwork will confirm the leisure potential values made by examining the Ordnance Survey map'.

- If completed after your fieldwork the results may be compared with the data from your fieldwork.

1. Allocate a value number between **1** and **5** for each leisure feature shown on your map such as **5** for a viewpoint, **4** for a car park, **3** for a pathway/woodland, **2** for flowerbeds/benches and **1** for statues. These are value judgements and you must be able to explain how you chose them.
2. Look very carefully at your map and, using a copy of your recording grid, allocate numbers for the features in each square. At the end, add up the total for each square.
3. Group the totals into classes. Choose a colour for each class and then colour the squares accordingly. Figure 155 shows the results of this technique used for the Dart Valley in the Dartmoor National Park based on 1 km grid squares.
4. Describe the distribution over your map of the values for leisure potential. Are there distinct areas of high potential at which you would expect to find large numbers of visitors?

Figure 155 Leisure potential in part of Devon assessed from the Ordnance Survey map of scale 1:25,000.

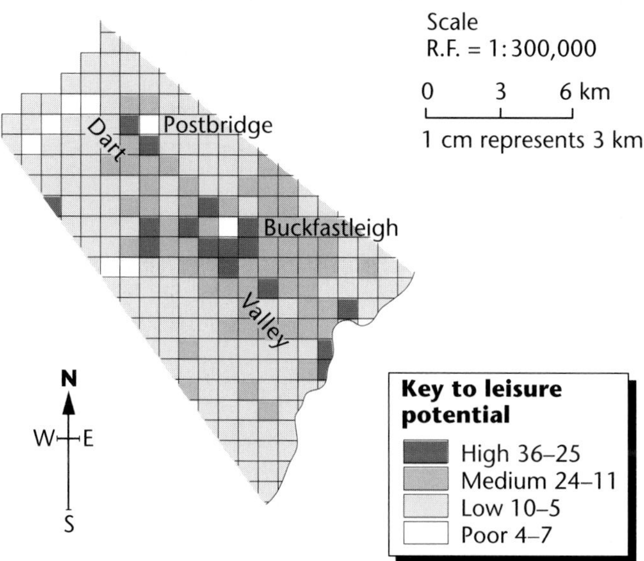

Before you begin

1. Prepare your base-map. An Ordnance Survey map of scale 1:2,500 is an ideal size to use (see Figure 157). The 1:10,000 scale of map can easily be used if the scale of the recording grid is enlarged by four times to scale it up to 1:2,500. This has been done in Figure 156.

   Using the grid lines already provided, divide your fieldwork area into small squares whose sides represent 25 m in length. This size of square is convenient for recording during fieldwork. Call them 'fieldwork squares'. Identify the fieldwork squares by letters and numbers as on the maps in A–Z guides and in some atlases.
2. On plain paper draw a recording grid as shown in Figures 156 and 157. Label your grid with the numbers and letters from the map. To help you to recognise exactly where you are during your fieldwork, copy any features shown on the Ordnance Survey map.
3. It will increase the accuracy of recording and save time during your fieldwork if you can easily recognise a distance of 25 m. Measure this with a tape measure at home or at school and then pace it out (see page 14). Practise recording features within this distance.
4. Consider carefully which age groups to record. The Trial Run concentrates on people under 16, between 16 and 60 and over 60 because the hypothesis involved people of 'working age' and 'others'. Here are two other suggestions intended to give you ideas.

Under 15 years	Under 5 years
16–35	6–10
36–60	11–16
Over 60 years	17–24
	25–39
	40–65
	Over 65 years

Avoid too many sub-divisions – don't attempt to use the right-hand list as it is. In your final report explain the reasons why you have chosen particular age groups. In the ***evaluation*** at the end you may consider whether or not they were the most appropriate for your leisure area.

Members of your family and friends will help you to become familiar with what people of different ages look like. Make sure that you can quickly place people fairly accurately into their age group. Practise estimating people's age groups as you wait in a queue at the bus stop or at the check-out in the supermarket.

Use coloured pens or pencils to indicate age groups: red = under 10 years; orange = 11–16 years; green = 16–35 years and so on. It is ideal if two of you can work together on recording the numbers of people and their age groups.

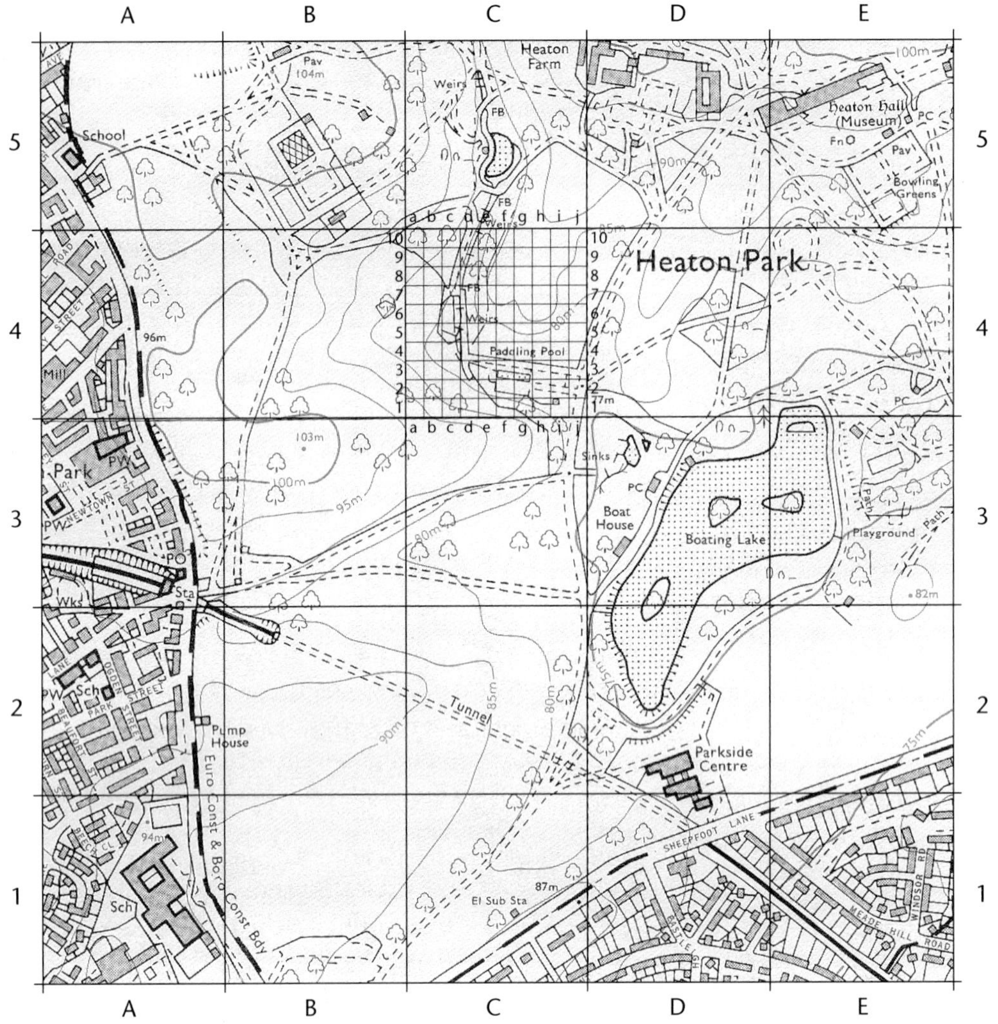

Figure 156 Part of Heaton Park in Manchester on a scale of 1:10,000 and enlarged recording grid.

The map was first divided into squares with sides representing 250 m. Square C4 has been sub-divided to make a recording grid of square with sides representing 25 metres

Scale
R.F. = 1:10,000

0 100 200 m

1 cm represents 100 m

A recording grid of square C4 enlarged to the scale of 1 : 2,500.

Features in the square have been copied from the map.

Scale
R.F. = 1:2,500

0 50 m

1 cm represents 25 m

Skill is needed to enlarge a map by hand. If you do this, explain in your *final report*, how and why you did it. You deserve to give yourself the credit.

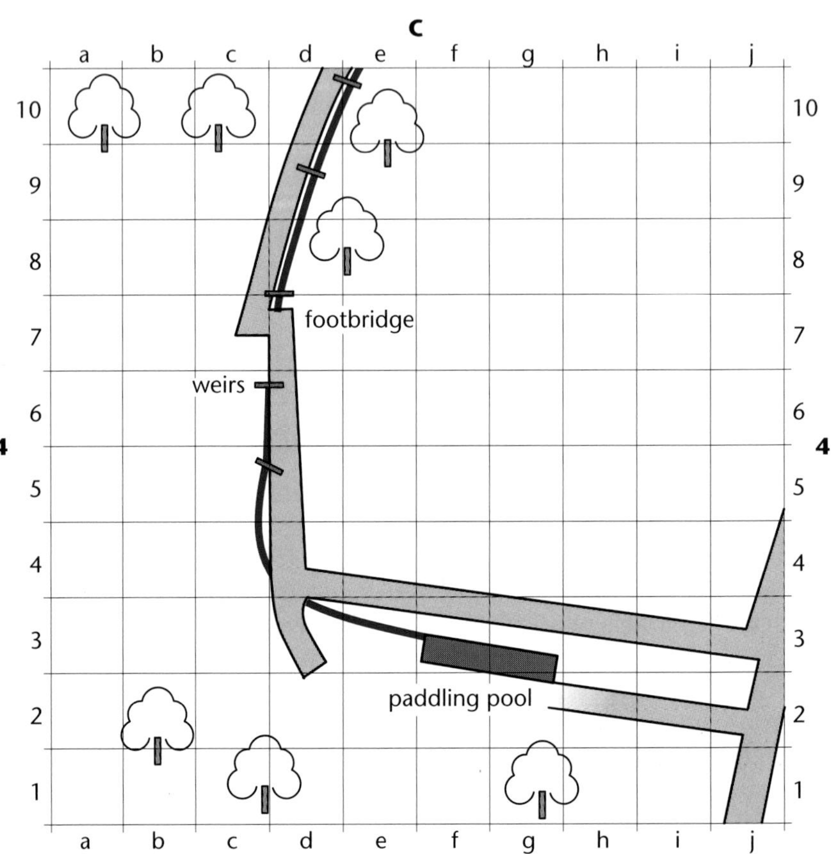

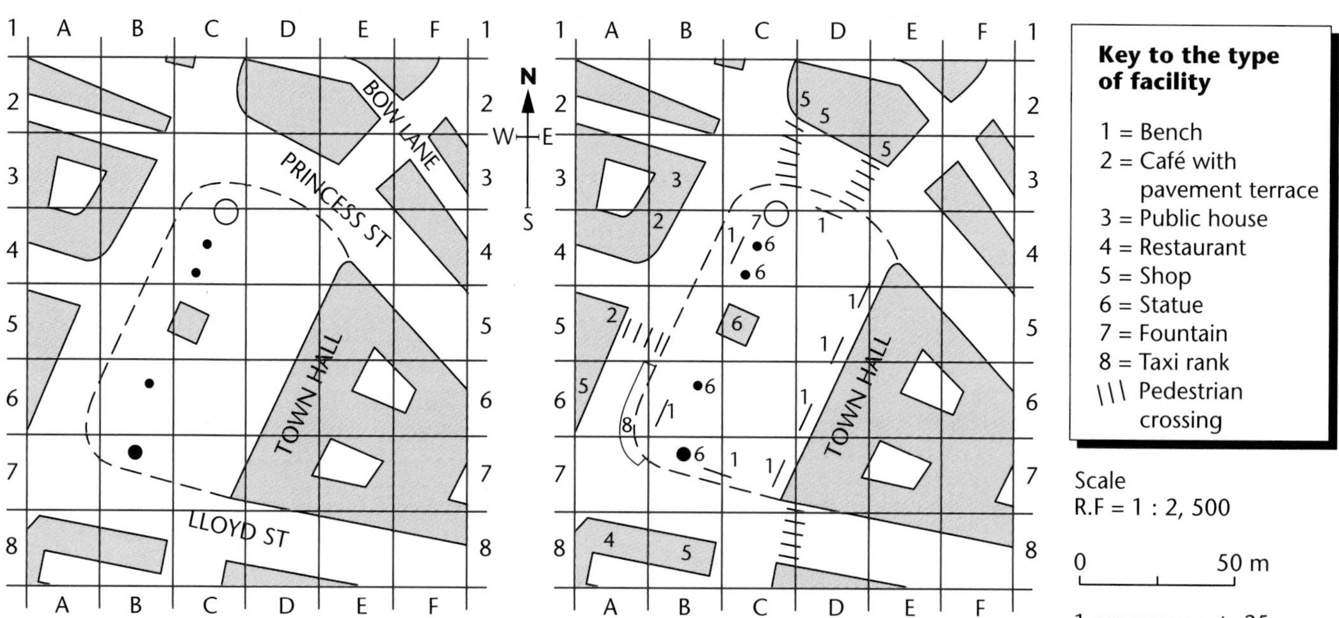

Figure 157 Albert Square, Manchester: map and recording grid on the same scale (1:2,500).

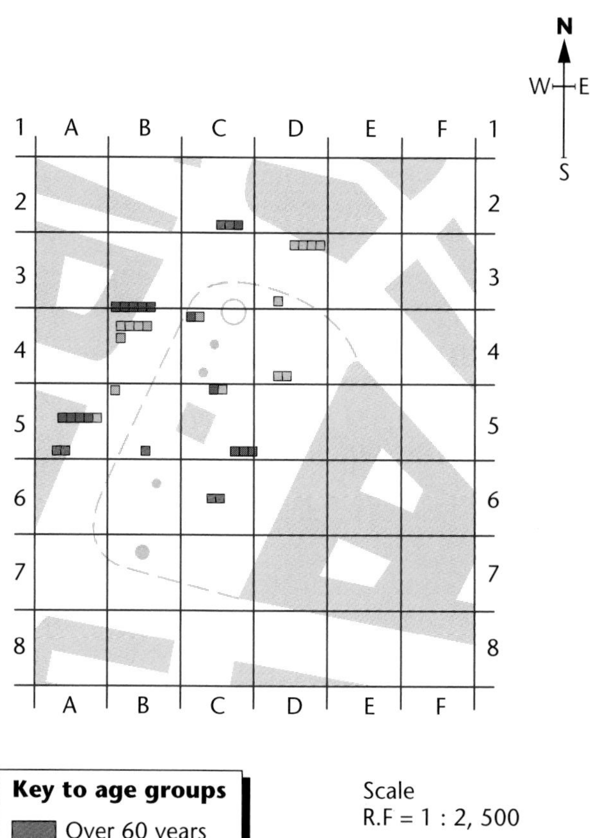

Figure 158 Numbers by age group using the facilities in Albert Square.

5. On a quick ***reconnaissance visit*** to the area:

   a Decide on the route you will take.

   b Look at the facilities that you will need to include in your list. Devise a simple way of recording them quickly and accurately so that they take up as little space as possible in the fieldwork squares on your recording grid. You could use numbers as in the list below, or a key similar to Figure 115 on page 119.

   List for recording leisure facilities

   1. angling area (stream or lake)
   2. bowling greens
   3. café
   4. flower garden
   5. grassy area for informal use

   c A person using the facilities is easily recorded by a tally stroke beside the facility. Use different colours according to the age group. For example, 10 people at a pavement café can be shown as 5 blue, 4 green and 1 pink (see square B4 in Figure 158). This does need some practice so try it out and find the way that works best for you. Describe how you did it.

   d Discover any background information available about the design and landscaping that has been done in your fieldwork area. A paragraph about this would be interesting in the Introduction to your final report.

e If your fieldwork area includes a town-centre space, become familiar with architectural styles and the materials of the buildings surrounding it (see pages 59–62).

f It is interesting to relate the location of features to the angle of slope, or to the local climate and weather as in Project Suggestion 2 on page 178. Consider whether to do this and where to take measurements. Make of note of these on your map.

You will need the following equipment:

- Base-map: Ordnance Survey map of scale 1:2,500 or 1:10,000 divided into fieldwork squares with sides representing 25 m in length.
- Recording grid on the scale of 1:2,500 as in Figures 156 and 157.
- 30 m tape measure or a 25 m length of cord. This may be useful in helping you to record accurately the exact location of particular facilities.
- List for Recording Leisure Facilities.
- Scheme for Recording Land Use in a Town (see page 119) adapted for an open space in the centre of a town. If you have made guides to architectural style and building materials (see pages 60–62) take them with you.
- Coloured pencils and your key to age groups if you have time to investigate this. Remember that it is helpful to have two geographers recording the people: one to count the numbers and the other to record the age groups using colours.
- Specialist equipment: Use a clinometer (see page 26) for measuring the angle of slope and for the local climate (weather elements) (see pages 28–36).

Fieldwork method

1. Follow your base-map along the routes you chose in your reconnaissance visit. Each time you walk into a new fieldwork square record the following in the corresponding square on your recording grid:

   a the facilities. In a town, in addition to recording benches, garden beds, fountains and so on, record the use of each building (see page 119). The architectural style and building materials may also be important.
   Remember that paths and paved areas are facilities.

   b the number of people using the facilities.

   c use your chosen colours to indicate the age groups of people.

   It is important to count the people immediately you see them because they may be moving around fairly quickly. This is especially true in a town square. Figure 158 shows you how to do the recording, including the age groups of people.

2. Take measurements of the angle of slope where it changes. Next, measure the weather elements in places of obvious sunshine, shadow and shelter. These measurements are to supplement the information which you will obtain from secondary sources (Head Gardener or Groundsman and the Ordnance Survey map). Explain this in your final report.

CAUTION: Do not trespass or cause damage.

Sources of secondary data

1. The people in charge of public spaces and parks often take surveys from time to time of visitor numbers and the ways in which the area is used. If you write to the person in charge (see pages 18–20) explaining why you would like this information, you will be given interesting and useful data. Allow two or three weeks for a reply.
2. The Head Gardener or Groundsman will be an expert on the ***local climate*** and ***microclimate*** and on the effects of slope angles. Write to them, explaining why you would like the information. It would be helpful to include with your letter a list of the information you would like, such as:
   - What effects does a shelter belt of trees/a walled garden/greenhouses have on the climatic conditions?
   - How do they affect the plants that are cultivated in the sheltered area?

   It would be interesting to find out whether there are any plants that are unusual for the area, i.e. exotic plants. Ask how much interest there is in these plants and whether they attract extra visitors in certain seasons.

Analysing and interpreting your data

1. Bar charts of the facilities available

From your recording grid, make a list of all of the different facilities available. Either divide the facilities into categories as suggested on page 15 or make a more detailed classification of the facilities you have investigated, such as:

roads and paths

scenic features such as woodland

water features

children's rides

areas for organised games such as tennis

Go back through your list again and make a tally chart of the number in each category. Illustrate them as a bar chart. Write one or two paragraphs to explain how you did this and describe what your results show.

2. A choropleth map to show the area covered by different facilities

From the list of facilities it will be obvious that particular types such as grassy areas and golf courses occupy a much larger area than picnic tables and flowerbeds. Cover your map with tracing paper, securing it with sticky tape at one edge to make a tracing overlay. Choose colours to represent the different categories of facility and shade on the tracing overlay the areas occupied by each. This will form a ***choropleth map***. Remember to add the key to your tracing overlay.

Use the grid for your fieldwork squares to calculate the total area covered by each category of facility. The method for calculating the area is explained in Section 2 on page 70. ***Rank*** the areas in order of the area occupied (see page 84). Extra weight may be added to your results if you calculate each of the different areas as a percentage of the total area (see page 86). Explain how you have analysed your data (drawing the choropleth map and ranking the areas). Describe your results.

3. The popularity of the facility

For each type of facility, either draw a bar chart (see pages 72–3) proportional to the number of people using it, or draw a proportional circle (see page 82). Proportional circles are slightly more complicated to draw, as the radius is drawn proportional to the number of people. Why not try them both and decide which you think is the better technique for the data? Explain that you did this in your final report.

To analyse the numbers in each age group, sub-divide your bar charts as in Figure 79. Proportional circles may be divided into pie sectors as follows:

a. Add up the total number of people of all ages who were using the facilities. Divide 360 (the number of degrees in a circle) by this number. The answer is the number of degrees in the circle which represent one person.

b. Multiply the number of degrees (your answer to 'a') by the number in each age group.

c. Use a protractor to measure the number of degrees for each age group. Begin at 'midnight' and work clockwise around your circle showing different age groups in turn.

d. Colour the pie sectors according to the colour key used in your fieldwork and on your choropleth map (see number 2 above). Make a key on the same page as your circles.

Describe the results shown by your bar charts or proportional circles:

- Which type of facility is the most popular irrespective of age group?
- Which is the most popular with the different age groups?
- Which is the least popular type of facility?
- From your knowledge of the area are you able to suggest reasons why?

4. Relating the distribution of leisure facilities to the relief and/or local climate of the area

If your base-map was of scale 1:2,500 or bigger, the height of the land will not have been shown as contours. Copy the contours from an Ordnance Survey map of scale 1:10,000 or 1:25,000. Add details of any slopes you have measured by ***annotating*** your map. Slope profiles can be drawn in the margin around your map and their exact location indicated by an arrow, like a desire-line to the correct place on the map. Similarly, add the results of your measurements of the weather elements.

Describe any ***inter-relationships*** that you can pick out. The replies to the enquiries you have made by letter should also help. Don't ignore the obvious things like benches that have been placed in sheltered spots or facing the sun.

Drawing conclusions

In this investigation there were two major aims:

1. to make an inventory of the facilities in the area, and
2. to assess the popularity of each facility (this will vary according to the age group of the users).

In your conclusions, first write a summary on the types of facility and their distribution/location. You may be able to relate the location(s) to the ***relief*** of the land, the ***local climate*** of the area, the nearness to the entrance gates or a car park, and so on.

Next, describe what your data analysis has shown about the popularity of different facilities. Comment on the age groups of people with whom different types of facility appeared to be particularly popular. In each case, suggest reasons.

Finally, can you conclude that the area is successful in providing leisure facilities? If you have completed the Further Suggestion explained earlier in this chapter you will be able to compare the extent to which the area fulfils its potential. In this respect, your investigation will have been like testing a hypothesis.

Evaluating your work

- Are any of the following likely to have affected the reliability of your fieldwork results:
  - the time of day
  - the day of the week
  - the season of the year
  - the month, as related to school holidays and terms
  - the weather conditions?

Suggest ways in which each of these could affect the number of visitors.

- Was your division of people into age groups successful? If you had used a different division would it have affected your results?
- Did you find the size of the fieldwork square helpful? If not recommend another size or another method.

Interesting extra ideas

1. From your fieldwork do you feel that there is a need for the provision of more facilities such as:
   a car parks, cafes and public conveniences
   b benches, picnic tables and litter bins
   c maps and signposts
   d more facilities for people who are blind, for those who are deaf, for those in wheelchairs?

   Where would you locate the extra amenities? Explain why.
2. Within the National Parks of England and Wales, roads and paths occupy only 3% of the total area, but most people visiting the parks stay near to them. They form a compact and economical way of using the land. Did you find a similar situation in your fieldwork area?
3. Imagine that you have overall responsibility for providing and maintaining leisure facilities in the area you have investigated. Suggest, with reasons such as site, safety or cost, whether you could close some, expand others and introduce new ones. Would you concentrate people by attracting them to facilities in one area, leaving more space for fewer people?
4. Discover the ***catchment area*** of the leisure area (park/public open space). Where do visitors come from? How do they reach the leisure area? What is the area over which the leisure area is advertised (on billboards/in newspapers/at railway stations and bus-stops/on the radio or television)? You will find help for this investigation on pages 00 and 00.
5. The population of the area surrounding a park can be calculated with accuracy by using the Small Area Statistics of the Census. Alternatively, use a map of scale 1:10,000 to count the number of houses in the area. Find out from the local authority the average number of people per household. Multiply the number of houses by the people per household to calculate the local population it serves.

Appendix 1 Further Project Ideas

The following is a list of other project ideas that you might also want to consider doing for your fieldwork or coursework project. These extra projects cover not only those topics included in Section 3 but also explore farming, advertising, gardens and allotments, industrial sites, supermarkets and urban landscapes through paintings.

The comments in italics suggest further ideas for your projects including which ones will have good links with other subjects you might be studying.

1. **The geography of the postal services in a village or town**

   (a) Where are pillar boxes located?

   (b) How big is the ***catchment area*** served by a pillar box? How many homes/shops/offices and other places of work are served by a pillar box?

   (c) Where is the post office in relation to the pillar boxes?

   (d) Town development can be traced through the inscription on the pillar box: VR, ERVII, GRV, GRVI and ERII. Contact:

   Post Office Archives
   Freeling House
   Phoenix Place
   London EC1A 1BB

   (e) The Collections and Deliveries Department of your post office will have records of the dates at which pillar boxes were established. They will also have details of the organisation of collections and deliveries.

   *A similar project could be done on the **geography of public telephones**.*

2. **Bus stop catchment areas**

   The average time taken to walk 250 m is 5 minutes.

   (a) On a map of scale 1:10,000 or bigger, plot the bus stops along one or more routes. Next, draw a circle with a radius representing 250 m around each. Are all of the houses on the map within a bus stop catchment area of 250 m radius? Count the number of houses within each catchment area. (You could use the 1:25,000 map but the radius of the circles would measure only 1cm. They might be difficult to draw.)

   (b) Interview people to discover where the watershed between bus stops really lies. Most people have an intense dislike of walking away from the direction in which they wish to travel even if the 'previous' bus stop is nearer to their home and the fare is the same.

3. **The sphere of influence of advertising**

   This would make a good link with Media Studies.

   Choose two or three events or products that are being advertised.

   (a) On a map mark the location of the billboards, bus shelters and railway stations where they are advertised.

   (b) Are the locations of the advertisements related to the following:

   the number of pedestrians passing by
   the number of vehicles passing by
   the number of buses
   the number of trains
   the socio-economic status of the area?

   (c) In which newspapers are the events/products advertised? Discover the area over which a local or regional newspaper is delivered/on sale.

   (d) Is the regional or national network of the radio or television used for the advertisements? What is the sphere of influence of the radio and television stations?

4. **Allotments**

   An ancient law entitles every householder in Great Britain to a plot of land somewhere within Britain on which to produce food for the family.

   (a) For your town, discover where the allotments are located. Calculate the area covered by allotments. Find out how many allotments exist, and how many are in use. Relate the location of the allotments to the density of households in the area. Are there enough allotments available locally to serve the town?

(b) Use historical sources to trace the allotments through time.

5. **Farm land use**

Does the way in which the fields are used vary according to the following:

- the distance on an individual farm from the farmhouse and steadings
- the distance along roads from the nearest market town
- the aspect (location in relation to the sun) in a deep valley which runs from east to west
- the height of the land
- the slope of the land as it affects the use of farm machinery, soil depth and drainage?

An interesting way of extending the project would be to include a section entitled 'How has the landscape changed in the last 75 years?'

Secondary data to help a project on farming may be obtained from:

The National Farmers' Union
Agriculture House
164 Shaftesbury Avenue
London WC2H 8HL

6. **Where, how and why does soil vary?**

Measure the depth of the soil and the ***infiltration rate*** and then collect a trowelful or a large spoonful of the topsoil to test for its colour, texture and acidity. Collect your samples from:

- the top, middle and bottom of a long slope, or
- from different cultivated environments such as:
  an arable field
  a field of ley grass (sown pasture)
  a garden flowerbed
  a football or hockey pitch

7. **An investigation of an industrial site through time**

This would make a good link with History.

The buildings at the site may have been replaced more than once. The company or companies using the site may have details in their Archive Department, and the Local History Section of your public library will also have information. Ask the present owner or manager about the use made of the site at the present time. Discover as much as you can about the following:

- the purpose of the factory at different times
- the source of power used
- where the employees lived and their journey to work
- where raw materials were brought from and how they were transported
- where the finished product(s) is/are sold

8. **Does the height of buildings decrease outwards from the centre of a large town?**

Identify the centre of the Central Business District, and then at intervals along ***transects*** outwards, count the number of storeys of the buildings.

9. **Are public car parks a good use of land?**

When a new underground car park in Mayfair, London, opened in 1998, the rent for a space was £48,000 per year. This is one of the most expensive car parks in the country but it illustrates how valuable they can be for earning money.

For your town:

(a) Locate the public car parks on a map.

(b) Count the number of spaces available.

(c) Find out the charges made.

(d) Calculate the potential value of the space. From the Valuation Office find out the value of land used for buildings near to the car parks and make comparisons.

(f) Imagine that you have been asked to produce a report and to advise on the future use of land which is at present occupied by car parks. Would you recommend the continued existence of the car parks, or would you recommend alternative ways of using this space?

10. **The geography of gardens**

How much of your fieldwork area is occupied by gardens, both public and private? Investigate the state of upkeep (attractiveness) of the gardens.

Where in your fieldwork area would you introduce more greenery? Consider the role of hanging baskets, tubs of flowers and shrubs in public places. Would you plant more trees along roadsides? Which species would you choose?

11. **A coursework project on towns through painting**

A coursework link with Art can be made by investigating paintings of towns by artists such as

Vermeer and Canaletto through to Adolphe Valette, L.S. Lowry and others.

- What kinds of buildings are shown in the pictures?
- What type of building materials were used?
- Describe the styles of architecture.
- Describe the roads, and the vehicles and people using them.
- What does the sky look like?

Does the picture reflect accurately your view of the urban geography of the period? Pages 59–62 may help. Also *The Impressionist and the City* by Brettell and Pissaro (Yale University Press, 1993) is one of several very helpful books.

12. Supermarket geography as a coursework project

(a) Write to the manager of one or more supermarkets asking for the layout of different types of goods – cheese, washing powder, frozen vegetables and so on – within the supermarket.

(b) Devise a questionnaire on the convenience of the clustering/adjacency of different goods when shopping, and interview members of your family and friends. (It could include which goods they would like to see next to one another on the shelves or on the same aisle, and how often they shop for particular items.)

(c) Analyse your data by awarding value numbers in terms of:
  (i) the frequency of purchase
  (ii) the location of goods within the supermarket: for people rushing in at lunchtime, for example.

(d) Write a report on the accessibility of goods in the supermarket and the reasons for the layout.

(e) Suggest re-organising the layout to promote particular items.

13. Glaciated uplands

(a) Can a corrie/cirque/cwm really be compared with a textbook example? Begin by studying a large-scale map, such as the Ordnance Survey 1:2,500. Record the following:
- measurements from the rocklip to the backwall and from one side to the other
- the height and appearance of the backwall
- evidence of freeze–thaw weathering and striations which indicate rotary movement of the glacier

(b) Are corries more distinct on the north-facing and east-facing sides of a valley?

(c) Do glaciated valleys/glacial troughs show different characteristics of soil, vegetation and farm land use along a transect from one side to the other?

(d) Is one area of a glacier/glaciated valley more important for tourism than another? Why?

(e) Is the glaciated upland important for water supply and the generation of hydro-electricity?

14. Fieldwork on a foreign holiday for a comparison with your home area

A comparison between your holiday destination and the area around your home or school would make an excellent project. One or more of the topics listed below can be investigated easily and quickly while you are on holiday:

- tourism
- building materials and architectural style
- a village
- farm land use
- shops and markets
- land use in a street in the town centre

Take care to be considerate of people's feelings and their privacy. The taking of photographs in particular can disturb people. Collect as much data on your topic as possible, bearing in mind that it is unlikely that you will be able to go back to check on details.

Appendix 2 Sources of Information

The following is a list of sources that you might use to obtain additional information and ***secondary data*** for your fieldwork project. The depth of the material provided in the different sources will vary. If you contact an Information or Publicity Officer directly by letter or telephone, explain exactly what information you wish to have, giving dates and details of your fieldwork area, possibly including grid references, and explain that you would like the information for your Geography Project. See the advice on writing letters of request on pages 18–20 of Section 2.

The secondary sources listed here are divided into four sections for your ease of reference:

- Books and other published work
- Information on CD-ROM and the Internet
- Companies, agencies and government departments
- Suppliers of specialist equipment

Remember that there are many other secondary sources that will also be able to provide you with useful data for your investigations.

This appendix is also available on the Website with updated information and full contact details for the organisations listed below.
Go to: *www.geography-fieldwork.nelson.co.uk*.

Books and other published work

These are books and other publications that you are likely to find in your public library. They can also be bought from good bookshops.

Often a summary appears at the beginning or end of books and reports. This may help you to write background information to introduce your reader to your topic and your fieldwork area.

Guide books to regions
The Blue Guide, Shell Guide, Rough Guide, and so on. Ward Locke's Red Guides, which were published until the 1980s, may provide an interesting historical view.

Whitaker's Almanack
This has been published every year since 1868. It is up-to-date from October–September of the year of publication. It includes information on the following:

Tide tables for the British Isles and for some parts of the North Sea and the English Channel.

Population for the United Kingdom for each of the Census years (1801 onwards).

Council tax: an explanation of the **valuation** of both residential property and the **non-domestic rate**.

Local government areas are described, including the most recent changes.

Conservation and heritage: details are given of the various types of conservation areas such as National Parks and the role of organisations such as the **Countryside Commission**.

A listing of buildings is included under **Historical Buildings and Monuments**.

Weather: records of weather in Britain for the last 30 years and detailed statistics for the previous year.

Periodicals: Trade, professional and academic periodicals are listed with the address of the publisher.

The names and addresses of the publishers of **Annual Reference Books**, such as *Britain: An Official Handbook*, the *Buses Year Book*, *Kelly's Business Directory*, *Municipal Year Book and Public Services Directory*, *Regional Trends*, *Water Services Year Book*.

Britain: An Official Handbook
This is prepared by the Office for National Statistics and published annually by The Stationery Office. Topics included are population density, environmental issues, agriculture and forestry, industry and transport.

Land Use – UK: A Survey for the 21st Century
Editor: Rex Walford, Publisher: The Geographical Association.

Chapter 5: The Overall Picture summarises the results of the Land Use-UK Survey of 1996 and compares them with the Land Utilisation Survey of the 1930s, the Second Lane Utilisation Survey of the 1960s, and the Department of the Environment's Countryside Survey of 1990.

Chapter 6: Rural Results.

Chapter 7: Urban Results.

Digest of Environmental Statistics
This has been published annually since 1978 by the Department of the Environment, Transport and the Regions (DETR). Information is given by Standard Region and includes the following:

- air quality
- inland water quality and use
- coastal and marine waters
- noise: road traffic, aircraft, industrial and
- commercial premises, noise on streets
- recycling
- land use
- wildlife

Ordnance Survey Statlas – UK
A statistical atlas of the United Kingdom, published by the Ordnance Survey, 1995.

Digest of United Kingdom Energy Statistics
Published annually by the Department of Trade and Industry (DTI).

Philip's Geographical Digest
Publisher: Heinemann-Philip Atlases. Published annually, this gives data on population, agriculture, energy, manufacturing industry, transport and pollution, country by country.

The State of the Environment 1991
Publisher: Organisation for Economic Co-operation and Development (OECD). On a world scale, this gives a summary and data on each of the following: agriculture, air quality, energy forests, industry, inland water, noise, transport, waste disposal and wildlife.

The Digest of Agricultural Census Statistics
Published annually by the Ministry of Agriculture, Fisheries and Food (MAFF). The information is the result of sample surveys of farms. It is given for England and Wales, Scotland and Northern Ireland at the scales of country, standard region and county.

Each edition contains reference tables for the previous 10 years so that trends can be seen. Information on the following is included: size of holdings, types of crops, farm animals, labour force.

The Surface Water Year Book of Great Britain
This was published annually by the government between 1936 and 1955 and so it is an excellent source of historical data. Details are given of gauging stations which are located by grid references, rainfall, geology of the drainage basin, average discharge and extreme discharge.

Kelly's Trades Directories
These were published annually for most towns in the United Kingdom from 1845 until 1969. They give the name and function of the occupant of the premises on a building-by-building and street-by-street basis. See the extract on page 68.

The Environment of England and Wales: A Snapshot
Publisher: Environment Agency. This contains maps, illustrations and descriptions of the geography, climate, population, land use and crop production.

The Census of Population

The Census of Population was first taken in England and Wales and Scotland in 1801, and in Northern Ireland in 1841. It has been taken every tenth year since, with the exception of 1941. The census returns for all of these years are available in public libraries.

The Census is a document on which planning is based. It is used by industrial and commercial firms as well as by government departments at national and local levels. In its early years bare figures were published, but since 1851 it has become more and more detailed.

The Census gives the following details:

Population numbers by sex

Population numbers by age

Population numbers by occupation

Population numbers by place of birth (useful for showing migration to the area)

Car ownership numbers

Journeys to work by the different means of transport

The census returns are published by ward in towns, and, if the ward is densely populated, it may be divided into sectors. Census returns are published by parish in rural areas. The returns provide very useful information on change through time. For dates earlier than 100 years ago, the people who occupied each individual house are named and their ages and occupation given.

The returns for different sizes of area are available as follows:

Administrative areas can be found in books in public libraries.
The **Small Area Statistics** are given by **ward** (in towns) and **civil parish** (in other areas) and by

postcode sectors in Scotland. These are available in public libraries where they may be kept on microfiche. See an example in Figure 159. **Enumeration district** figures are called **Local Base Statistics** and are available in the local town hall or on CD-ROM. See an example in Figure 160.

The Census returns for each administrative area include a useful summary of the data at the beginning of each report. The population for each census return since 1891 is also listed at the beginning of each bound volume. Tables of particular use to geographers include the following:

- Table 21 Car availability and cars in households
- Table 74 Occupation
- Table 76 Occupation and industry
- Table 82 Travel to work and socio-economic group (SEG)
- Table 83 Travel to work and car availability
- Table 99 Standard occupational classification

The 1991 census returns at all levels are published by Chadwyck-Healey and entitled *The 1991 Census on CD-ROM*. The CD-ROM contains instructions on how to use it.

Addresses where census data may be obtained are given in the Sources of Information on the Website.

Figure 159 Small Area Statistics for the district of Wigan (county Greater Manchester), 1991

Table 20. Households with residents; residents in households

		Tenure of households in permanent buildings								
		Owner occupied		Rented privately						
Amenities	All perman-ent	Owned outright	Buying	Furnished	Un-furnished	Rented with a job or business	Rented from a housing assoc-iation	Rented from a local authority or new town	No permanent accomo-dation	No car
a	b	c	d	e	f	g	h	i	j	k
TOTAL HOUSEHOLDS	**118,513**	**30,248**	**52,707**	**1,298**	**2,744**	**1,058**	**1, 911**	**28,547**	**61**	**41,588**
Exclusive use of bath/shower	117,835	30,102	52,682	1,176	2,607	1,052	1,906	28,310	44	40,963
Exclusive use of inside WC	117,598	29,979	52,657	1,164	2,555	1,048	1,904	28,291	34	40,783
With central heating - all rooms	80,279	19,294	41,740	594	733	737	1,566	15,615	14	21,634
- some rooms	16,776	3,813	4,987	122	219	143	235	7,257	3	7,993
No central heating	20,543	6,872	5,930	448	1,603	168	103	5,419	17	11,156
Shared use of WC	15	-	3	2	3	-	-	7	-	14
With central heating - all rooms	11	-	2	1	2	-	-	6	-	11
- some room	-	-	-	-	-	-	-	-	-	-
No central heating	4	-	1	1	1	-	-	1	-	3
No inside WC	222	123	22	10	49	4	2	12	10	166
With central heating - all rooms	32	14	8	1	1	-	2	6	4	20
- some room	26	14	5	-	5	-	-	2	-	16
No central heating	164	95	9	9	43	4	-	4	6	130

Figure 160 Local Base Statistics for Central ward Manchester, 1991

1991 Census Local Base Statistics

Table 23. Persons per room: Households with residents: residents with households

Tenure	TOTAL HOUSEHOLDS	Up to 0.5 persons per room	Over 0.5 and up to 1 person per room	Over 1 and up to 1.5 persons per room	Over 1.5 persons per room
TOTAL HOUSEHOLDS	**4,249**	**2,891**	**1,229**	**103**	**21**
All permanent buildings	4,247	2,890	1,228	103	21
Owner occupied - owned outright	95	72	20	1	0
- buying	309	220	82	5	0
Rented privately - furnished	74	42	30	3	1
- unfurnished	21	14	7	0	0
Rented with a job or business	137	88	40	6	2
Rented from a housing association	405	316	87	2	0
Rented from a local authority or new town	3,206	2,138	962	86	18
Non-permanent accommodation	2	1	1	0	0
TOTAL PERSONS IN HOUSEHOLDS	**8,690**	**3,929**	**4,062**	**582**	**117**

Information on CD-ROM and the Internet

Some of the following may be available on CD-ROM at your local public library:

Newspapers: *Daily Telegraph, The Guardian, The Independent, Independent on Sunday, The Observer, Sunday Telegraph, Sunday Times, The Times* and *Financial Times*.

The British Humanities Index (BHI Plus) contains details of articles published since 1985 in a wide range of periodicals.

United Kingdom Official Publications lists the publications of The Stationery Office, government departments and other official bodies.

The Internet is also a useful source of information. See the advice on Using the Internet to Conduct Research on page 22. You can use a search facility to look for web sites that contain secondary data or background information that might be relevant to your project. However, you need to be very careful not to overload your project with too much detail or include information that you do not understand. The range and depth of materials you find on the Internet could be massive indeed, and you will need to choose only the most important and up-to-date details for your project. Ask your teacher for advice if you are unsure what will be useful to you and what you should ignore.

There are several Internet addresses hotlinked from the Sources of Information section on the Website. Go to: *www.geography-fieldwork.nelson.co.uk*. Most government departments and local councils now have web sites that you can access for information and many businesses throughout the country also have information available. Remember though that finding information on the Internet can take up a lot of valuable time so think carefully about what you want before starting.

Companies, agencies and government departments

When you contact the Information Office at any of the following organisations make sure that you have written down precisely what information you need. It is a good idea to have the grid references of your fieldwork area written down. Always approach people politely and explain at the outset that you wish to have the information to help you to complete your Geography Project.

Suggestions on how to write a letter to request information are given on pages 18–20. If you need a written reply, remember to include an envelope stamped and addressed to yourself. A short letter of thanks after you have received the information always pleases the people involved.

The addresses and contact details for these organisations are supplied and updated on the Website.

Statistics

The Office for National Statistics

The Office for National Statistics is responsible for the maintenance of a central database of key economic and social statistics.

The Stationery Office

There are branches of the Stationery Office in London, Cardiff, Manchester, Bristol, Birmingham, Edinburgh and Belfast.

Weather

Contact: **The Meteorological Office** and **The Royal Meteorological Society**.

Census

There are Census offices for England and Wales, Northern Ireland and Scotland. Another useful source of information is the Family Records Centre.

Government Departments

Department of the Environment, Transport and the Regions (DETR)

The Department of the Environment, Transport and the Regions is responsible for environmental protection, roads, transport, railways and aviation.

General enquiries on **environmental statistics** may be made to the **Environmental Protection Statistics and Information Management Division**. The *Environment in your Pocket* is available on request.

There are Regional Offices of the Department of the Environment in many large towns.

Air quality information is available from the DETR's laboratory: **AEA National Environmental Technology Centre** at Abingdon.

Water quality monitoring is the responsibility of **The Environment Agency** (for England and Wales). The regional offices of the Environment Agency are given in the telephone directory.

Also contact: **National Society for Clean Air and Environmental Protection and The Atmospheric Research and Information Centre**.

The Ministry of Agriculture, Fisheries and Food (MAAF)

This department publishes the results of the Agricultural Census and of a range of sample surveys of farms. The main office is in London but there are other offices in York, Cardiff, Edinburgh and Belfast.

The European Community Farm Structure Survey is conducted by member states every two or three years. This survey provides a wide range of census-type data on broadly consistent definitions for each of the twelve countries of the Community. Contact your public library or the offices of MAFF for details.

Department of Trade and Industry

The DTI is responsible for policies on energy and it incorporates the Office of Science and Technology.

Department of Heritage

The following are responsible for sport and recreation, historic buildings, monuments and tourism: **Department of Heritage** (part of the Department of Culture, Media and Sport), **Historic Buildings Council for Wales**, **Historic Buildings Council for Scotland** and **The Countryside Commission**. There are seven regional offices of the Countryside Commission.

The Department of Transport

The Department of Transport is part of the DETR. It publishes annual reports on transport nationally and for metropolitan and county areas. These include reports on the following: travel to work, air quality, car ownership, public transport, traffic on major roads, expenditure on roads.

Transport

Highways Agency

For England, this is part of the DETR. The agency for Wales is the Transport and Highways Division in the National Assembly for Wales. For Scotland it is the National Roads Directorate.

The Highways Agency is responsible for the management and maintenance of the **motorway and trunk road network** and its extension.

More locally, roads and traffic are the responsibility of:

- county councils: major roads
- non-district councils: urban roads and offstreet car parks
- unitary authorities: major and urban roads and offstreet car parks

The Freight Transport Association Limited

This association publishes annually a yearbook which contains details about the weight, length, width and height of vehicles allowed on roads in the United Kingdom.

Sustrans (Sustainable Transport Systems)

Sustrans is a registered charity that is helping to create the National Cycle Network.

Geology

The British Geological Survey

Maps may be bought and information obtained from the Information Office.

Soil and land capability

The three 'branches' involved in soil research combined in the late 1990s to produce the first complete soil map of the United Kingdom on the scale of 1:250,000. More detailed soil maps and land capability maps, as well as schools resource packs, are available from the following organisations: **Soil Survey and Land Research Centre, Macaulay Land Use Research Institute, Department of Agriculture and Environment (Belfast), Forestry Commission (Scotland)** and **Forestry Research**.

HM Land Registry

The Land Registry classifies property into detached (old and new), semi-detached, terraced and flats, and publishes a summary of trends in each type every quarter. The summaries refer to areas similar to those used by the Population Census.

Local authorities

The departments and addresses of local authorities are to be found in public libraries.

Who is responsible for what?

In Scotland, Wales and Northern Ireland a single tier of unitary authorities has been in control since 1994. However since there was the devolution of power to Scotland and Wales in 1999 you should contact *The Scottish Parliament* and *The National Assembly for Wales* for Information.

In England the organisation outside the unitary authorities is as follows:

- County councils are responsible for education, traffic, transport and major roads, fire service, refuse disposal, and smallholdings.
- Non-district councils are responsible for local planning, housing, urban roads, offstreet car parks, building regulations, refuse collection, and cemeteries.
- All councils are responsible for recreation (parks, playing fields and swimming pools), museums, encouragement of the arts, tourism and industry.

Suppliers of specialist equipment

Ordnance Survey
Maps of the United Kingdom at the following scales:

1:250,000

1:50,000

1:25,000

1:10,000

1:2500 (rural areas)

1:1250 (urban areas)

Geographers' A – Z Map Company
Street maps

Experian Goad Limited
Shopping centre maps.

Read Scientific
Read Scientific will supply single items, and will repair and service instruments.

Your teacher will have the details and catalogues of most of the larger suppliers.

Glossary

The glossary is intended to help you find quickly the meanings of some terms. If you cannot find the one you need, look it up in the index or in a dictionary of geography.

Acid rain	Rain which has been polluted by chemicals so that it is more acidic than pH 5.
Analysis	Processing information or **raw data** (e.g. by mapping, **tabulating**, **annotating** etc) so that patterns and **inter-relationships** appear.
Annotate	To add notes to a map, picture or diagram to emphasise features (see Figure 4 on page 13).
Anticyclone	A weather system with high pressure at the centre
Aspect	The position of a feature or an area in relation to the sun.
Bed	A layer of sedimentary rock.
Bedding plane	A crack which separates one bed of sedimentary rock from another.
Bibliography	A list of secondary sources used in your project.
Calibrate	To create a measuring scale on an instrument.
Catchment area	The area from which water drains into a river. The same as a **drainage basin** or **water catchment**. Also the area from which people come to use the services of a town or city.
Choropleth map	A map with areas shaded in different colours or densities of dots or lines to represent particular features or values.
Correlation	The links between two or more sets of data.
Cost–benefit analysis	An approach adopted by planners to assess whether the financial costs of a scheme will be more than covered by the benefits.
Data	Information which is written or in the form of numbers, pictures or maps. Information before it has been **analysed** is called **raw data**.
Depression	A weather system containing fronts with low pressure at the centre
Discharge of a river	The quantity of water passing through a section of channel each second. It is measured as the cross sectional area x the speed of flow and is often expressed as **cumecs** (cubic metres per second).
Distribution	Whereabouts on a map or in an area, particular features are found e.g. in the SW corner; below 500m; close to a main road.
Ecosystem	The system within an area large or small in which plants, animals and the environment are closely linked together.
Evaluation	Looking at your work to assess whether and how it could have been done better.
Expectations	Expectations can be formed during a reconnaissance visit. They are more than a hunch and are what you would expect your project to prove. Hypotheses can be based on expectations.

Frequency	The number of times something occurs within a certain length of time or a particular number occurs within a set of number data.
Function	(of a building) The main purpose for which a building is used.
Functional zone	(of a town) A certain area specialising in a particular function, e.g. shopping, entertainment, residential.
Groyne	A barrier built outwards across a beach to trap and stabilise beach materials (sand and shingle).
Hierarchy	A system which arranges information in an order of importance from the most important to the least important.
Honeypot	A leisure facility which attracts a great many people.
Hypothesis	The statement of an expectation or hunch about the topic you intend to investigate. A hypothesis can be tested and either proved to be correct or disproved.
Infiltration rate	The rate, usually in seconds, at which a measured volume of water soaks into the soil.
Interpretation	Using your geographical knowledge to bring out and make clear the meaning of your **data**, so that whoever reads your final report will understand it easily (like someone translating a foreign language).
Inter-relationships	Connections between facts, e.g. when the river flows slowly less load is carried.
Inventory	A detailed list of features observed during fieldwork or from secondary sources.
Isopleth	A line on a map joining points of equal value, e.g. a contour on a relief map.
Load of a river/stream	The material transported by a river/stream. Can be sub-divided into: **suspension** load; **saltation** load; **bottom traction** load (bedload) and **solution** load.
Local climate	The temperature, wind and other weather conditions within a localized area such as a shopping area or playing field.
Longshore drift	Waves breaking diagonally on the shore result in the movement of beach materials along the coast.
Matrix	A table in which the horizontal lines of squares are called rows and the vertical lines of squares are called **columns**.
Meander	A large bend in a river. Named after the River Meander in Turkey.
Microclimate	The temperature, wind and other weather conditions within a small area such as a balcony, flowerbed, small garden or yard.
Objective	Not being influenced by personal likes or dislikes; unbiased.
Order of importance	Your information arranged in a logical sequence to help your **analysis** and **interpretation**. The order depends on your aims, but should range from facts of high importance to facts of low importance.
Particle sizes	British soil survey sizes: the diameter of clay is less than 0.002 of a millimetre (2 microns); silt from 0.002 to 0.02mm; sand from 0.02 to 1.9mm; shingle from 2 to 4mm; pebbles from 5 to 59mm; cobbles from 60 to 200mm; boulders more than 200mm.

Pollution	Altering the environment so that it is spoiled in some way.
Precipitation	Water falling as rain, drizzle, sleet, snow or hail.
Primary data	Information which you obtain in the field by direct observation and measurement, interviewing etc.
Rank order	Numbers placed in order from the biggest to the smallest.
Reconnaissance visit	A preliminary visit to your fieldwork locations to assess the possibilities for your investigation and your safety and equipment needs.
Relief	The height and shape of the land.
Sample	A small amount of information or material collected which represents the whole picture. Some methods of **sampling** are random, systematic and stratified.
Secondary data	Information published, e.g. books, leaflets, magazines, CD-ROMs and the Internet. These are all **secondary sources**.
Sketch map	A map drawn freehand and not traced.
Socio-economic status	'Social' means the way people behave and 'economic' means how they earn their living. The two are closely related.
Sphere of influence	The area served by a settlement for shopping, entertainment and professional services.
Stream order	Every stream within a network of streams is placed into an order of importance according to the number of tributaries it has received. Two streams of the same order from any part of the world can therefore be compared.
Subjective	Giving your own views or using your own judgement.
Tabulate	To arrange data in the form of a table.
Topological map	A transport map in which routes are drawn as straight lines and neither the distance nor the compass direction matters. Places on the map are termed **nodes** and the routes between them **edges**.
Total population	If you were able to obtain every single piece of information it would be the total population.
Transect	A line followed in fieldwork for data gathering. It may be a line on a map or a route on the ground.
Trend line	A line drawn on a scattergraph to emphasise the main patterns (trends) in the data shown. Two types are **line of best fit** and **regression line**.
Weathering	The break-up of rock by the weather without the broken fragments being moved away.

Index